D0810266

HYDROGEN BONDING IN SOLIDS

FRONTIERS IN CHEMISTRY

Ronald Breslow and Martin Karplus, Editors
Columbia University

CONTRIBUTIONS TO THE THEORY OF CHEMICAL KINETICS
T. A. Bak, *Københavns Universitet*

MOLECULAR ORBITAL THEORY
C. J. Ballhausen, *Københavns Universitet*
H. B. Gray, *Columbia University*

NONCLASSICAL IONS
P. D. Bartlett, *Harvard University*

OPTICAL PUMPING
R. A. Bernheim, *The Pennsylvania State University*

AN INTRODUCTION TO ELECTRON PARAMAGNETIC RESONANCE
M. Bersohn, *University of Toronto*
J. C. Baird, *Brown University*

BIOORGANIC MECHANISMS
T. C. Bruice, *University of California, Santa Barbara*
S. J. Benkovic, *The Pennsylvania State University*

HYDROGEN BONDING IN SOLIDS
W. C. Hamilton, *Brookhaven National Laboratory*
James A. Ibers, *Northwestern University*

THERMODYNAMICS OF SMALL SYSTEMS
T. L. Hill, *University of Oregon*

LIGAND SUBSTITUTION PROCESSES
C. H. Langford, *Amherst College*
H. B. Gray, *Columbia University*

LECTURES ON QUANTUM THEORY OF MOLECULAR
ELECTRONIC STRUCTURE
R. G. Parr, *Johns Hopkins University*

THE BIOSYNTHESIS OF STEROIDS, TERPENES, AND ACETOGENINS
J. H. Richards, *California Institute of Technology*
J. B. Hendrickson, *Brandeis University*

OXIDATION MECHANISMS
R. Stewart, *University of British Columbia*

MOLECULAR PHOTOCHEMISTRY
N. J. Turro, *Columbia University*

COMPUTER PROGRAMMING FOR CHEMISTS
K. B. Wiberg, *Yale University*

HYDROGEN BONDING
IN SOLIDS

Methods of Molecular Structure Determination

WALTER C. HAMILTON
Brookhaven National Laboratory

JAMES A. IBERS
Northwestern University

W. A. BENJAMIN, INC.   1968
New York   Amsterdam

Library
I.U.P.
Indiana, Pa.

546.2 H18h
c. 1

HYDROGEN BONDING IN SOLIDS:

Methods of Molecular Structure Determination

Copyright © 1968 by W. A. Benjamin, Inc.
All rights reserved

Library of Congress Catalog Card Number 67-29602
Manufactured in the United States of America

*The final manuscript was put into production on March 2, 1967;
this volume was published on January 31, 1968*

W. A. BENJAMIN, INC.
New York, New York 10016

To Joyce and Marjorie

Preface

The phenomenon of hydrogen bonding is the best-studied specific inter-molecular interaction. Practically every technique of structural chemistry has been applied toward the end of elucidating the nature of the hydrogen bond. Although the excellent book by Pimentel and McClellan and the published contributions to the Ljubljana Symposium have provided an encyclopedic coverage of hydrogen bonding, we feel there is a need for a book that will critically examine the various structural techniques used in the study of the hydrogen bond—a book that not only gives examples of the applications of these various techniques but also describes the kind of information each method can or cannot give. Such is the intent of the present volume.

The book is written at a level which should make it useful as a text for a graduate or advanced undergraduate course in structural chemistry. It may also serve as a useful supplementary text in advanced physical or inorganic chemistry. The only prerequisites are elementary organic and physical chemistry. The book may also be useful to research workers in peripheral fields who would like to be brought up to date on the current state of the structural investigation of the hydrogen bond in solids.

We have not attempted to make the book or the treatment of any one topic an exhaustive review of the work in this field. Rather, we have presented what we feel to be the more pertinent facts concerning the nature of the hydrogen bond. By relating facts to experiments, we hope we have given the reader a good feeling for some of the pitfalls that are not always apparent in a paper describing a molecular structure determination. Having read this book, the student should be well prepared for a critical reading of the literature in hydrogen bonding and in structural chemistry generally. The many references to original papers are not intended to form a complete bibliography. They were selected with the aim of providing the student convenient entry points into the vast literature that exists on this subject.

We have restricted our discussion to the investigation of the hydrogen bond in the solid state because it is here that the hydrogen bond—being fixed in position—is best studied by many structural techniques. Further-more, all evidence points to the fact that the hydrogen bond differs very little in any important respect as it is found in the solid, liquid, and vapor phases.

In Chapter 1, we discuss the concept of molecular structure and the definition of a hydrogen bond. What do we mean when we say that a molecular structure has been determined? What do we mean when we say that a hydrogen bond exists?

In Chapter 2, we present the elements of diffraction methods for the determination of molecular structure and give a thorough discussion of the systematic errors in diffraction experiments which may affect the validity of the derived geometric structure of the molecule. The importance of neutron diffraction in the determination of hydrogen atom positions is emphasized.

In Chapter 3, the application of infrared spectroscopy to hydrogen-bonded systems is discussed. The combination of spectroscopy and diffraction has led to our best understanding of some simple hydrogen-bonded systems, and these are treated in some detail. This chapter also includes a brief discussion of the application of nuclear magnetic resonance to the determination of hydrogen positions in solids.

Nuclear magnetic resonance can also give valuable information on the motions of hydrogen atoms in solids, and this application is discussed in Chapter 4. Most of Chapter 4, however, is devoted to a discussion of neutron inelastic scattering as an important structural tool. This is treated in somewhat more detail than are the more conventional spectroscopic methods. Since the essentials of the method have not yet become a part of the standard physical chemistry curriculum, it seems appropriate that somewhat more weight be given to it here.

In Chapter 5, some examples of hydrogen bonding in organic crystals are presented. Hydrogen bonds are extremely important in biological sys-tems, and the details of their geometry in proteins and nucleic acids are set down.

Chapter 6 is devoted to hydrogen bonding in inorganic chemistry, with particular emphasis on the structure of water, both in ice and in crystalline hydrates. Next to water, the most commonly occurring hydrogen-bonding species in inorganic compounds is the ammonium ion, and the structures of several ammonium salts are discussed in some detail.

Chapter 7 concludes the discussion of hydrogen-bonded inorganic com-pounds but is restricted to ferroelectric materials, in which the ferroelectric transition is directly related to changes in hydrogen bonding.

Chapter 8 presents a brief prognosis of future developments in this field.

One of the unique features of this volume is the illustration of many of the structures by stereoscopic drawings which require the viewer found inside the back cover of the book.   These drawings were produced by use of the elegant computer program written by Dr. C. K. Johnson of the Oak Ridge National Laboratory, and we are indebted to Dr. Johnson for supplying not only the program but also four of the drawings.   Most of the other drawings were competently prepared by Sam La Placa and Anisbert Sequeira.

WALTER C. HAMILTON
JAMES A. IBERS

Upton, New York
Evanston, Illinois
August 1967

Acknowledgments

A number of our colleagues have been extremely cooperative in communicating to us the results of their unpublished work in this field, and we are appreciative of the discussions that we have had with them.

One of us (W. C. H.) would like to thank the members of the chemistry department of Princeton University for the hospitality extended when he lectured on the subject matter of this book during the tenure of an FMC lectureship in the spring of 1965. Thanks are also due to members of the chemistry department of the State University of New York at Stony Brook for similar hospitality during the fall semester of 1966.

Both of us feel privileged to have had the opportunity of receiving our early training in structural chemistry under the tutelage of Professor Verner Schomaker, whose critical insight and deep interest in all branches of physical chemistry have been greatly stimulating to us through the years.

We are indebted to members of the staffs of the Brookhaven National Laboratory and Northwestern University for their help in preparing this book for publication. We would particularly like to express our appreciation to Mrs. Bonnie Wesolowski for her efficient and accurate preparation of the final manuscript.

We gratefully acknowledge the cooperation of the following publishers and editors for granting permission to use previously published figures: E. Arnold, Ltd., the W. H. Freeman Co., the Cambridge University Press, and the editors of *Acta Crystallographica*, *Inorganic Chemistry*, the *Journal of the American Chemical Society*, the *Journal of Chemical Physics*, the *Journal de Physique*, *Physical Review Letters*, the *Proceedings of the Royal Society*, the *Proceedings of the Physical Society*, *Solid State Communications*, and the *Zeitschrift für Elektrochemie*.

W. C. H.
J. A. I.

Contents

Contents

chapter	# Some Definitions
one	# and Motivations

In confining ourselves in this book to the structural investigation of the hydrogen bond in *solids*, we are open to the question, "Why are you interested in solid state structure at all?" There are two obvious answers: We are interested in studying the structure of the solid state in order to learn something about the structures of individual molecules that compose the solid state, and we are interested in studying the structure of the solid state in order to learn something about the peculiar characteristics of this state itself.

From the first point of view, we look upon the crystal [1] simply as a device for holding the molecule down so that we can take a good look at it. Any special effects due to the crystalline condition—distortions due to the requirements of intermolecular packing for example—may be looked upon as being undesirable but unavoidable side effects which may partially obscure the information we are really after, namely molecular structure. In the extreme of the second point of view—that of the solid state physicist who is happiest when studying a monatomic, cubic solid—it is effects associated with the crystalline order which are of primary interest, and the molecule may be looked upon as an evil to be avoided if at all possible.

The chemist may often be interested in the crystalline state, not only to learn something about molecular structure, but to learn something about the interactions of molecules with each other as well. The study of hydrogen-bonded systems, for example, falls somewhere in between the two extremes described above. As we shall see throughout this book, we are interested

[1] In this book, we shall hold the terms *crystal* and *solid* to be synonymous unless otherwise stated. This usage is not intended to imply that hydrogen bonds are unimportant in noncrystalline solids.

in the structure of crystalline materials containing hydrogen bonds, not only because studies of these materials can tell us something about the general nature of possibly isolated hydrogen bonds, but also because the presence of hydrogen bonds often plays the determinative role in the packing of the molecules which make up the crystal structure. Then practically all the properties of the solid are strongly dependent on the presence of the hydrogen bond.

1-1 SPECIFIC INTERMOLECULAR INTERACTIONS AND HYDROGEN BONDS

In the solid state, many substances appear to crystallize in such a way that the packing of the molecules approaches some kind of close packing. That is, the molecules may be considered to be composed of spherical atoms with constant radii—the van der Waals radii. These objects with well-defined boundaries then pack together so as to leave as little empty space as possible. If the molecules are spherical, we get some fairly simple arrangements, for example that in Figure 1-1. If they are oddly shaped, the arrangements may get more complicated (Figure 1-2). If the van der Waals radii are constant, the efficient space filling by these molecular lumps is the important point; there are no specific directional effects or interactions between molecules. The close packing of oddly shaped molecules has been the subject of extensive study by Kitaigorodskii (1957), and some structures have even been predicted on the basis of these packing considerations. (See, for example, Williams, 1965.) This simple model in

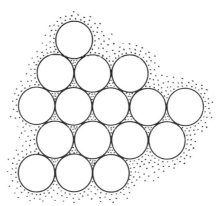

Figure 1-1 *A regular packing of regular objects in the plane. The hexagonal array shown is the closest possible packing of circles.*

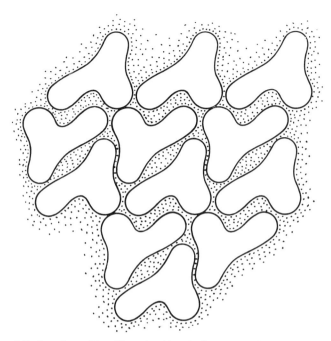

Figure 1-2 *A regular packing of irregular objects in the plane.   There may be other arrangements which fill space more densely.   The symmetry of the lattice is determined by the shape and packing of the molecules.*

fact seems to account for much of the detailed structure of such complex molecules as proteins.   (See, for example, Scott and Scheraga, 1966.)

There are, however, a number of rather specific intermolecular interactions which can influence the packing significantly.   A naive description of these says that the van der Waals spheres are distorted, but to be fair we must ask for the reasons behind these distortions.   These specific interactions can often be qualitatively explained on the basis of simple electrostatic considerations.   For example, such interactions often occur between charged species or between portions of molecules rich or deficient in electron density. The availability of empty π orbitals to aid in intermolecular bonding is often an important factor as well.   Examples of charge transfer complexes such as the benzene-I_2 complex immediately come to mind.   The short carbonyl oxygen-aromatic carbon distances to be found in alloxan (Figure 1-3; Bolton, 1964) and similar compounds provide other good examples. Specific attractions between the charged —NH_3^+ portions of amino acids in the zwitterion form and double bonds in adjacent molecules are also apparently common.

By far the most ubiquitous and widely studied specific intermolecular interaction which affects the structure of condensed states is that known as the *hydrogen bond*. Now many chemists have been primarily concerned with the study of the hydrogen bond in the liquid state, for consideration of the hydrogen bond is indeed important for many of the details of reactions in aqueous media, and the interesting properties of many common liquids are closely related to the hydrogen-bonding properties of the molecules in these liquids. The high melting and boiling points of H_2O provide the most obvious example. It is, however, in the solid state, where the experimental results are least ambiguous, that the hydrogen bond is best studied.[2] Many of the things that we learn about the nature of the hydrogen bond in solids can be carried over to an understanding of the hydrogen bonding in other states of matter. That the hydrogen bond in the solid must be very similar to that in the liquid state is supported by thermodynamic measurements. The energy associated with the formation of the O—H $\cdots$ O hydrogen bond in solid phenol is 4.2 kcal mole^{-1}, while that for the same bond in a carbon tetrachloride solution is 4.3 kcal mole^{-1}. There are many such examples. (See Pimentel and McClellan, 1960, Chapter 7.)

[2] Possible exceptions to this rather strong statement are the few studies of hydrogen-bonded dimers or complexes in the vapor phase.

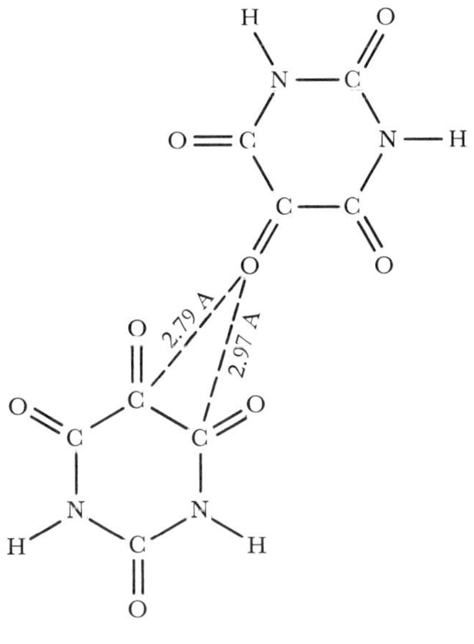

Figure 1-3 *Two molecules of alloxan as found in the crystal. The two labeled C $\cdots$ O intermolecular distances provide examples of unusually short nonbonded contacts where hydrogen bonds are not involved. The two molecules are not coplanar; the C $\cdots$ O distances are less than the O $\cdots$ O distances.*

Thus our reasons for wishing to study the hydrogen bond in solids are similar to our reasons for wanting to study any structure in the solid state. On the one hand, we use the crystal simply as a matrix for tying down the system of interest—the isolated hydrogen bond—while we study it. On the other hand, we are interested in the beauties—the simplicities and complexities—of the solid state itself. Primarily though, we are interested in the thorough study of a particular strong intermolecular attractive force.

1-2 WHAT IS A CRYSTAL?

Since we are to be discussing the structures of hydrogen-bonded crystals, it behooves us to understand what we mean by *crystal structure* and what we mean by the *hydrogen bond*. Let us address ourselves to the first question. What do we know about a crystal when we say that we know its structure? This question may be answered from two principal points of view because the elucidation of solid state structure has depended on two techniques: x-ray crystallography and infrared spectroscopy. The first answer of the x-ray crystallographer to the question "Do you know the structure of this crystal?" will be "Yes, I know where all the atoms are." The spectroscopist on the other hand will answer, "Yes, I know the energy levels of this system." The former answer perhaps appeals most to the practical man and pre-twentieth-century physicist in all of us; the latter point of view perhaps appeals more to that part of our intellect which understands that the information about energy levels alone will allow us to calculate all the thermodynamic functions of interest.[3] The truth of course lies somewhere in between, and our opinion is that we are all happiest when we are able to build a model out of cork balls which indicates the approximate locations of the atoms in a molecule and at the same time understand all the spectroscopic measurements which have been made on the system.

1-3 WAVE AND DENSITY FUNCTIONS

It is the current view of most chemists that the solution of the Schrödinger wave equation would tell us all that we need to know about a molecule. If

[3] This part of our intellect would also assert that thermodynamics is the foundation, cornerstone, and pinnacle of all of chemistry. We should of course include nonequilibrium thermodynamics in this statement to cover many of the interesting problems of chemistry.

a molecule is composed of n particles—nuclei and electrons—the position of each being specified by a vector r_i, it seems fair to say that we would have a complete description of the structure of this molecule if we had precise knowledge of the n-particle wave functions and energy levels for the ground state and all excited states [4]:

$$\Psi_0(r_1, r_2, \ldots, r_n) \quad E_0$$
$$\Psi_1(r_1, r_2, \ldots, r_n) \quad E_1$$
$$\cdot \qquad \qquad \cdot$$
$$\cdot \qquad \qquad \cdot$$
$$\cdot \qquad \qquad \cdot \qquad \qquad (1\text{-}1)$$
$$\Psi_i(r_1, r_2, \ldots, r_n) \quad E_i$$
$$\cdot \qquad \qquad \cdot$$
$$\cdot \qquad \qquad \cdot$$
$$\cdot \qquad \qquad \cdot$$

Because of the extreme mathematical complexity of the wave functions for all but the simplest systems, it is not a practical matter to calculate the wave functions for molecules with an interestingly large number of nuclei and electrons. The chemist who is interested in the subtleties of molecular structure wisely turns to experiment rather than to the computer for his information.

Closer to reality than the wave function Ψ is the density function $\rho(r_1, r_2, \ldots, r_n)$, which gives the probability of finding particle number 1 at r_1, particle 2 at r_2, and so on:

$$\rho(r_1, r_2, \ldots, r_n) = \Psi^*\Psi = |\Psi|^2 \qquad (1\text{-}2)$$

For many purposes, as a matter of fact, it is sufficient to know the second- and first-order density functions given by

$$\rho_{II}(r_i, r_j) = \int_{\substack{k \neq i \\ k \neq j}} \rho(r_1, r_2, \ldots, r_n) \, dr_k \cdots \qquad (1\text{-}3)$$

$$\rho_I(r_i) = \int_{k \neq i} \rho(r_1, r_2, \ldots, r_n) \, dr_k \cdots \qquad (1\text{-}4)$$

The second-order density function (1-3) tells us the probability of finding particle i at r_i and particle j at r_j at the same time. It thus gives us information about the correlation of the positions of the particles, as well as informa-

---

[4] If we are interested in chemistry, we are also interested in the probabilities of transition between these states and between states of related molecules under specified circumstances. Obviously, one of the reasons we study structure is to be able to say something about the interactions between molecules—which is what chemistry is really all about.

We shall of course also be interested in solutions of the wave equation in the presence of electric and magnetic fields—both static and periodic.

tion about the positions of each individually. The first-order density function (1-4) on the other hand gives us information only on the position of a single particle. The first-order density function is, for example, sufficient to determine the mean position of a particle,[5]

$$\langle \mathbf{r}_i \rangle = E\{\mathbf{r}_i\} = \int \mathbf{r}_i \rho_{\mathrm{I}}(\mathbf{r}_i) \, d\mathbf{r}_i \tag{1-5}$$

as well as the mean square deviation of the particle position,

$$E\{(\mathbf{r}_i - \langle \mathbf{r}_i \rangle)^2\} = \int (\mathbf{r}_i - \langle \mathbf{r}_i \rangle)^2 \rho_{\mathrm{I}}(\mathbf{r}_i) \, d\mathbf{r}_i \tag{1-6}$$

In order to define the mean separation between particles i and j, however, we need the two-particle density function [6]:

$$\text{Mean separation} = E\{|\mathbf{r}_i - \mathbf{r}_j|\} = \int |\mathbf{r}_i - \mathbf{r}_j| \rho_{\mathrm{II}}(\mathbf{r}_i, \mathbf{r}_j) \, d\mathbf{r}_i \, d\mathbf{r}_j \tag{1-7}$$

Although the treatment up to this point has been perfectly general, in most of what follows the particles at positions $\mathbf{r}_i$ will be the nuclei of the system, and much of what we have to say about molecular structure will be in terms of the wave functions describing the positions of the nuclei in the molecule. Thus, $E\{\mathbf{r}_i\}$ will be the mean position of atom i, and $E\{|\mathbf{r}_i - \mathbf{r}_j|\}$ will be the *bond length*, the calculation of which requires knowledge of the two-nucleus density function. A mean bond angle, which requires three distances for its determination, can only be calculated exactly if the three-nucleus density function is known.

The mean separation as defined in (1-7) is not the only possible definition for the bond length. This may not at first be apparent to the student who is accustomed to thinking about a molecule in terms of balls separated by rigid sticks. The nuclei do not remain at a fixed separation as such a model would imply. Because of zero-point vibrational energy the nuclei are in constant motion relative to one another, even at the lowest temperature, and the concept of bond length necessarily becomes a bit fuzzy. The definition of bond length as mean separation probably is the closest to the common-sense definition.

The relative motion of two atoms may also be calculated from the two-particle density function. For example, we may obtain the mean square displacement Δ^2 from the mean bond length as follows:

$$\Delta^2 = E\{|\mathbf{r}_1 - \mathbf{r}_2|^2\} - E^2\{|\mathbf{r}_1 - \mathbf{r}_2|\} \tag{1-8}$$

where

$$E\{|\mathbf{r}_1 - \mathbf{r}_2|^2\} = \int |\mathbf{r}_1 - \mathbf{r}_2|^2 \rho(\mathbf{r}_1, \mathbf{r}_2) \, d\mathbf{r}_1 \, d\mathbf{r}_2 \tag{1-9}$$

[5] We introduce here the notation $E\{x\}$, read *expected value of x*, to denote the mean value of x over the density function ρ. $E\{x\}$ is also called the first moment of the density function. Similarly, $E\{x^n\}$ is called the nth moment.

[6] The vertical bars signify that the absolute value is to be taken.

In general, it is necessary to specify all the moments of a distribution to define completely the distribution—or density function. However, the use of a model plus the experimental determination of a few moments may allow us to specify the distribution completely. As we shall see, in a typical diffraction experiment only the first-order density function is obtained, and a model must be assumed in order to obtain mean bond distances.

1-4 PERIODIC STRUCTURES

The results of Section 1-3 are perfectly general in that they apply to any atomic or molecular system. Let us now consider the structures of crystals in greater detail.

A perfect crystal may be described in terms of a three-dimensional translational lattice defined by three noncoplanar vectors, a_1, a_2, a_3.[7] If there is an atom at position R, there is an atom at the position $R + n_1a_1 + n_2a_2 + n_3a_3$ where n_1, n_2, n_3 are integers (positive, negative, or zero). In terms of the density function,

$$\rho(R + n_1a_1 + n_2a_2 + n_3a_3) = \rho(R) \qquad (1\text{-}10)$$

Given any vector X, the region of space bounded by the parallelepiped with vertices X, $X + a_1$, $X + a_2$, $X + a_3$, $X + a_1 + a_2$, $X + a_1 + a_3$, $X + a_2 + a_3$, $X + a_1 + a_2 + a_3$, is a *unit cell* of the crystal. Because of the translational periodicity expressed by (1-10), a description of the contents of one unit cell of a crystal is a description of the entire crystal.[8]

In this concept of a perfect crystal, at any instant of time we cannot tell the difference between the environment of a point in one unit cell and the environment of a point related to the first one by a lattice translation. If this is true at all times, then any motions which the atoms in the crystal undergo must be collective motions: if an atom in unit cell one moves 0.1 A in the positive a_1 direction, the corresponding atoms in all unit cells must move 0.1 A in the positive a_1 direction at the same time. This is certainly not true for all the motions which the atoms and molecules in crystals undergo. We expect though that in a perfect crystal the motions which an atom in one unit cell makes are identical with those that the corresponding atom in another unit cell makes, even though there may not be a definite phase rela-

---

[7] These vectors are not necessarily orthogonal.

[8] Strictly speaking, for a finite crystal we must also specify the dimensions of the crystal and give a description of the surface. In this book, we shall not be concerned with surface effects and will thus consider a knowledge of the unit cell contents to be sufficient.

tion between the two. If we average over a time period which is long compared with one cycle of the periodic atomic motions, this time average distribution will be identical from one unit cell to the next. If there is randomness of the phases of the motions, the average over all unit cells at a single instant of time gives the same result as an average over one unit cell for a long period of time. Let us, for example, consider that a complete description of the contents of the unit cell identified by the lattice translation $\mathbf{L}_i$ at time t be given by a density function $S(\mathbf{L}_i, t)$. The average of this function over a time period $t_1 < t < t_2$, perhaps the time of an observation of some kind, is

$$S_t(\mathbf{L}_i) = \frac{1}{(t_2 - t_1)} \int_{t_1}^{t_2} S(\mathbf{L}_i, t) \, dt \qquad (1\text{-}11)$$

Similarly, the average over the N unit cells which make up the whole crystal at a single time will be given by

$$S_{\mathbf{L}}(t) = \frac{1}{N} \sum_{i=1}^{N} S(\mathbf{L}_i, t) \qquad (1\text{-}12)$$

If all unit cells are indeed identical, we may assert that

$$S = S_{\mathbf{L}}(t) = S_t(\mathbf{L}_i) \qquad \text{for all } i \text{ and all } t \qquad (1\text{-}13)$$

What we normally mean by the description of a crystal structure is the description S of the average unit cell. If the crystal is in a stationary state, that is, has a definite energy, the most general form of the function S for describing the crystal is the many-particle wave function, which *is* of course periodic on the crystal lattice. There is no finite number of experiments which will allow us to determine completely the wave function for a molecular system. As we shall see in Chapter 2, the average single-particle density function is the function most easily determined by a diffraction experiment, and this is what the x-ray crystallographer is usually talking about when he says he knows the structure of a crystal. From a practical point of view, the crystal may be described by a sum of density functions for each particle in the unit cell. We might, for example, give an electron density function plus a distribution function for the position of every nucleus in the cell.

During the period of observation, a crystal will probably exist in many different stationary states, due to thermal excitation, and we may wish to make a further average of the density functions—not the wave functions— over all these states.

That the zero-point motions and thermal excitation cause the periodicity of the crystal not to be exact may be described by saying that the crystal is disordered. These effects may be called *dynamic* disorder, because they arise from the motions of the atoms. In addition to this dynamic disorder, over which we must average, any real crystal will also have defects or *static* disorder which may cause departures from true periodicity. Molecules or atoms may be missing here or there, or molecules may occasionally pack in a way different from the ideal. In any real crystal, the description of the average unit cell will take these effects into account, again by performing the average over many unit cells. (See Figure 1-4.)

Disorder of atomic positions between two equivalent energy states is covered by the averaging over all occupied stationary state wave functions discussed in the preceding paragraph.

Thus although the ideal description of a crystal might demand a knowledge of the wave function for a single stationary state, or even separate knowledge of the wave function for all stationary states of interest, in actual fact the best that we can do is to obtain an average description of the unit cell in terms of an average density function. We may then try to infer

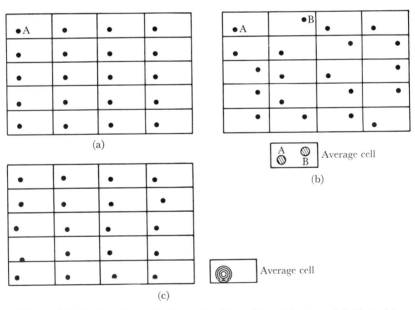

Figure 1-4 (a) *A perfectly ordered crystal. The position of the atoms A is identical in each unit cell. (b) A statistically disordered crystal. The atom is at position A in about half the unit cells and at position B in the other half. The average unit cell consists of half an atom at A and half an atom at B. (c) The effect of motion in an ordered crystal. The atom is displaced from its mean position A because of zero-point energy. This displacement varies with time and with the particular unit cell. The average unit cell has a distribution of atomic positions which may be represented by a contour map, the contours giving the probability of finding the atom at a particular position.*

something about the individual wave functions or the potentials which gave rise to them from our knowledge of the average densities and the use of some sort of model for the factors which have been averaged in the experiment.

1-5   ENERGY LEVELS AND STRUCTURE

Although we have briefly spoken of stationary states and energy levels in the preceding sections, the emphasis in Section 1-4 unavoidably strayed to the point of view of the x-ray crystallographer, who says that he knows a structure when he knows where everything is.   Most of modern physics, however, is concerned not with where things are but with what energy differences exist between various states of the system.   At first sight, one might be tempted to say that this emphasis is dictated by the fact that spectroscopy—the measurement of energy differences—is a technique which is adapted to many situations and has been very widely used in many different energy ranges.   This is perhaps partly true, but it is also true that this measurement of energy level differences strikes at the very heart of chemistry, since it is chemical change or the reaction of one molecule with another which is the real concern of the chemist.   Since the direction and rate of chemical change are intimately tied up with the energies of the reacting molecules, the understanding of molecular energetics may be the most important area of chemistry.

Since the energies of stationary states of the system and the wave functions of these states are dependent on the potential energy of interaction of one particle with another, a knowledge of the energy levels can allow one to work backward to obtain knowledge of the potential energy.   The consequent information regarding the nature of intermolecular and interatomic interactions can be of great value in interpreting not only chemical reactions but also the behavior of matter in dense phases.   Since one of the more interesting problems connected with hydrogen bonding is the potential energy surface which describes the interaction giving rise to the hydrogen bond, spectroscopy has had as much of an impact on the study of hydrogen bonding as has any other technique.

The most important spectroscopic studies relating to hydrogen-bonded systems have been in the areas of vibration-rotation spectroscopy, using mainly infrared radiation.   This study of nuclear motions is usually interpreted in the framework of the Born-Oppenheimer approximation, which allows us to consider nuclear and electronic motions separately because of the large differences in mass.   In principle (but not in practice, as we have noted earlier), we may consider a molecule in which the nuclei are at fixed positions, denoted collectively by $\mathbf{R}$, and solve the Schrödinger equation for the motions of the electrons (with positions $\mathbf{r}_i$) alone:

$$\left\{ - \sum_i \left[\frac{h^2}{8\pi^2 m_i} \nabla_i^2 + V(\mathbf{r}_i, \mathbf{R}) \right] - E_{\mathrm{el}}(\mathbf{R}) \right\} \psi_{\mathrm{el}}(\mathbf{r}) = 0 \qquad (1\text{-}14)$$

The sum of kinetic energy operators extends over all electrons. V is the electrostatic potential energy and includes terms due to interactions between all electrons and nuclei in the molecule. The electronic wave function $\psi_{\mathrm{el}}(\mathbf{r})$ depends also on $\mathbf{R}$, but only because $\mathbf{R}$ enters as a parameter in the potential energy. It gives no information on the position density of $\mathbf{R}$. The electronic energy $E_{\mathrm{el}}(\mathbf{R})$ is now taken as the potential energy for the solution of the Schrödinger equation for the nuclear motions:

$$\left\{ - \sum_i \frac{h^2}{8\pi^2 M_i} \nabla_i^2 + E_{\mathrm{el}}(\mathbf{R}) - E_{\mathrm{total}} \right\} \psi_{\mathrm{nuclear}}(\mathbf{R}) = 0 \qquad (1\text{-}15)$$

The sum extends over all nuclei with masses M_i. Since the energy levels obtained in the solution of (1-15) depend on the potential E_{el}, a measurement of the transition energies can tell us something about the variation of the total molecular energy with changes in the positions of the nuclei and hence something about the electronic wave function.

We shall also see in Chapter 4 how other types of spectroscopy have been useful in studies of the hydrogen bond. The use of NMR (nuclear magnetic resonance) spectroscopy has had important applications, both in its use as a probe of the electronic wave function and as a measure of inter-hydrogen distances. Neutron inelastic scattering for the study of low-frequency motion has also been important.

1-6 WHAT IS A HYDROGEN BOND?

Now that we have discussed what a structure—particularly a crystal structure—*is*, we shall discuss what the hydrogen bond is. The concept of the hydrogen bond was first introduced some 47 years ago by Latimer and Rodebush (1920) in the following way:

"Thus, in terms of the Lewis theory, a free pair of electrons on one water molecule might be able to exert sufficient force on a hydrogen held by a pair of electrons on another water molecule to bond the two molecules together.

Structurally this may be represented as

$$
\begin{array}{c}
\text{H} \\
\ddot{} \quad \ddot{} \\
\text{H} : \text{O} : \text{H} : \text{O} \\
\ddot{} \quad \ddot{} \\
\text{H}
\end{array}
$$

. . . . Such an explanation amounts to saying that the hydrogen nucleus held between two octets constitutes a weak bond."

Since that time there has been considerable discussion of a suitable definition of the hydrogen bond (e.g., see Hadži, 1959). We adopt here an operational definition which is most closely related to that used by Pimentel and McClellan (1960).

A hydrogen bond exists when a hydrogen atom is bonded to two or more other atoms.

This seems an appropriate definition, since in the electron-pair theory of chemical bonding, a hydrogen atom is capable of forming only one bond. Thus this definition of hydrogen bond suggests that there is something at least slightly out of the ordinary in a hydrogen bond. Use of the above definition requires us to answer the further question, "What is a bond?" As we have suggested in Section 1-1, a bond might best be defined as existing between two atoms when there is a specific, directional interatomic attractive force which causes these two atoms to be in proximity when the system is at equilibrium. Thus there are two criteria:

(1) a geometrical criterion involving distance and direction;
(2) an energetic criterion.

It is not an accident that there is a one-to-one correspondence between these criteria and the two principal general methods of molecular structure determination—diffraction and spectroscopy. For in the end, one must adopt a definition by which one can define the existence or nonexistence of a hydrogen bond on the basis of an experiment. As we shall see below, the presence of hydrogen bonds is often inferred either from the geometrical arrangements found by diffraction methods or by the characteristic changes in the vibrational spectra of molecules when hydrogen bonds are formed.

There is perhaps a difficulty in nomenclature when one speaks of the hydrogen bond. The definition above defines a *situation* in which the hydrogen bond is said to exist, but what do we mean when we say *the hydrogen bond?* Usually this name refers to the entire group of three or more atoms which are involved in a configuration X—H—Y. In most cases of hydrogen bonding, one of the two or more bonds formed by hydrogen is much stronger than the others.[9]

[9] The strength of a bond can be measured in several different ways. Perhaps the simplest is to consider the bond to be stronger if the bond dissociation energy is greater.

The weaker of the two bonds is sometimes called the hydrogen bond to distinguish it from the stronger, and presumably covalent, bond. Such a bonding situation is often indicated diagrammatically by

$$X—H \cdot \cdot \cdot Y$$

There are important cases of hydrogen bonding where the two bonds are equal in strength and length; these may be written

$$X—H—X$$

Among the known examples are F—H—F in the bifluoride ion and O—H—O in the acid salts of several monobasic acids.

Although the bridge bonds in the boron hydrides satisfy the operational definition, there is a marked difference between them and most of the hydrogen bonds we discuss in this book. The bridge bonds in the boron hydrides can best be discussed in terms of a *single* electron pair bond extending over three nuclei B—H—B. The more conventional hydrogen bonds with which we are concerned involve *two* electron pairs extending over the three nuclei involved. For B—H—B, we might write the single filled bond orbital as

$$\psi_{bond} = aB_1 + bH + aB_2$$

whereas in the symmetric O—H—O case, we might write two filled bond orbitals as

$$\psi_1 = aO_1 + bH + aO_2$$

$$\psi_2 = O_1 - O_2$$

We shall not consider the boron hydrides further in this book. The interested reader should consult the excellent monograph by Lipscomb (1963).

It also would not appear to be particularly useful to consider the ionic hydrides—such as LiH, which has the sodium chloride structure—as being hydrogen bonded.

1-7 VAN DER WAALS RADII AND THE HYDROGEN BOND

In previous sections of this chapter, we have said that there exists geometrical evidence for hydrogen bonding—that is to say, geometrical evidence that a hydrogen atom is involved in more than one bond. What is this evidence?

It is found that in molecular crystals, when there are no specific directional interactions between molecules, the molecules are packed together so that the distances of closest approach for a given pair of atomic species are nearly constant from crystal to crystal. This fact may be formalized by assigning to each a characteristic packing radius. These characteristic radii are known as the van der Waals radii and have been tabulated by Pauling (1960) and more recently by Bondi (1964). The van der Waals radius of oxygen, for example, is 1.4 A. We thus expect that when two molecules pack in such a way that oxygen atoms on the molecules are adjacent the distance between the oxygen atoms is about 2.8 A. We are prepared to say that something unusual is going on if two oxygen atoms are much closer together than that, and if the distance is much greater than that we do not usually consider that there is a contact between the atoms which is important in the packing. The general criterion that has been applied in inferring the presence of hydrogen bonds when the positions of only the nonhydrogen atoms are known is that two electronegative atoms be closer together than the sum of the van der Waals radii. Furthermore it must be possible to have a hydrogen atom bonded to one of these atoms in a normal covalent way and positioned nearly along the line of centers joining the two heavy atoms. Thus a short distance and a possible linear hydrogen bond have been the requirements. We shall see in a later chapter that the requirement of linearity is not particularly stringent.

The importance of this criterion based on heavy atom positions is that many x-ray crystal structure determinations in the past have not resulted in the determination of hydrogen atom positions (for reasons that we shall examine in Chapter 2), and it has been necessary to make inferences based on heavy atoms positions. If the hydrogen bonds are weak, the criterion that the distance be less than the sums of the heavy atom van der Waals radii is not necessarily valid, and in complex structures, particularly inorganic hydrates, the assignment of hydrogen atoms to specific hydrogen bonds may be ambiguous. A far more restrictive criterion for weak hydrogen bonding, which is based on knowledge of the hydrogen atom position, is that the distance from the hydrogen atom to the more weakly bound atom be considerably less than the sum of the van der Waals radii of hydrogen and the heavy atom. Here there can rarely be any ambiguity. This point may be made clear by an examination of the data in Table 1-1, where we present some characteristic distances which are relevant to a number of different hydrogen bond types. Except for F—H—F, these figures refer to typical, nonsymmetric hydrogen bonds. The distances labeled A · · · B (calc) are the sums of the appropriate van der Waals radii as adapted from Pauling (1960). The distances H · · · B (calc) are defined in a similar way. The columns labeled A · · · B (obs) and H · · · B (obs) are values determined by diffraction methods.

There is a range of A · · · B and H · · · B distances observed in hydrogen bonds; this range extends from bonds about 0.2 A shorter than those presented in the table in each case to distances which are so long that

Table 1-1 *Van der Waals Contact Distances and Observed Hydrogen Bond Distances (in A) for Some Common Types of Hydrogen Bonds*

Bond type	A · · · B (calc)	A · · · B (obs)	H · · · B (calc)	H · · · B (obs)
F—H—F	2.7	2.4	2.6	1.2
O—H · · · O	2.8	2.7	2.6	1.7
O—H · · · F	2.8	2.7	2.6	1.7
O—H · · · N	2.9	2.8	2.7	1.9
O—H · · · Cl	3.2	3.1	3.0	2.2
N—H · · · O	2.9	2.9	2.6	2.0
N—H · · · F	2.9	2.8	2.6	1.9
N—H · · · Cl	3.3	3.3	3.0	2.4
N—H · · · N	3.0	3.1	2.7	2.2
N—H · · · S	3.4	3.4	3.1	2.4
C—H · · · O	3.0	3.2	2.6	2.3

the van der Waals criterion on the A · · · B distance no longer identifies the hydrogen bond. There is uncertainty of the order of 0.1 A in the van der Waals diameters, as the concept of a constant van der Waals radius is an oversimplified, average description of intermolecular packing.

It should be noted from Table 1-1 that the observed heavy atom separation is rarely more than 0.3 A shorter than the predicted van der Waals separation and is sometimes even longer. On the other hand, the difference between the H · · · B distance observed and that predicted is large and unmistakable; the difference ranges from near 1 A for the stronger hydrogen bonds to 0.3 A for the rather weak C—H · · · O hydrogen bonds. The table has in fact been arranged so that the strongest bonds, in terms of this distance criterion, lie at the top of the table. A heavy atom distance less than the van der Waals distance is perhaps a sufficient, but not necessary, condition for the presence of hydrogen bonding. A good operational criterion for the existence of the hydrogen bond is that at least two heavy atom-hydrogen atom distances less than the sum of the van der Waals radii be present.

1-8 CHEMICAL REQUIREMENTS FOR HYDROGEN BOND FORMATION

In the last section we omitted any discussion of why hydrogen bonds form. There seems to be no generally applicable answer to this question. In fact Bernal (1959) has said, "It seems to me that all quantum treatments of the hydrogen bond suffer from the defect that there are too few experimental facts." Nevertheless there are a few observations that have general validity.

What do the hydrogen bonds in Table 1-1 have in common in terms of the chemical characteristics of the atoms involved? The requirement for hydrogen bond formation is the simultaneous presence of an acidic hydrogen atom and a basic acceptor. The charge distribution in a hydrogen bond can be described partially by the following diagram:

$$A^- \!\!-\!\! H^+ \cdot \cdot \cdot B^-$$

A requirement for the *donor* molecule in a hydrogen bond is that there be a hydrogen atom attached to an electronegative atom A, which has withdrawn some electrons from the hydrogen atom to give it a slightly positive or acidic character.[10] The *acceptor* molecule may contain a region B which has high electron density capable of interacting strongly with the acidic hydrogen. Lone pair electrons in the acceptor molecule are ideal for this purpose.

As we shall see in Chapter 6, many of the geometrical aspects of hydrogen bond formation can be adequately explained on the basis of simple electro-static models. On the other hand, a rigorous quantum mechanical model is necessary to calculate quantitatively the potential energy surface for the motion of the hydrogen atom along the internuclear line in a hydrogen-bonded system.[11]

The most common hydrogen bond donor molecular segments are F—H, O—H, and N—H. The groups Cl—H, S—H, and P—H also act as hydro-gen bond donors in some situations, but the hydrogen bonds so formed are very much weaker than those formed by the first-row atoms. This seems clear evidence that high electronegativity of the heavy atom, leading to an acidic hydrogen, is of great importance. There is also very good evidence that C—H can act as a hydrogen-bonding donor. This usually occurs where the whole C—H group has a net positive charge.

The criterion that a lone pair be available seems to be a good one for selecting acceptor atoms for hydrogen bond formation. C apparently never acts as an acceptor, while F, N, and O are all good acceptors. The other

---

[10] After the hydrogen bond is formed, the hydrogen may be either slightly basic or acidic, as NMR chemical shifts indicate.

[11] There have been many heated discussions as to whether the hydrogen bond is electro-static or quantum mechanical in nature. Couched in these terms, there is no real argument, for the quantum mechanical treatment of molecular structure uses an electrostatic potential; thus all chemical bonding is a result of electrostatic potentials. There are two related and real questions. Can a simple electrostatic model explain a great deal of the energetics of hydrogen bond formation? Does the hydrogen bond have a substantial amount of ionic (as opposed to covalent) character? The answer to both questions is "In many cases, yes."

halogen atoms can probably act as acceptors as well, but the halogen ions
F^-, Cl^-, Br^-, and I^- are even better, although hydrogen bonds to I^- are
weak. S and sometimes P may also act as weak acceptors in hydrogen bonds.

1-9 HYDROGEN BOND NETWORKS

Descriptions of hydrogen-bonded structures often become exceedingly
complex. Some attempts have been made to classify the different types of
hydrogen-bonding networks that occur (Wells, 1962). We shall briefly
discuss one possible classification.

In the discussion of the network structure of hydrogen-bonded molecular
crystals, it is convenient to consider each molecule as a single point with
lines representing hydrogen bonds extending from it.

We shall consider only a single hydrogen-bonded species to be present in
the crystal. The simplest hydrogen bonding will occur when there is only

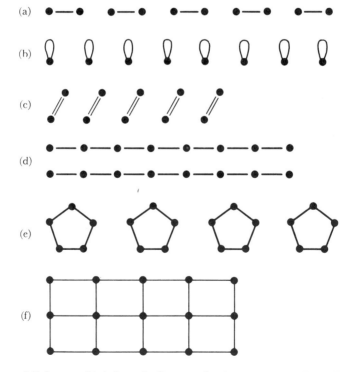

Figure 1-5 *Some possible hydrogen-bonding networks of a simple type, as described in the text.*

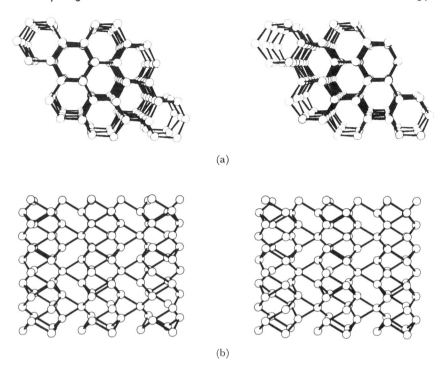

Figure 1-6 *The structure of trigonal acetamide. Each molecule is represented as a single sphere to illustrate better the infinite three-dimensional hydrogen bond network. This is a stereo pair. (See Preface.) (a) View approximately down the trigonal axis. In addition to being hydrogen bonded in the hexagonal sheets, the sheets are connected by other hydrogen bonds, so that each molecule is hydrogen bonded to four others. (b) View normal to the threefold axis showing that a three-dimensional hydrogen-bonded array is formed.*

one hydrogen atom available for hydrogen bonding for every two molecules, as for example in potassium hydrogen bisbenzoate, where the hydrogen atom is shared equally between the two anions[12]:

$$K^+ \quad A\text{—}H\text{—}A^-$$

There is only one hydrogen-bonded structure involving more than one molecule, namely, a structure of singly hydrogen-bonded dimers. This may be represented as in Figure 1-5a. The trivial but interesting case of a single internal hydrogen bond, as in potassium hydrogen maleate, may be repre-

---

[12] Many such structures have been examined by Speakman and co-workers. (See for example, Golic and Speakman, 1965.) Most of them have very short O—H—O hydrogen bonds. These are discussed further in Section 5-4.

sented as in Figure 1-5b. Consider now a molecule which has available one hydrogen atom per molecule to engage in hydrogen bonding. Only three types of structures are possible: The first is a structure composed of hydrogen-bonded dimers (Figure 1-5c) which are not further hydrogen-bonded to each other. The second is a structure composed of infinite linear hydrogen-bonded chains (Figure 1-5d). The third is a structure composed of cyclic complexes M_n, where $n > 2$. This structure is illustrated in Figure 1-5e for $n = 5$.

When there are as few as two hydrogen-bonding hydrogen atoms per molecule, the possibilities for different types of networks are very extensive. One of the simplest of these is a structure in which the principal element is an infinite planar network (Figure 1-5f). Two other cases are illustrated by the dimorphism of acetamide, which crystallizes in both an orthorhombic (Hamilton, 1965) and a trigonal form (Senti and Harker, 1940). The latter can be described in terms of an infinite three-dimensional network as illustrated in Figure 1-6. It is possible to go from any one molecule in the structure to any other by traveling along hydrogen bonds from molecule to molecule. On the other hand, in the orthorhombic form, illustrated by Figure 1-7, one can travel an infinite distance in one direction through the crystal but only one molecule from side to side in the other two directions. The structure consists of hydrogen-bonded dimers which are stacked in hydrogen-bonded columns, but the columns are not hydrogen bonded together.

Two useful pieces of information which may be given in the description of any hydrogen-bonded structure are the number of hydrogen bonds per

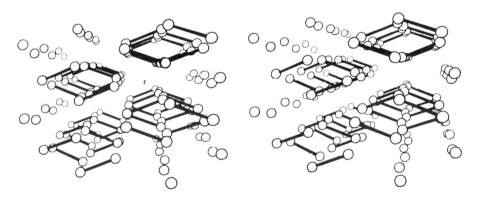

Figure 1-7 *The structure of orthorhombic acetamide, one sphere per molecule, as in Figure 1-6. Infinite two-dimensional columns (perpendicular to the plane of the drawing) of hydrogen-bonded dimers predominate in the structure. The hydrogen bonds connecting the dimers in the columns are not shown. There are no hydrogen bonds between the columns.*

molecule and the number of other molecules to which any one molecule is hydrogen bonded. This does not describe the topology of the structure completely, but it does tell much about the individual molecular environment. This part of the structure could, for example, be described in terms of two numbers

$$(N, M)$$

where N is the number of hydrogen bonds per molecule and M is the number of molecules to which a given molecule is hydrogen bonded. Thus hydrogen bond networks of the types illustrated in Figure 1-5 could be described respectively as $(\frac{1}{2}, 1)$, $(\frac{1}{2}, 0)$, $(1, 1)$, $(1, 2)$, and $(2, 4)$. The fact that the single pair of numbers is not a sufficient description is illustrated not only by a comparison of Figures 1-5d,e but also by a comparison of the structure in Figure 1-5f with trigonal acetamide, both of which may be described as $(2, 4)$. In one case, an infinite two-dimensional network is the extent of the hydrogen bonding; in the other a three-dimensional network is found. Orthorhombic acetamide may be described as $(2, 3)$.

This is an area where further systematic work would be useful.

REFERENCES

Bernal, J. D. (1959), in *Hydrogen Bonding* (D. Hadži, ed.), p. 360. Pergamon Press, New York.

Bolton, W. (1964), The Crystal Structure of Alloxan, *Acta Cryst.* **17,** 147.

Bondi, A. (1964), Van der Waals Volumes and Radii, *J. Phys. Chem.* **68,** 441.

Golič, L., and Speakman, J. C. (1965), The Crystal Structures of the Acid Salts of Some Monobasic Acids. X. Potassium, Rubidium, and Cesium Hydrogen Ditrifluoroacetate, *J. Chem. Soc.*, p. 2530.

Hadži, D. (1959), *Hydrogen Bonding*. Pergamon Press, New York.

Hamilton, W. C. (1965), The Crystal Structure of Orthorhombic Acetamide, *Acta Cryst.* **18,** 866.

Kitaigorodskii, A. I. (1961), *Organic Chemical Crystallography*. Consultants Bureau, New York.

Latimer, W. M., and Rodebush, W. H. (1920), Polarity and Ionization from the Standpoint of the Lewis Theory of Valence, *J. Am. Chem. Soc.* **42,** 1419.

Lipscomb, W. N. (1963), *Boron Hydrides*. W. A. Benjamin, New York.

Pauling, L. (1960), *The Nature of the Chemical Bond*, 3rd Ed. Cornell Univ. Press, Ithaca, New York.

Pimentel, G. C., and McClellan, A. L. (1960), *The Hydrogen Bond*. W. H. Freeman, San Francisco.

Scott, R. A., and Scheraga, H. A. (1966), Conformational Analysis of Macromolecules. III. Helical Structures of Polyglycine and Poly-L-alanine, *J. Chem. Phys.* **45,** 2091.

Senti, F., and Harker, D. (1940), The Crystal Structure of Rhombohedral Acetamide, *J. Am. Chem. Soc.* **62,** 2008.

Wells, A. F. (1962), *Structural Inorganic Chemistry*, pp. 294–315. Clarendon Press, Oxford.

Williams, D. E. (1965), Crystal Packing of Molecules, *Science* **147,** 605.

Diffraction Methods for the Study of the Hydrogen Bond

chapter two

In the half-century since von Laue's discovery of the diffraction of x-rays by crystals and the brilliant work of the Braggs and others in applying the newly discovered phenomenon to the elucidation of the structures of crystals, diffraction methods have provided an immense amount of detailed information about the microstructure of the crystalline state. These methods alone are capable of providing precise locations for every atom in the unit cell of a crystal, and hence the main feature of what we have called *the* crystal structure.

In this chapter our aim is to describe some of the theory and approximations involved in diffraction studies of crystal structures, and to point out some of the differences between x-ray, electron, and neutron diffraction, especially as applied to the study of the hydrogen bond.

2-1 GENERAL ASPECTS OF DIFFRACTION METHODS

When electromagnetic radiation or a particle beam is scattered from an object which has a periodic structure, the scattered waves interfere to produce detectable diffraction effects if the wavelength of the radiation is comparable to the repeat period of the object. The most common example is the diffraction of visible light by a regularly ruled plane grating. A crystal may be thought of as a three-dimensional diffraction grating, with characteristic

23

periods of the order of magnitude of 1 A. Any radiation of a comparable wavelength which is scattered from the crystal will produce diffraction effects. Not only electromagnetic radiation, but also particle beams, can produce these effects. The details of these diffraction effects depend on the structure of the crystal, and careful measurement of the diffraction pattern of a crystal can lead to a determination of the molecular and crystal structure.

If the crystal is described in terms of a periodic lattice with unit cell translation vectors $\mathbf{a}_1$, $\mathbf{a}_2$, $\mathbf{a}_3$, any point in the crystal may be described by a vector

$$\mathbf{r} = x_1\mathbf{a}_1 + x_2\mathbf{a}_2 + x_3\mathbf{a}_3 \tag{2-1}$$

The quantities x_1, x_2, and x_3 are the coordinates of the point $\mathbf{r}$ with respect to the axis system $\{\mathbf{a}_i\}$. (The notation $\{\mathbf{a}_i\}$ refers to the set $\{\mathbf{a}_1, \mathbf{a}_2, \mathbf{a}_3\}$.) A specification of the coordinates of every atom with

$$0 \leqslant x_1 \leqslant 1 \qquad 0 \leqslant x_2 \leqslant 1 \qquad 0 \leqslant x_3 \leqslant 1 \tag{2-2}$$

that is, every atom in the unit cell of the crystal, serves because of periodicity to specify the position of all atoms in the crystal. The atomic coordinates satisfying the conditions (2-2) are called the fractional coordinates of the atoms.

If the coordinates x_1, x_2, and x_3 in (2-1) are integers n_1, n_2, and n_3, and these integers are allowed to take on all possible values, the set of points $\mathbf{r}$ so generated is the *crystal lattice*.

The equation

$$h_1 x_1 + h_2 x_2 + h_3 x_3 = m \tag{2-3}$$

where m takes on all integral values, defines a set of parallel planes in the crystal. Radiation is scattered from a crystal elastically (with no change in energy) and coherently (with definite phase relationships producing diffraction effects) only if the crystal and x-ray beam are so oriented that the incident x-ray beam and the reflected x-ray beam make equal angles with a plane of form (2-3), where h_1, h_2, and h_3 are integers. This geometrical relationship is illustrated in Figure 2-1. The integers h_1, h_2, and h_3 are called the Miller indices of the plane. If the distance between these planes is d, diffraction occurs only when the angle θ satisfies the Bragg equation

$$\lambda = 2d \sin \theta \tag{2-4}$$

A plane may also be defined by describing the vector which is normal (perpendicular) to the plane. The vector perpendicular to the planes defined by equation (2-3) may be written as

$$\mathbf{H} = h_1 \mathbf{a}_1{}^* + h_2 \mathbf{a}_2{}^* + h_3 \mathbf{a}_3{}^* \tag{2-5}$$

Library
I.U.P.
Indiana, Pa.

546.2 H18h
C.1

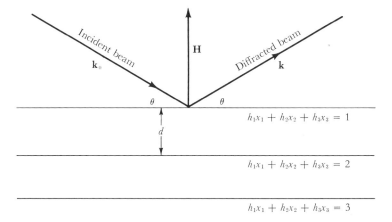

Figure 2-1 *Bragg diffraction from a crystal plane occurs only if the angle of incidence is equal to the angle of reflection θ, and if the plane has integral coefficients h_1, h_2, and h_3. The plane may also be described in terms of its normal, the vector $\mathbf{H} = h_1\mathbf{a}_1^* + h_2\mathbf{a}_2^* + h_3\mathbf{a}_3^*$.*

provided that the basis vectors $\mathbf{a}_1^*$, $\mathbf{a}_2^*$, $\mathbf{a}_3^*$ are related to the unit cell vectors $\mathbf{a}_1$, $\mathbf{a}_2$, $\mathbf{a}_3$ in the following way:

$$\mathbf{a}_i \cdot \mathbf{a}_i^* = 1 \tag{2-6}$$

and

$$\mathbf{a}_i \cdot \mathbf{a}_j^* = 0 \qquad \text{for} \quad i \neq j \tag{2-7}$$

Thus, $\mathbf{a}_1^*$ is perpendicular to $\mathbf{a}_2$ and $\mathbf{a}_3$, $\mathbf{a}_2^*$ is perpendicular to $\mathbf{a}_1$ and $\mathbf{a}_3$, and $\mathbf{a}_3^*$ is perpendicular to $\mathbf{a}_1$ and $\mathbf{a}_2$. The vectors $\mathbf{a}_1^*$, $\mathbf{a}_2^*$, $\mathbf{a}_3^*$ define the reciprocal unit cell of the crystal, and the set of points defined by (2-5), where h_1, h_2, and h_3 take on all integral values, defines the *reciprocal lattice*. Thus to every set of rational planes in the crystal [those planes defined by (2-3), where the coefficients are integers], there corresponds a point in the reciprocal lattice.

The distance d^* of a reciprocal lattice point from the origin is given by

$$d^{*2} = \sum_{i=1}^{3} \sum_{j=1}^{3} h_i h_j \mathbf{a}_i^* \cdot \mathbf{a}_j^* \tag{2-8}$$

This distance d^*, which is the length of the vector $\mathbf{H}$, is just the reciprocal of the interplanar spacing d:

$$d = \frac{1}{d^*} \tag{2-9}$$

Thus the Bragg condition (2-4) tells us that diffraction will take place only when the crystal is so oriented that a vector $\mathbf{H}$ with integral coefficients bisects the angle between the incident and diffracted beams, and that furthermore the scattering angle 2θ must be related to the length of the vector **H** by the equation equivalent to (2-4),

$$\sin \theta = \frac{d^*\lambda}{2} = \frac{|\mathbf{H}|\lambda}{2} \tag{2-10}$$

From the positions of the diffracted beams (the Bragg reflections), we can thus derive the dimensions of the unit cell. It is from the *intensities* of the Bragg reflections that we can determine the contents of the unit cell—that is, the positions and shapes of all the atoms in the cell.

Intensities and Structure

Let **r** be a vector within the real unit cell,

$$\mathbf{r} = x_1\mathbf{a}_1 + x_2\mathbf{a}_2 + x_3\mathbf{a}_3 \tag{2-11}$$

The intensity $I(\mathbf{H})$ of a Bragg reflection is related to a quantity known as the structure factor $F(\mathbf{H})$ by the expression[1]

$$I(\mathbf{H}) = K(\mathbf{H})F(\mathbf{H}) \cdot F(\mathbf{H})^* \tag{2-12}$$

where $K(\mathbf{H})$ is a known quantity involving physical constants and geometrical factors and where F^* is the complex conjugate of F. The structure factor is related to the density of matter in the unit cell by the equation[2]

$$F(\mathbf{H}) = \int_{\text{cell}} \rho(\mathbf{r}) \exp(2\pi i \mathbf{H} \cdot \mathbf{r}) \, d\mathbf{r} \tag{2-13}$$

The scattering density $\rho(\mathbf{r})$ is defined in a way characteristic of the radiation used.

For purposes of molecular structure determination, it is convenient to divide the total scattering density into contributions from the various atoms j

---

[1] This is strictly true only in the case of an *ideally imperfect* crystal. Such a crystal is made up of a large number of smaller subunits or mosaic blocks that are slightly misaligned with respect to one another. Except for very perfect crystals, such as diamond, such mosaicity is the rule.

[2] The integral is over one unit cell of the crystal. We may separate F into two parts such that $F = A + iB$ and thus $F^*F = A^2 + B^2$. A and B are given by

$$A = \int_{\text{cell}} \rho(\mathbf{r}) \cos(2\pi\mathbf{H} \cdot \mathbf{r}) \, d\mathbf{r}$$

and

$$B = \int_{\text{cell}} \rho(\mathbf{r}) \sin(2\pi\mathbf{H} \cdot \mathbf{r}) \, d\mathbf{r}$$

In a *centrosymmetric* crystal, that is, a crystal where $\rho(\mathbf{r}) = \rho(-\mathbf{r})$, the integral defining B vanishes, and $F = A$.

centered at positions $\mathbf{r}_j$.   The atomic scattering factor is defined by

$$f_j(\mathbf{H}) = \int \rho_j(\Delta) \exp(2\pi i \mathbf{H} \cdot \Delta) \, \mathbf{d}\Delta \tag{2-14a}$$

where $\rho_j(\Delta)$ is the scattering density of atom j at rest.   If the atom is in motion, with a distribution $\rho_j^{\text{motion}}(\Delta)$ around its mean position, we define a temperature factor

$$T_j(\mathbf{H}) = \int \rho_j^{\text{motion}}(\Delta) \exp(2\pi i \mathbf{H} \cdot \Delta) \, d\Delta \tag{2-14b}$$

If there are n atoms in the unit cell, we may then express the structure factor as

$$F(\mathbf{H}) = \sum_{j=1}^{n} f_j(\mathbf{H}) \, T_j(\mathbf{H}) \exp(2\pi i \mathbf{H} \cdot \mathbf{r}_j) \tag{2-15}$$

There is no loss in generality in going from equation (2-13) to (2-15). If all the atoms are vibrating with simple harmonic motion, the temperature factor $T_j(\mathbf{H})$ is given by

$$T_j(\mathbf{H}) = \exp\left(-8\pi^2 \frac{\sin^2 \theta}{\lambda^2} \langle r_\mathrm{H}^2 \rangle \right) \tag{2-16}$$

where $\langle r_\mathrm{H}^2 \rangle$ is the mean square amplitude of vibration in the direction of $\mathbf{H}$. Although the deviations from harmonic motion in crystals are of interest and importance, this harmonic approximation suffices for most structure determinations.   The function T may be complex for more realistic (but infrequently assumed) models of thermal motion.

The two principal distinguishing characteristics of x-ray, electron, and neutron diffraction are the strengths of their interactions with matter and the forms taken by f_j for the various elements.   These will be discussed later in this chapter.   The function f is in general complex, either as a result of absorption or as a result of the scattering from a noncentrosymmetric and nonspherical atom (in which case there may also be a dependence of the scattering on the orientation of the atom with respect to $\mathbf{H}$).   The final important result from diffraction theory is the relation between the structure factor F and the scattering density $\rho(\mathbf{r})$:

$$\rho(\mathbf{r}) = V^{-1} \sum_{h_1, h_2, h_3 = -\infty}^{\infty} F(\mathbf{H}) \exp(-2\pi i \mathbf{H} \cdot \mathbf{r}) \tag{2-17}$$

where V is the volume of the unit cell.[3]

---

[3] This is the Fourier transform of (2-13) when the density is repeated on an infinite periodic lattice.

Determination of the Structure

It is clear that if the magnitudes and phases of the complex quantities $F(\mathbf{H})$ were known for a sufficient number of terms, then by direct summation (2-17) one would obtain the scattering density and hence a knowledge of the positions of the scatterers within the unit cell. The problem here, the so-called *phase problem*, is that while the magnitudes of F are known from the experimentally observed intensities (2-12), the phases of F are not. There is a variety of methods available for solving the phase problem,[4] but none is invariably successful. Some of the successful methods are based on Patterson's (1934) discovery that the Fourier series

$$P(\mathbf{r}) = V^{-1} \sum_{h_1,h_2,h_3 = -\infty}^{+\infty} F(\mathbf{H})F(\mathbf{H})^* \cos(2\pi\mathbf{H} \cdot \mathbf{r}) \qquad (2\text{-}18)$$

which is clearly related to the series for $\rho(\mathbf{r})$, but calculable purely from *observed* quantities, is equal to

$$P(\mathbf{r}) = V^{-1} \int_{\text{cell}} \rho(\mathbf{u})\rho(\mathbf{u} + \mathbf{r}) \, d\mathbf{u} \qquad (2\text{-}19)$$

$P(\mathbf{r})$, now called the Patterson function, has a simple interpretation in terms of the structure. The interpretation is that $P(\mathbf{r})$ has maxima when maxima of scattering density are separated by $\mathbf{r}$: that is, $P(\mathbf{r})$ is a representation of all interatomic vectors translated to a common origin and is often referred to as a vector map. The problems of unraveling the Patterson function may be considerable, and some of the more promising techniques depend for their successful application on the high-speed computer.

The so-called *direct methods* for solution of the phase problem attempt to assign a nearly correct set of phases to the observed structure amplitudes without the necessity of going through the Patterson function. The criteria generally imposed are that the scattering density be everywhere positive— certainly a reasonable condition if the scattering density $\rho(\mathbf{r})$ is (as in x-ray diffraction) the electron density, but not a valid condition for neutron diffraction—and that the atoms be isolated, that is, that the total density is the sum of individual nonoverlapping atom density functions. The most successful of the phase-determining methods is based on a relationship between

---

[4] There is no unique solution of the phase problem. Each of the experimentally measured structure factor magnitudes may have an arbitrary phase assigned to it when it is included in the summation (2-17). If these phases are not correct, the calculated density will not in general be interpretable in terms of isolated atoms at chemically reasonable distances from one another. The various methods available for solution of the phase problem all depend on limiting the possible phases by imposing in a systematic way the criterion that the structure revealed by (2-17) satisfy certain conditions of chemical reasonableness.

the signs of structure factors discovered by Sayre (1952) and by Zachariasen (1952) and vigorously pursued by Karle and Karle (1963) and others.   The interested reader should refer to the Karles' paper and also to the proceedings of the symposium on direct methods held by the American Crystallographic Association (1966).

Refinement of the Structure

To complete this brief and general discussion of diffraction methods we remark that once the phase problem has been solved and in some manner a trial structure has been derived from approximate phases for some of the structure factors, the structure may be improved (or refined) in several ways.   The two most generally used methods are (1) successive Fourier refinement and (2) a nonlinear least-squares refinement.   These will be discussed in more detail later on in this chapter.   Both of these methods depend in some degree on the assumption of a specific model with variable parameters for the description of the contents of the unit cell and hence of the scattering density.

2-2   SCATTERING AMPLITUDES AND CROSS SECTIONS

The only diffraction methods in common use today, and probably the only likely ones for some time to come (because of the necessity for intense sources) are x-ray diffraction, electron diffraction, and neutron diffraction. The differences in the interaction of x-rays, electrons, and neutrons with the atoms in the scattering crystal, as manifested by differences in the magnitudes, relative values, and angular dependence of the atomic scattering factors f, lead to some important differences in the applications of these techniques. In this section we shall indicate briefly how these differences arise.

Scattering of Particle Beams

Before considering the individual methods in detail, it is useful to review some of the elementary concepts of particle scattering.   If a beam of particles with intensity I_0 is incident upon an infinitely thin sample containing N atoms per unit area, and if the number of particles scattered by a given process is I_s, the ratio

$$\frac{I_s}{I_0} = \sigma N \qquad (2\text{-}20)$$

defines the total cross section σ of a single atom for this process.   The cross section has the dimensions of area.   The linear absorption coefficient μ of the material for this process is given by

$$\mu = \frac{\sigma}{V} \tag{2-21}$$

where V is the volume per atom.

In terms of the scattering of waves, if a plane wave with amplitude ϕ_0 is incident on the material, the scattered wave will have at a distance R from the scattering atom the amplitude

$$\phi_s(R) = \left(\frac{a}{R}\right)\phi_0 \tag{2-22}$$

The preceding equation defines the scattering amplitude or scattering length a, which may be a function of the scattering angle. The total scattering cross section is obtained by integrating the square of the scattering amplitude over all solid angles, that is, over the surface of a sphere:

$$\sigma = \int a^2 \, d\Omega = \int a^2 \sin \theta \, d\theta \, d\phi \tag{2-23}$$

where $d\Omega$ is the element of solid angle. For isotropic scattering, this integral reduces to

$$\sigma = 4\pi a^2 \tag{2-24}$$

Although for traditional reasons units other than scattering amplitudes in centimeters are usually employed in x-ray and electron diffraction papers, it will be useful to use the same units of centimeters for the absolute scattering amplitudes when discussing the differences between the methods.

x-Ray Scattering Amplitudes

Let $\mathbf{k}$ and $\mathbf{k}_0$ be vectors of length $2\pi/\lambda$ along the reflected and incident directions and let a vector $\mathbf{S}$ be defined as

$$\mathbf{S} = \mathbf{k} - \mathbf{k}_0 \tag{2-25}$$

Thus $\mathbf{S} = 2\pi\mathbf{H}$, and the magnitude of $\mathbf{S}$ is

$$s \equiv |\mathbf{S}| = 4\pi\lambda^{-1} \sin \theta \tag{2-26}$$

Then in terms of the atomic electronic wave functions ψ_j, the scattering factors for x-rays are given by [5]

$$f_j(\mathbf{S}) = \int \psi_j^* \psi_j \exp(i\mathbf{S} \cdot \mathbf{r}) \, d\mathbf{r} \tag{2-27}$$

Note that the charge density $\psi_j\psi_j^*$ need not be spherically symmetric, and in general the scattering will be a function of $\mathbf{H}$ (i.e., $\mathbf{S}$). For purposes of

---

[5] In this formulation for coherent elastic scattering it has been assumed that the frequency of the incident radiation is large compared with any atomic transition frequencies.

illustration (but also because it is a usual assumption), let us assume that the charge density is spherically symmetric. Then the mean scattering factor $\bar{f}$ depends only on s, not $\mathbf{S}$, and is simply

$$\bar{f}(s) = 4\pi \int_0^\infty \psi\psi^* \left(\frac{\sin sr}{sr}\right) r^2 \, dr \qquad (2\text{-}28)$$

Thus the mean, spherically symmetric atomic scattering factor is readily computed from the individual atomic wave functions, and extensive tabulations of calculated values for these quantities are available[6] (International Tables for X-ray Crystallography, 1962). Note that at zero scattering angle, f must equal Z, the number of electrons in the atom. With increasing scattering angle, interference occurs because of the extension of the electron density in space, so that f drops off monotonically with increasing scattering angle (increasing s). Figure 2-2 shows this dependence for a few representative atoms. Since it is the electrons that interact with the x-rays, the scattering density derived from an x-ray diffraction experiment is generally termed "electron density" and is usually expressed in the units of electrons A^{-3}

If the scattering factor in electrons is multiplied by the scattering amplitude for a single electron (e^2/mc^2), we obtain the scattering amplitude for the atom in centimeters:

$$a_x = \left(\frac{e^2}{mc^2}\right) f$$

$$= 0.28 \times 10^{-12} f \qquad (2\text{-}29)$$

It is the factor of the mass of the scattering species in the denominator which renders the scattering of x-rays by the nucleus unimportant.

Electron Scattering Amplitudes

The scattering process for electrons is different. It can be considered as the scattering of the electrons by the electrostatic potential of the atom. If it is assumed that the interaction between the electrons and the atom is small (a valid assumption if the electrons are traveling fast enough or if the potential is small enough), and if it is further assumed that the atom is spherically symmetric, one can obtain the atomic scattering amplitude for

---

[6] The calculations of wave functions for many-electron atoms are necessarily approximate, and the use of the consequently approximate scattering factors based on these calculations can represent a source of error in crystallographic work. The calculated scattering factors are for free atoms, not atoms in solids; this represents another source of error. Except for the location of hydrogen atoms, these uncertainties are probably not very important in present x-ray structure determinations.

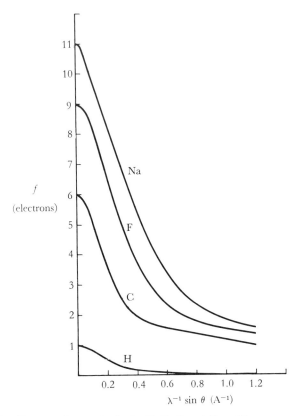

Figure 2-2 x-Ray scattering amplitudes for H, C, F, and Na.   The curves are for atoms at rest; for moving atoms, the curves decrease more rapidly with scattering angle.   Adapted from data in International Tables for X-Ray Crystallography (1962).

electrons as

$$f^B(s) = \left(\frac{8\pi^2 me^2}{h^2}\right)\frac{(Z - \bar{f})}{s^2} \tag{2-30}$$

where Z is the atomic number and $\bar{f}$ is the mean atomic scattering factor for x-rays.   The term in Z arises from scattering by the nucleus and that in $\bar{f}$ from scattering by the electrons in the atom.   It should be noted that f^B is real.   Equation (2-30) is not suitable for the calculation of $f^B(0)$ because $\bar{f}$ is equal to Z for a neutral atom, while s^2 also vanishes.   Rather, $f^B(0)$ is given by

$$f^B(0) = \left(\frac{4\pi^2 me^2}{3h^2}\right)\langle r^2\rangle \tag{2-31}$$

where $\langle r^2 \rangle$ is the mean square radius of the atom:

$$\langle r^2 \rangle = \int r^2 \rho(r) \, dr \tag{2-32}$$

and $\rho(r)$ is the first-order electron density function for the atom. Figure 2-3 shows the form of f^B for the same atoms whose x-ray scattering was shown in Figure 2-2. The scattering amplitude depends on λ, θ, and Z, but for small values of $\lambda^{-1} \sin \theta$ is considerably greater than that for x-rays. The quantity $(8\pi^2 m e^2 / h^2)$ has the value 3.78×10^8 cm^{-1}. The scattering amplitude in angstroms for $\theta \neq 0$ is thus given by

$$f^B = 0.0239(Z - \bar{f}) \left(\frac{\lambda}{\sin \theta} \right)^2 \tag{2-33}$$

with λ expressed in angstroms and $\bar{f}$ in electrons. A structure factor for

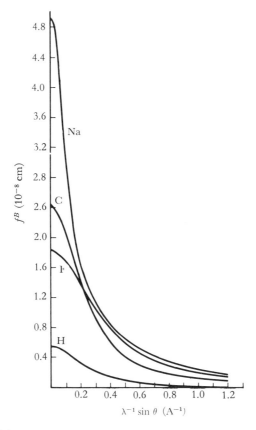

Figure 2-3 *Electron scattering amplitudes for the same atoms as in Figure 2-2.*

electrons $\Phi(hkl)$ may be defined in a manner completely analogous to equation (2-15) for x-rays by the substitution of f^B for f. Thus $\Phi(hkl)$ would have the units of angstroms. Since the scattering of electrons is from an electrostatic potential, it is usual to express this structure factor in the units of volts. This is accomplished in accordance with the formula

$$\Phi(hkl) \text{ (volts)} = \frac{K\Phi(hkl) \text{ (angstroms)}}{V} \tag{2-34}$$

where V is the volume of the unit cell in cubic angstroms. The constant $K [= h^2/(2\pi me)]$ has the value 47.87 for the units of equation (2-34).

Neutron Scattering Amplitudes

Whereas the scattering of x-rays is largely from the electrons, and the scattering of electrons has both an electronic and nuclear dependence, the scattering of thermal neutrons is largely from the nucleus. The only important exception is the scattering caused by the interaction of the magnetic moment of the neutron with the magnetic moments of unpaired electrons which may be present in the system under study. This scattering leads to intensity in the Bragg reflections only when the magnetic moments are ordered in the unit cell, that is, in ferromagnetic, antiferromagnetic, and ferrimagnetic materials. Although neutron diffraction studies have contributed immensely to our knowledge of the nature of magnetism in solids, the magnetic scattering is of little importance in the study of hydrogen-bonding systems, and we shall not consider it further.

The scattering amplitudes of nuclei for thermal neutrons cannot be reliably predicted or calculated, as can the corresponding amplitudes for x-rays or electrons. If we consider that a nucleus presents a geometric cross section to an incident beam approximately proportional to $A^{2/3}$,[7] where A is the atomic mass number of the nucleus, then the scattering amplitude increases as $A^{1/3}$. This, on the average, is true. Recalling that the scattering amplitude of an atom for x-rays increases (at least at zero scattering angle) linearly with atomic number, we see that the scattering amplitudes of all nuclei for thermal neutrons are of the same order of magnitude, while those for x-rays vary by a factor of 100. This $A^{1/3}$ dependence is only an average behavior, and the stronger or weaker interactions of individual nuclei with neutrons cause great departures from this average. In fact, scattering amplitudes for neighboring nuclei can even have opposite signs. (The sign of the scattering amplitude is positive when the scattered wave is 180° out of phase with the incident wave. The sign is negative if the phases

[7] If each nucleon occupies a constant volume, the volume of the nucleus is proportional to A. If the nucleus is spherical, the radius is then proportional to $A^{1/3}$ and any circular cross-sectional area is proportional to $A^{2/3}$.

are the same. For x-ray scattering and most neutron scattering the signs are positive.)

The radius of the nucleus is approximately 10^{-4} A. As a scattering source it is thus effectively a point source for particle beams with wavelengths of about 1 A. The amplitude of the scattering is independent of scattering angle, that is, the scattering is isotropic. In Table 2-1 we list the scattering amplitudes (expressed in the units of 10^{-12} cm) for some common isotopes. The scattering density derived from a neutron diffraction experiment is nuclear scattering density and is generally expressed in the units of 10^{-12} cm A^{-3} or occasionally as fermis A^{-3}.[8]

Comparisons of Amplitudes for the Three Methods

From Figures 2-2 and 2-3 and Table 2-1, it is clear that for the detection of hydrogen atoms in the presence of other scatterers the preferred method is neutron diffraction, followed by electron diffraction and x-ray diffraction.

Because of the different strengths of interaction of the various radiations with the crystal, the method may well be dictated by the size of the crystal specimen available. A good feeling for the size of crystal appropriate to the

[8] One fermi is 10^{-13} cm.

Table 2-1 *Coherent, Elastic, Scattering Amplitudes for Electrons, x-Rays, and Neutrons for a Scattering Angle of 0°. The Units Are 10^{-12} Cm*

Element	Electron[a]	x-Ray	Neutron[b]
H	5,290	0.28	−0.38
D	5,290	0.28	0.65
C	24,500	1.69	0.66
N	22,000	1.97	0.94
O	20,100	2.25	0.58
F	18,400	2.54	0.55
Si	60,000	3.94	0.42
^{31}P	54,000	4.22	0.53
S	47,000	4.51	0.31
Cl	46,000	4.79	0.99
Br	73,000	9.86	0.67
^{127}I	101,000	14.93	0.52
Xe	102,000	15.22	0.48
^{238}U	141,000	25.92	0.85

[a] These numbers are known no better than the x-ray figures. The extra zeros are not significant.

[b] Unless otherwise indicated, these values are for the elements in their natural abundances.

various methods may be obtained by considering the thickness $(t_{1/2})$ of crystal required to attenuate the beam by a factor of 50%:

$$\frac{I}{I_0} = \exp(-\mu t_{1/2}) = 0.50 \qquad (2\text{-}35)$$

Several processes can contribute to the beam attenuation, the scattering process giving rise to the Bragg reflections being the one which gives us a measure of the strength of the interesting interaction of the beam with the crystal. If the half-thickness for this scattering process is small, we may use a very small crystal in the experiment; if this half-thickness is large, we must use a large crystal in order to obtain enough intensity in the scattered beam. There are other processes which also contribute to the attenuation of the scattered beam; these include other scattering processes as well as pure absorption. We lump all these effects together under "absorption" and note that if the half-thickness for this absorption is small, we cannot use a large crystal, even if it would appear desirable from the point of view of the Bragg scattering.

In Table 2-2, we present the half-thicknesses for both scattering and absorption for crystals of a number of the elements. These values are dependent on the wavelength, particularly for electrons and x-rays, and they are quoted for wavelengths commonly used in experiments. Although the half-thicknesses are quoted separately for the scattering and absorption processes, the combined half-thickness is given by

$$\frac{1}{t_{1/2}\text{ (total)}} = \frac{1}{t_{1/2}\text{ (scattering)}} + \frac{1}{t_{1/2}\text{ (absorption)}} \qquad (2\text{-}36a)$$

Note that absorption by x-rays is by far the dominant process, whereas for

Table 2-2 *Thicknesses of Crystalline Materials Characteristic of 50%
Transmission for Various Radiations. All Thicknesses Are in
Centimeters, and Are Quoted to Only One Significant Figure*

Element	x-Ray (λ = 1.54 A)		Neutron (λ = 1.07 A)		Electron scattering (λ = 0.05 A)
	Scattering	Absorption	Scattering	Absorption	
H	2000	20	7	0.2	2×10^{-4}
Be	20	0.2	0.7	1000	5×10^{-6}
Al	2	0.005	8	90	2×10^{-6}
Fe	0.3	0.0003	0.7	5	6×10^{-7}
Cd	0.2	0.0004	8	0.005	5×10^{-7}
Pb	0.06	0.0003	2	200	3×10^{-7}

Table 2-3 *Approximate Crystal Sizes Required for Diffraction Studies*

x-Rays	0.05–1.00 mm on an edge
Neutrons	0.5–5.0 mm on an edge
Electrons	10–500 A in the beam direction

neutrons it sometimes is but usually is not. The numbers quoted for the scattering apply strictly only to nonordered samples. In crystals giving Bragg diffraction, the scattering will depend sensitively on the orientation of the crystal, and the numbers give only a feeling for the relative strengths of the interaction.

In general, very small crystals are appropriate for electron diffraction studies, while very large crystals are needed for neutron diffraction (see Table 2-3). But the necessary size also depends on the composition of the crystal and the intensities of the x-ray, electron, and neutron beams available. These details will be discussed later in the chapter.

From a practical point of view it is worth pointing out that the availability of equipment to carry out the experiment may play an important part in determining the method used. x-Ray diffractometers capable, in the hands of an experienced and careful crystallographer, of producing results of high accuracy are commercially available. Many problems in hydrogen bonding can certainly be solved by the appropriate use of x-ray diffraction techniques. Good neutron diffraction facilities exist at only a few major research centers, and the equipment is expensive to build and operate. For problems in which the highest accuracy is important, neutron diffraction provides the best technique, but the cost of the experiment must be weighed against the importance of the problem.

2-3 ELECTRON DIFFRACTION

The scattering theory presented thus far, in which equation (2-12) is valid, depends on the strength of the interaction being small enough so that the amplitude of the incident wave is constant throughout the crystal. In this *kinematic theory*, the scattering from each volume element in the sample is treated as being independent of that of other volume elements. In *dynamical theory*, one attempts to take account of all wave interactions within the crystalline particle. This is necessary when the strength of the scattered beam is such that the interactions of incident and diffracted beams cannot be ignored. As we indicated in footnote 1 of this chapter, for a crystal with many small mosaic blocks the size of the diffracting region is small enough so that (2-12) holds for an x-ray diffraction experiment. Nevertheless (2-12) is not a general result and dynamical effects are manifested in the diminution of strong x-ray reflections, a phenomenon that is known as primary extinction. For scattering from a very large perfect crystal, a rare object, the intensity of scattering is directly proportional to the magnitude of the structure factor, rather than to its square.

The interaction of electrons with a crystal is almost always sufficiently strong for dynamical effects to be of extreme importance (see Table 2-2). It is only with exceedingly small crystals that these can be ignored and the usual kinematical theory applied. One of the problems in the interpretation of electron diffraction data is the determination of the limits of applicability of the kinematic theory. These limits depend on the composition of the crystal, the degree of perfection of the crystal, and the wavelength of the electron beam. It is a generally fair statement that these limits cannot be determined and one does not know how to relate the intensities of scattering to the structure factors. There are other difficulties in the electron diffraction method. These include the experimental difficulties of orienting minute single crystals and of collecting three-dimensional data, since it is difficult to obtain crystallites of the same material that are thin in different directions; these also include theoretical difficulties concerned with the atomic scattering amplitudes: Does the Born approximation hold?[9] What does one take for the degree of ionization of the atom? For electron scattering, the degree of ionization has a pronounced effect; for x-ray scattering, it does not.

There have been a number of apparently successful applications of electron diffraction to the study of crystal structures and the location of hydrogen atoms. This is possible for simple structures where even with structure factors of low accuracy one can determine the general features correctly. A similar situation obtained in the early days of x-ray diffraction when it was possible to obtain correct (but imprecise) structures using *strong*, *medium*, and *weak* as measures of the intensities.

Kinematic theory should be valid for electron diffraction if there is disorder in the direction of the beam. Electron diffraction techniques do indeed yield interesting information about such crystals. Examples include studies of the intercalated compounds of graphite (ferric chloride-graphite, Cowley and Ibers, 1956; molybdenum chloride-graphite, Johnson, 1966)

---

[9] In scattering theory, the approximation that the amplitude of the scattered wave is small compared with that of the incident wave is known as the Born approximation. If the strength of the interaction is very large, as it is for electron scattering, this approximation breaks down even for scattering for a single atom. The calculation of the atomic scattering factor therefore becomes much more difficult. This is a particularly severe problem for heavy atoms.

where electron diffraction has yielded structural information that, because of the disorder, is unobtainable from x-ray studies.

Further discussion of the electron diffraction method does not seem worthwhile in view of its limited applicability as a structure determining tool for crystals.   Accordingly we turn now to a more detailed discussion of x-ray and neutron diffraction.

2-4   X-RAY DIFFRACTION

x-Ray diffraction remains the most common technique for the determination of crystal structures.   As we have noted earlier, this is partly due to the wide availability of commercial diffraction equipment and also because of the ease of manipulation of samples of suitable size.   The course of a crystal structure investigation and the handling of the data are identical in x-ray and neutron diffraction methods, so that in this section we shall discuss some topics which are applicable to both techniques.   In Section 2-5 we discuss some of the unique features of neutron diffraction.

Crystal Structure Determination

It is well to remind the reader here of the sequence of events that takes place in a typical crystal structure investigation:

(1) *Choice of the problem.*   Given a chemical problem of interest, is a crystal structure investigation the best way of solving this problem, either completely or in connection with other methods?

(2) *Selection of a sample.*   Single crystals of a size suitable to the technique (Table 2-3) must be obtained.   These must be examined optically and with x-rays to ascertain their quality.   A chemical analysis should be performed to ascertain that the crystals are in fact crystals of the interesting material. An accurate density determination can also be of great importance.   If the unit cell volume determined by x-rays is V, if the formula weight of the compound is denoted by M and Avogadro's number by N, the number of formula units Z in the unit cell is related to the density ρ as follows:

$$Z = \left(\frac{N}{M}\right) V \rho \qquad (2\text{-}36\text{b})$$

For a pure compound of known composition, this number should be integral. If it is not, one can suspect an improper chemical analysis or the presense of disorder in the crystal.

(3) *Collection of the diffraction data.*   The intensities of many Bragg reflections must be measured, either photographically or by use of a radiation

counter. There are many sources of error in this part of the experiment. These are sufficiently serious and common so that we devote Section 2-7 to their discussion. During the period of data collection, one must be sure that the crystal is not changing with time by decomposition or reaction with components of the atmosphere. Often the crystal must be sealed in an inert environment.

(4) *Reduction of the intensity data to structure amplitudes.* The correction of the data for many experimental factors must be made. Systematic errors can easily be introduced at this stage. Have, for example, the effects of absorption and extinction been appropriately considered?

(5) *Solution of the phase problem.* An approximate structure must be obtained, either by interpretation of the Patterson function or by direct solution of the phase problem. This approximate structure must contain most of the atoms, located closer than about 0.3 A to their correct positions.

(6) *Refinement of the structure.* That set of parameters describing the positions and motions of the atoms which gives the best agreement between observed and calculated structure amplitudes must be obtained.

(7) *Analysis of the results.* The parameters determined in (6) must be analyzed in such a way that the meaningful chemical information is most evident. What are the bond lengths? What information has been obtained concerning potential energy functions for atomic motions?

(8) *Choice of a new problem.* At this point, new insight into the chemistry of the problem will have been obtained, and it will be apparent that other structural studies may lead to more meaningful information on the same or related points. We return to (1).

Contribution of an Atom to the Structure Factor

In judging the suitability of a diffraction technique for the solution of a chemical problem, we must ask ourselves how well we wish to know an atomic position. In this connection, it is instructive to consider the following point. On the average, the fractional contribution of atom A_i with atomic factor scattering f_i to the square of the structure factor F^2 is

$$\frac{f_i^2}{\sum_j f_j^2} \tag{2-37}$$

where the sum is over all atoms in the unit cell.

Let us now consider a compound in which there is one hydrogen atom for each carbon atom. In accordance with (2-37) the intensity of the average Bragg x-ray reflection will be $\frac{1}{37}$ from hydrogen and $\frac{36}{37}$ from carbon. The actual contribution of hydrogen will be somewhat smaller for the following reasons: The hydrogen atomic scattering factor falls off more rapidly with scattering angle than does the carbon scattering factor (see Figure 2-2); the damping effects of thermal motion are generally greater for hydrogen than for carbon because the hydrogen atoms have a smaller mass and also occupy terminal positions on the molecule. Even at absolute zero these motions will be appreciable because of zero-point energy. Thus the hydrogen contribution to the average structure factor is somewhat less than 2% in this example. This means that if we wish to know the hydrogen contribution to the average structure factor to 10% accuracy, then we must be able to measure the total intensity to an accuracy of about 0.25%. Usually there will be a considerable number of reflections to which the hydrogen makes more than an average contribution, so that the unattainable accuracy of 0.25% is not necessary in order to determine hydrogen positions. Although it is difficult to give a general estimate of the accuracy (as distinct from precision) of intensity measurements, it is safe to say that for modestly complex crystals one does not expect to achieve an accuracy of better than 3% error in intensity, even under the most exacting and careful conditions of measurement (American Crystallographic Association, 1965).

Refinement by Least Squares Methods

We assume that at this point the intensities have been correctly reduced to structure amplitudes and a trial structure obtained. This trial structure constitutes a model containing certain free parameters—usually the positional coordinates of all the atoms of the structure and quantities describing the amplitudes of thermal vibration of these atoms. The procedure by which we obtain the best possible values for these parameters is known as a refinement. The structure factors will usually be known to an accuracy of no better than a few percent. It is thus desirable to have more observations than there are parameters. Examination of equation (2-15) will indicate that the relationship between the structure factors and the parameters r_i and T_i is by no means simple.

In situations where there are many more observations than parameters, it is reasonable and traditional to define the best parameter set as that set which minimizes the sum of squares S of differences between the observed quantities F_k (obs) and those calculated F_k (calc) from the parameter set:

$$S = \sum_{\substack{\text{all} \\ \text{observations} \\ k}} (F_k \text{ (obs)} - F_k(\text{calc}))^2 \qquad (2\text{-}38)$$

More properly, we should include in the definition of S a factor for each term of the sum which takes account of the fact that some of our observations are better than others. We may define a weight w_k such that w_k is large for good observations and small for observations which we know to be more uncertain. S is then usually defined as

$$S = \Sigma w_k (F_k(\text{obs}) - F_k(\text{calc}))^2 \qquad (2\text{-}39)$$

A method that leads to a minimum of S is known as the method of least squares. We assume that we have values x_i^0 for the parameters and wish to improve these to values $x_i = x_i^0 + \Delta x$. The new values will result in changing $F_k(\text{calc}) (x_i^0)$ to a new value $F_k (\text{calc}) (x_i)$ which, if the experiment were perfect, should be equal to $F_k (\text{obs})$. We may write

$$dF_k = \sum_i \frac{\partial F_k}{\partial x_i} dx_i \tag{2-40}$$

and assuming that

$$\Delta F_k = F_k (\text{obs}) - F_k (\text{calc}) (x_i) \tag{2-41}$$

is small and that all the Δx_i are small, we may write (2-40) as

$$\Delta F_k = \sum_i \frac{\partial F_k}{\partial x_i} \Delta x_i \tag{2-42}$$

If there are n observations and m unknown parameters, the set of equations is overdetermined. If the criterion is imposed that the proper solution be the solution that minimizes the sum of squares S, it is shown in most books on statistics (Hamilton, 1964, for example) that this solution is the solution of the m independent normal equations

$$\sum_{k=1}^{m} b_{ij}\Delta x_j = a_i \qquad i = 1, \ldots , n \tag{2-43}$$

where the coefficients b_{ij} and a_i are defined as follows:

$$b_{ij} = \sum_{k=1}^{n} w_k \left(\frac{\partial F_k}{\partial x_i}\right) \left(\frac{\partial F_k}{\partial x_j}\right) \tag{2-44}$$

$$a_j = \sum_{k=1}^{n} w_k \left(\frac{\partial F_k}{\partial x_j}\right) \Delta F_k \tag{2-45}$$

The weights w_k are appropriately chosen as proportional to $1/\sigma_k^2$, where σ_k^2 is the variance of the observation F_k.[10]

[10] In methods of data collection based on particle counting, estimates of this variance may be based partially on the known Poisson distribution of the counts. It is important to note, however, that these *counting statistics* do not usually represent the major portion of the error in an x-ray diffraction experiment.

In the present discussion of the least squares equations, F refers to a general observable quantity. It may be taken as the structure factor amplitude $|F|$ or as the squared structure factor amplitude $|F|^2$.

The least squares procedure yields estimates not only of the parameters x_i but also of the variances $\sigma^2(x_i)$ of these parameters.   Examination of these variances gives us a feeling for the precision of the structure determination as it affects the estimate of a single parameter.   If there are many more observations than parameters, the estimate of x_i has a normal (Gaussian) probability distribution with standard deviation $\sigma(x_i)$.   For example, if the true value of the parameter x_i is x_i (true), there is a probability of 0.95 that the estimate $\bar{x}_i$ lies in the range

$$x_i \text{ (true)} - 1.96\sigma(x_i) < \bar{x}_i < x_i \text{ (true)} + 1.96\sigma(x_i) \qquad (2\text{-}46)$$

The variance $\sigma^2(x_i)$ is known as the marginal variance of the parameter x_i. The range defined by (2-46) is valid without regard to the values of the other parameters $\{x_j\}$.   This marginal variance is given by the ith diagonal element of the inverse $\mathbf{B}^{-1}$ of the matrix $\mathbf{B}$ of the normal equations

$$\mathbf{B} = \{b_{ij}\} \qquad (2\text{-}47)$$

It is instructive to consider what factors enter into the estimate of $\sigma(x_i)$; when is it small, and when is it large?   For the purpose of this analysis, we shall consider the conditional variance.   This quantity may be used to define a probability range as in (2-46) but the range so defined is valid only if all other parameters $\{x_j\}$ are assumed to be fixed, either at the estimated values or at some other arbitrary set of values.   Since this is a more restrictive condition than the complete freedom given to the parameters $\{x_j\}$ in the definition of the marginal variance, the conditional variance is necessarily smaller than the marginal variance.   Nevertheless, in most problems the marginal and conditional variances will be of the same order of magnitude, and for the purposes of this qualitative discussion we shall use the latter— and simpler—quantity.

The conditional variance is given simply by the inverse of the ith diagonal element of $\mathbf{B}$ itself,

$$\sigma^2(x_i) = b_{ii}^{-1} = \left[\sum_{k=1}^{n} \left(\frac{1}{\sigma_k^2}\right)\left(\frac{\partial F_k}{\partial x_i}\right)^2\right]^{-1} \qquad (2\text{-}48)$$

Equation (2-48) implies that the precision of the estimate of the parameter x_i will increase if

(1) the variances of the observations are small;
(2) the derivatives of the structure factors with respect to the parameters are large; or
(3) the number of terms in the summation is large.

Thus the observations must be accurately made; they must be sensitive to the parameters of interest; the more observations that are made, the better (as long as the observations are sensitive to the parameters of interest). What this means for the location of hydrogen atoms is that we want very accurate measurements of intensities at relatively small scattering angles, where the hydrogen atoms are still contributing to the intensities. Since we also need as many observations as possible, this implies that location of hydrogen atoms is best achieved using counter methods rather than film methods, both because of the higher accuracy and because "weak" reflections, unobserved in the film methods, can often be observed in the counter methods. Moreover, because of the necessity of a large number of terms at low scattering angle, it is desirable that the unit cell of the crystal be large (at least in terms of volume per hydrogen atom).

Refinement by Fourier Techniques

Since the most pictorial representation of the diffraction data is obtained by calculation of the Fourier series (2-17), it seems natural to use this equation in the improvement of a trial structure. As we have noted, we do not have experimental knowledge of the phases of the structure factors that enter into this summation. We may, however, calculate structure factors using the trial structure. Each of these structure factors will have a calculated amplitude and calculated phase. If the observed amplitudes and calculated phases are used in the Fourier summation, we expect that the scattering density will have peaks which are closer to the true positions than are the positions on which the calculated structure factors were based. We repeat the procedure, using the new peak positions for the new structure factor calculation. This sequence of events is known as a *Fourier refinement* and may converge to the correct structure. (The refinement has converged if there are no further changes in phase.) Although the procedure has the disadvantage of not being as automatic as a least squares refinement and does not provide such convenient estimates of probable errors in the parameters, it is certainly a better procedure, particularly at early stages of the refinement, for recognizing when something is grossly wrong with a trial structure. Missing atoms in the trial structure may be easily identified by their appearance in the scattering density map; the least squares procedure would never reveal them directly.

Use of the Fourier technique to reveal missing atoms is in fact the technique that is most often applied for the determination of hydrogen atom positions in hydrogen-bonded and other compounds. If the positions of all atoms but the hydrogen atoms are known, we know that the scattering density for these other (heavy) atoms is

$$\rho_{\text{heavy}} = V^{-1} \sum_{\mathbf{H}} F_{\text{heavy}} \text{ (calc) } \exp(-2\pi i \mathbf{H} \cdot \mathbf{r}) \qquad (2\text{-}49)$$

(The sum over $\mathbf{H}$ is over all values of the Miller indices h_1, h_2, and h_3.)   Also, we know that we may write

$$\rho_{\text{total}} = V^{-1} \sum_{\mathbf{H}} F(\text{obs}) \exp(-2\pi i \mathbf{H} \cdot \mathbf{r}) \tag{2-50}$$

if the phases of $F(\text{obs})$ are known.
Since

$$\rho_{\text{total}} = \rho_{\text{heavy}} + \rho_{\text{hydrogen}} \tag{2-51}$$

we find that

$$\Delta\rho = \rho_{\text{hydrogen}} = \rho_{\text{total}} - \rho_{\text{heavy}}$$

$$= V^{-1} \sum_{\mathbf{H}} [F(\text{obs}) - F_{\text{heavy}}(\text{calc})] \exp(-2\pi i \mathbf{H} \cdot \mathbf{r}) \tag{2-52}$$

A calculation of $\Delta\rho$—the *difference map*—assigning the phase of F_{heavy} (calc) to $F(\text{obs})$, should result in indications of hydrogen atom positions.   The phases are not quite correct, of course, but one hopes that they are nearly right because of the small contribution of hydrogen to the structure factors.   If the structure is centrosymmetric, so that the phases are either 0 or π, this assumption is probably a good one; if the structure is noncentrosymmetric then the situation is much worse and the positions of the hydrogen atoms may not be obvious.   Of course, in interpretation of the difference map one uses chemical intuition; in fact, one usually knows approximately where to look for the hydrogen atoms.   Once these are found, the Fourier refinement can continue, based on phases that have been improved by the addition of the hydrogen atom contributions.

As we emphasized above, it is important to include terms in the Fourier summation to which the hydrogen atoms contribute.   The standard deviation $\sigma(\rho)$ in the electron density at an average point is

$$\sigma(\rho) = \frac{1}{V} \left\{ \sum_{\mathbf{H}} [F(\text{true}) - F(\text{obs})]^2 \right\}^{1/2} \tag{2-53}$$

On the other hand the observed electron density for an atom is given approximately by

$$\rho(r) = \frac{1}{2\pi^2} \int_0^{s_0} f(s) \, T(s) \left\{ \frac{\sin sr}{sr} \right\} s^2 \, ds \tag{2-54}$$

where s_0 is that value of s corresponding to the maximum scattering angle. $\rho(0)$, the peak height, increases with the number of terms (increasing s_0) in the Fourier summation until the product $f(s) \cdot T(s)$ becomes negligible. An important quantity for detectability of a hydrogen atom in a Fourier map is $\rho(0)/\sigma(\rho)$ and this goes through a maximum for some value of s_0.[11] It is difficult to predict this maximum scattering angle. Although other quantities might be used to define detectability, for example some measure of the curvature of the hydrogen atom peak versus the average noise level of the Fourier map, such quantities suffer from the difficulty of predicting in advance what the proper value of s_0 should be to ensure maximum detectability. A more practical procedure is to compute difference Fourier maps for various values of s_0; a hydrogen atom should be distinguishable from noise in the map if it shows a predictable change in height with change in s_0. A good example of the application of this procedure is described by La Placa and Ibers (1965) in the location of the hydrogen atom attached to Rh in the compound $RhH(CO)(P(C_6H_5)_3)_3$.

Because of the small contributions of hydrogen atoms to the structure factors, any errors in either the data or the model make their location difficult. Our discussion of errors above was based on the assumption that these are random errors only. The estimates of errors in the parameters are meaningful only if the intensities are indeed linear in the parameter changes over intervals comparable with the estimated standard deviations, if the least squares problem has been correctly and completely solved, if the weights are correct to within a single overall scale factor, and if the model being refined is correct.

2-5 NEUTRON DIFFRACTION

Neutron diffraction provides information on the location of the nuclei of hydrogen atoms to nearly the same accuracy as it does on other atoms in the structure. It is thus from neutron diffraction studies that the precise details of the geometry in many hydrogen-bonded crystals have been derived.

We remarked earlier that the neutron scattering factor is isotropic. Since the intensities of the peaks decrease less rapidly with scattering angle, more accurate data can be obtained at high angles than with x-rays of the same wavelength. There is an experimental difficulty in neutron diffraction which balances this apparent advantage. With x-rays a nearly monochromatic beam of high intensity is easily obtained because of the presence of characteristic sharp lines in the x-ray spectrum. With neutrons, on the other hand, an approximately Maxwellian distribution of neutrons with no sharp peaks is available from a nuclear reactor. One must select from the Maxwell distribution a band of neutron wavelengths, usually by reflection from a

[11] This is true only if the hydrogen scattering falls off more rapidly than the scattering for other atoms. This is almost always a valid assumption.

crystal monochromator. In order to obtain workable intensities for the diffraction experiment, this band must be rather broad. In a typical neutron experiment, the peak of the "monochromatic" wavelength band may be 1.1 A, but the width of the band may be 0.1 A. From the Bragg equation, we see that

$$\Delta \sin \theta = \frac{d^* \Delta\lambda}{2} \tag{2-55}$$

or

$$\Delta\theta = \frac{d^* \Delta\lambda}{2 \cos \theta} \tag{2-56}$$

Equation (2-56) gives the effective peak width $\Delta\theta$ as a function of the wavelength band width $\Delta\lambda$ and the Bragg angle θ. At high angles the peak width becomes large, and the ability to resolve two neighboring peaks becomes more difficult. Thus, with crystals with large unit cells, it is still difficult to get well-resolved, high intensity data at high scattering angles.

A more important advantage of the isotropic scattering factor for neutrons is that the scattering density map (if based on an infinite series) gives us directly a picture of the thermal motion or disorder in the crystal. If there were no thermal motion or disorder, the scattering density map would be simply a sum of Dirac delta functions at the atomic positions.[12] Any smearing out of the atoms that we see is due to the motion of the atoms (or due to our necessary use of an incomplete Fourier series). Another way of looking at this advantage of neutron diffraction is that we can refine the values of the thermal parameters without the necessity of making any assumptions about the shape of the atomic scattering factor or the electron distribution on which it is based. Many people have suggested simultaneous neutron and x-ray diffraction studies of the same compound to obtain accurate information on electron density distributions. The neutron diffraction study is used to obtain the thermal vibrational parameters, which are then kept fixed in the x-ray diffraction study. Any additional departures from spherical symmetry in the atomic densities determined from the x-ray data may be ascribed to bonding electrons.[13] Such studies are not to be undertaken lightly, for it

[12] The Dirac delta function is an infinitely sharp function which may be defined by the following conditions:

$$\delta(x) = 0 \qquad \text{for} \quad x \neq 0$$

$$\int_{-\infty}^{+\infty} \delta(x) = 1 \qquad \int_{-\infty}^{+\infty} \delta(x)f(x) = f(0)$$

[13] But only if for each atom the nucleus and electron cloud have the same thermal motion.

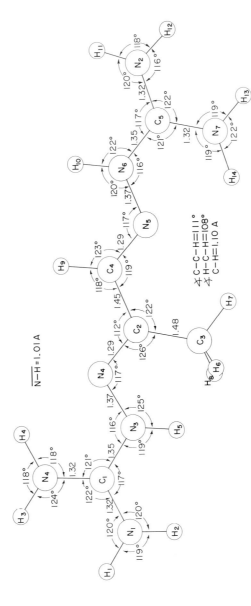

Figure 2-4 The chemical structure of methylglyoxal bisguanylhydrazonediacid. The bond lengths between heavy atoms are averages of those given by the x-ray and neutron diffraction studies; there were no significant differences between the two. The bond lengths involving hydrogen are from the neutron diffraction study. (See also Figure 5-19.)

48

is extremely difficult in any diffraction study to obtain thermal parameters on an absolute scale in which one can place any confidence.   Many systematic errors in data collection are easily absorbed into nonmeaningful vibrational parameters.

We close this section by remarking that the chief advantage of neutron diffraction for hydrogen-bonding studies is that the ratio of the hydrogen scattering factor to that for the other elements is so favorable.   For our hypothetical C_nH_n molecule, the hydrogen contribution to the scattering is

$$\frac{0.38^2}{0.38^2 + 0.66^2}$$

or 25%, as compared with 3% at zero scattering angle in the x-ray experiment.   If a deuterium-substituted crystal is used, the contribution goes up to 50%.

A Comparison between x-Ray and Neutron Diffraction Studies

Although we shall discuss many structures in detail in later chapters, it is useful at this point to compare briefly the results (Hamilton and La Placa, 1967) of an x-ray diffraction and a neutron diffraction study of a large organic compound: methylglyoxal bisguanylhydrazone dihydrochloride monohydrate (Figure 2-4).   The number of data was approximately the same in both studies.   Although the final agreement between observed and calculated intensities was better for the x-ray data than for the neutron data, it seems likely that the quality of the data was about the same.   The possible systematic errors from multiple scattering of neutrons are probably matched by possible systematic errors introduced by the visual estimation of x-ray intensities.

An examination of the difference density syntheses ($\rho_{obs} - \rho_{heavy}$) in Figure 2-5 will easily convince the reader of the superiority of neutron diffraction for hydrogen atom location.   The hydrogen atoms *are* visible in the x-ray structure, although there are regions of noise just as large as the hydrogen atoms; unless one knew exactly where to look, in the plane of the molecule, for instance, it is possible that all the hydrogen atoms might not be found.

The agreement between the thermal motion parameters for the heavy atoms in the two studies was good, as was the agreement for the heavy atom bond lengths.   On the other hand, the results in Table 2-4 for the heavy atom-hydrogen atom bond lengths are typical.   The apparent shortening of these bond lengths in the x-ray studies will be discussed further in Section 2-7. We only note here that bond lengths involving hydrogen derived from x-ray diffraction studies are notoriously unreliable.   The hydrogen atom positions

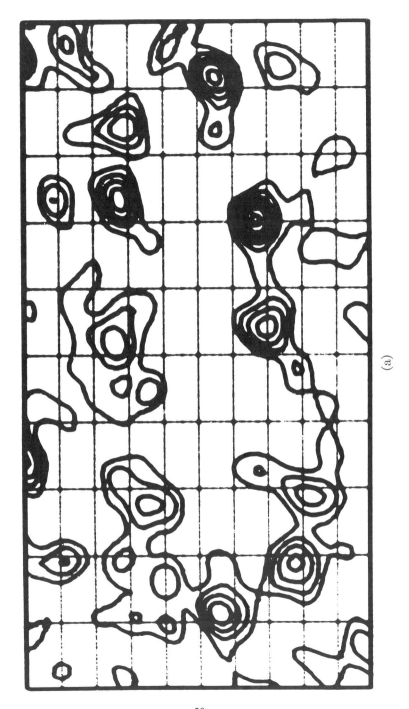

(a)

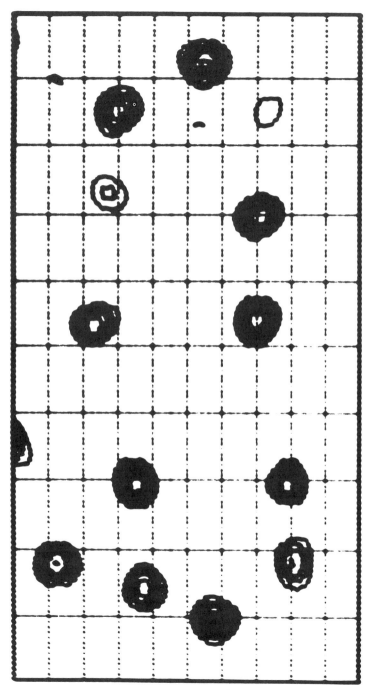

(b)

Figure 2-5 *Difference scattering density maps, in the principal molecular plane, showing hydrogen atom scattering only for (a) x-ray and (b) neutron diffraction data on methylglyoxal bisguanylhydrazone dihydrochloride monohydrate. The peaks are much better defined by the neutron diffraction data.*

Table 2-4 *Heavy Atom to Hydrogen Atom Bond Lengths (A) in Methylglyoxal Bisguanylhydrazone Dihydrochloride Monohydrate. Range, Mean (μ), and Standard Deviation (σ) of Mean*

	x-Ray			Neutron		
	Range	Mean	σ	Range	Mean	σ
N—H	0.59–1.00	0.84	0.04	0.97–1.04	1.013	0.008
C—H	0.76–1.16	0.97	0.09	1.04–1.15	1.101	0.025
O—H	0.73–0.88	0.80	0.08	0.99–1.02	1.006	0.012

in the x-ray study were refined using the thermal parameters from the neutron study and the best spherical scattering factor of Stewart, Davidson, and Simpson (1965).

Other Results

Since neutron diffraction has given the most precise results regarding actual hydrogen atom location, we present as the Appendix a table giving the interesting geometrical parameters concerning hydrogen bonds which have been studied by neutron diffraction and reported in full papers in the literature. Although several structures which have been refined with neutron diffraction data will be discussed in later chapters, one general result should be quoted at this time. If one looks at a class of compounds containing the same type of hydrogen bond, and we take the O—H · · · O hydrogen bond as an example, one finds that there is a definite correlation between the O · · · O distance and the O—H covalent bond length. As the O · · · O distance grows shorter, the O—H bond length grows longer. The points for all compounds which have been done to date are plotted in Figure 2-6. The best quadratic line through the points is also shown. This line has limited predictive value. There is considerable variation of the points from the best curve through them, but the trend is nevertheless real, and its existence is the basis of some theories regarding the potential function for hydrogen atom motion and for explanation of the deuterium isotope effect to be discussed in Chapter 3. As the O · · · O distance decreases to about 2.5 A the bond becomes symmetric.

In Figure 2-7 data for the same compounds are shown but O—H bond length is plotted against the H · · · O distance. The same trend is again observed. The two curves differ in detail because most of these hydrogen bonds are not linear.

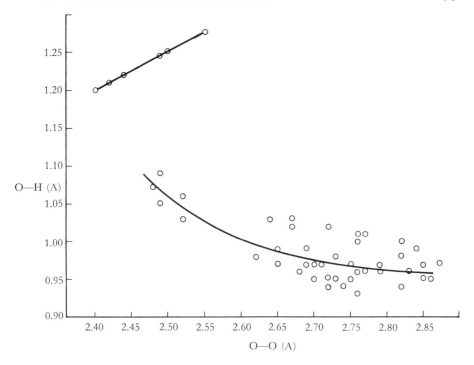

Figure 2-6 *O—H distance as a function of O · · · O distance as determined by neutron diffraction for a number of compounds containing O—H · · · O hydrogen bonds. The curved line represents the best least squares fit to the points, but the deviations of the points from the line are significant in many cases. In particular, the O · · · O distance characteristic of the shift from an asymmetric to a symmetric hydrogen bond is not well defined.*

2-6 FURTHER REMARKS ON THE PHASE PROBLEM

The Heavy Atom Method

If a crystal contains a very few atoms which dominate the scattering in the sense of (2-27), the structure solution may be simplified. To a first approximation, we consider that the only structure to be determined is that involving these few atoms; the coordinates of these atoms may be obvious from the Patterson function. The difference Fourier technique as described above is then used to determine the positions of the other atoms. The Fourier refinement should continue until it is clear that no atoms remain to be found; the final parameter refinement will usually be carried out by least squares techniques. Except that the location of hydrogen atoms by x-rays

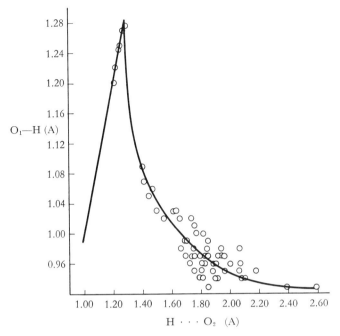

Figure 2-7 *Bonded O—H distance as a function of nonbonded H · · · O distance for the same compounds included in Figure 2-6. The significance of the correlation is only obvious for the shorter hydrogen bonds.*

is essentially a heavy atom technique, where the structure is solved in two stages, the heavy atom technique may be of little interest for hydrogen-bonding problems. Where there is a very heavy atom—a transition metal for example—the presence of which leads to a very straightforward structure solution, it is unlikely that the hydrogen atoms will be detectable with any precision at all.

In neutron diffraction studies, the heavy atom method in the usual sense is of very limited applicability because most neutron scattering amplitudes are of the same order of magnitude. A neutron diffraction problem thus may often be more difficult to solve than the x-ray diffraction problem for the same compound. Since the hydrogen atoms contribute an amount to the scattering that is comparable with what the other atoms contribute, the structure solution cannot be broken down into two distinct parts—heavy atom and hydrogen atom—but a trial structure for all atoms must be found initially. The phase problem is more difficult. For this reason, many neutron diffraction studies in the past have been preceded by x-ray diffraction studies. The positions of the heavy atoms obtained from the x-ray study generally permit a determination of the approximate phases for the neutron study that are close enough to the true phases so that the hydrogen atoms may be readily located in difference maps from which the hydrogen atom contributions have been omitted. The double work of two determinations will become less common as neutron fluxes increase and as our techniques for solving the phase problem improve.

Isomorphous Replacement Method

The phase problem can be solved if two or more crystals are found which have identical structures except for the replacement of a single atom (or perhaps at most a few atoms). Such crystals are said to be isomorphous.[14] Let us consider an isomorphous pair of crystals, both having atoms with scattering factors f_i at positions R_i. Let one of the crystals have an atom at position X with scattering factor f_A and the other crystal an atom at the same position with scattering factor f_B. Let V_{ij} represent the vector in the Patterson function between atoms at R_i and R_j. This vector will have a weight $f_i f_j$. In an ideal Patterson function, the peak height will be proportional to this weight. We may thus represent the two Patterson functions as

$$P(A) = f_A{}^2 V_{XX} + \sum_i f_A f_i V_{Xi} + \sum_{ij} f_i f_j V_{ij} \qquad (2\text{-}57)$$

and

$$P(B) = f_B{}^2 V_{XX} + \sum_i f_B f_i V_{Xi} + \sum_{ij} f_i f_j V_{ij} \qquad (2\text{-}58)$$

The difference Patterson function

$$P(A) - P(B) = V^{-1} \sum_{\mathbf{H}} (F_A{}^2 - F_B{}^2) \cos (2\pi \mathbf{H} \cdot \mathbf{r}) \qquad (2\text{-}59)$$

thus has peaks

$$\Delta P = P(A) - P(B) = (f_A{}^2 - f_B{}^2) V_{XX} + \sum_i (f_A - f_B) f_i V_{Xi} \quad (2\text{-}60)$$

Thus the difference Patterson function produces, aside from the peak at the origin (V_{XX}), an image of the structure V_{Xi} as seen from the replaceable atom. Although we have looked at the method as a means of simplifying the Patterson function, it can also be interpreted as a direct method of phase determination.

---

[14] Strictly speaking, they are *isostructural*. *Isomorphous* implies only that the crystals are identical in form, shape, or morphology—not necessarily in structure. It is, however, common practice among x-ray crystallographers to apply the term isomorphous only if the crystals are isostructural as well.

Deuterated Crystals

Although the substitution of deuterium for hydrogen will affect x-ray structure factors only if the substitution has a direct effect on the structure, in a neutron diffraction study the effects on the structure factors will be profound. D and H have different scattering amplitudes for neutrons, namely 0.65 and -0.38. The comparison of a normal structure and one in which a single hydrogen has been replaced by deuterium is exactly the problem of isomorphous replacement. The difference Patterson function will reveal the structure as seen from the replaceable hydrogen atom. The generalization to a structure with N_H hydrogen atoms and N_A other atoms gives the result that

$$\Delta P = (b_D{}^2 - b_H{}^2) \sum_{Hi=1}^{N_H} \sum_{Hj=1}^{N_H} V_{Hi,Hj}$$
$$+ (b_D - b_H) \sum_{Hi=1}^{N_H} \sum_{Aj=1}^{N_A} b_{Aj} V_{Hi,Aj} \quad (2\text{-}61)$$

The peaks in the Patterson function have been reduced in number by $N_A(N_A - 1)$, a fact which should make the difference Patterson function far easier to interpret.

There is another interesting consequence of the fact that H and D have scattering amplitudes of opposite sign. If it is assumed that the crystal can be deuterated with random substitution of deuterium for hydrogen, then a system whose hydrogen content is made up of approximately 63% H and 37% D will exhibit no coherent scattering from (H, D) and hence the size of the problem is reduced. If the phase problem can be solved for the remaining atoms, then collection of data from a pure H or pure D crystal may subsequently be carried out to locate the hydrogen nuclei.

2-7 SYSTEMATIC ERRORS

In any diffraction experiment or in its interpretation, there are possible systematic errors which not only may affect the precision of the location of an atom (and of other parameters) but also our estimate of this precision. In order to give the reader a feeling of what he should look for in a quality diffraction investigation, we discuss some of these possible errors here, particularly as they apply to the detection of hydrogen atoms. It is convenient to divide the errors into two broad classes: errors in the model and errors in the data.

By errors in the model we mean the inadequacies in our description of the structure that lead us to calculate structure factors incorrectly, to refine the wrong parameter sets in our least squares refinements, and to interpret incorrectly our results.   These include the following specific trouble points:

(1) *Poor chemical characterization of the compound.*   We may not know the stoichiometry of the material we are studying.

(2) *Incorrect trial structure.*   There may be missing atoms, too many atoms, or groups of atoms in wrong positions.   These may not always be revealed in the course of the Fourier and least squares refinements.

(3) *Improper model for thermal motion.*   The harmonic approximation is usually assumed.   It may be far from adequate in many hydrogen-bonded systems.

(4) *Improper model for atomic scattering.*   If the incorrect atomic scattering factors have been used, if anomalous scattering has been neglected, or if there are bonding effects, incorrect calculations of structure factors will occur, and difference maps and calculated phases will thus be incorrect.

By errors in the data we mean those mistakes which cause the intensities to be measured incorrectly and also those which affect the reduction of the intensities to structure factors.   These may include (among others, no doubt) the following problems:

(1) absorption;
(2) extinction;
(3) multiple diffraction;
(4) poor crystal quality;
(5) malfunctioning equipment.

We shall discuss these problems in turn.

Poor Chemical Characterization

The work of the crystallographer is of course far easier if he knows the chemical *structure* of the material on which he is working.   At the very least, the chemical *composition* is important.   Chemical analysis for small amounts of hydrogen and for water content can be a difficult matter if the amount of sample is limited.   Thus it often happens that the crystallographer will find that through the structure determination he has actually done a better job of chemical analysis than was possible by wet chemical techniques. For this reason, it is essential to calculate a difference Fourier map at the end of a structure investigation to be sure that there are no atoms present which have not been included in the model.   Also, unusually large thermal parameters on an atom may indicate that it is either not really present or present in smaller amounts than assumed.

Improper Structure Model

If the model for the structure being refined is incorrect, one can of course place little credence in the numerical values for the parameters in the model; indeed they may have no meaning. Perhaps the most common mistake of this type is the assumption of an ordered structure when in reality the structure is disordered.[15] If the refinement of a structure does not result in agreement between observed and calculated structure factors that is as good as the precision of the measurements would predict, one should examine the possibility of the structure model being inadequate. (Systematic errors in the raw data may also be responsible.) Disorder occurs in many hydrogen-bonded systems, particularly in inorganic salts containing the ammonium ion. Various ammonium compounds exist in several solid phases, stable at different temperatures, and the higher temperature phases almost always involve disorder of the hydrogen atoms. Since the result of a diffraction experiment is a description of the contents of the average unit cell, the following situation arises when there is disorder. If there are N different possible locations for a hydrogen atom in the unit cell, all equally probable, then the average unit cell will contain one Nth of a hydrogen at each of these N locations. For example, if position r_1 is occupied in half the unit cells and position r_2 in the other half, the average unit cell will have half an atom at r_1 and half an atom at r_2. In an attempt to find the structure of the average unit cell from the diffraction data we shall not be able to apply the criteria that all "atoms" be a minimum distance apart or that their scattering densities be resolved from one another. The vectors r_1 and r_2 may differ only very slightly, and the scattering densities may overlap sufficiently so that there is but one broad peak in the scattering density function. The scattering density might be represented as well by an ordered model with the atom in the unique position undergoing vigorous and anisotropic motion about its mean position. This problem, along with those brought about by the attempt to decide on the static or dynamic nature of the disorder, will be discussed in greater detail in ensuing chapters devoted to simple hydrogen-bonded systems. Here we simply emphasize that if there is disorder, it is not always possible to derive a unique model from the diffraction data. It is sometimes possible to do this by the combination of diffraction and spectroscopic information.

Thermal Motion

We shall now discuss the very important effects of thermal motion on a diffraction experiment, both as it affects the structural model and as it affects some of the quantities derived from the structure refinement.

---

[15] A possible error is also the use of a disordered model to obtain agreement between observed and calculated intensities when an entirely different ordered model might be more satisfactory.

In addition to the mean positions of atoms, the x-ray or neutron diffraction experiment gives information concerning the thermal motions of the atoms. The scattering density map gives a peak at the atomic position which should represent the shape of the atom averaged over all motion (and disorder, if any). In least squares refinements, it is usual to assume a model of thermal motion which corresponds to three-dimensional harmonic motion of each atom. The scattering density is given by

$$\rho(\mathbf{r}) = \rho_0 \exp[-\tfrac{1}{2}\{U_{11}x_1{}^2 + U_{22}x_2{}^2 + U_{33}x_3{}^2$$
$$+ 2U_{12}x_1x_2 + 2U_{13}x_1x_3 + 2U_{23}x_2x_3\}]$$

or more concisely[16]

$$\rho(\mathbf{r}) = \rho_0 \exp(-\tfrac{1}{2}\mathbf{r}'\mathbf{U}\mathbf{r}) \tag{2-62}$$

where $\mathbf{U}$ is a tensor from which may be derived the mean square amplitudes of vibration in any direction. This model results in the atomic scattering factor being similarly modified by an exponential function

$$f(\mathbf{H}) = f_0 \exp(-\{h^2\beta_{11} + k^2\beta_{22} + l^2\beta_{33} + 2hk\beta_{12} + 2hl\beta_{13} + 2kl\beta_{23}\})$$

or more concisely[17]

$$f(\mathbf{H}) = f_0 \exp(-\mathbf{H}'\mathbf{B}\mathbf{H}) \tag{2-63}$$

Typically the components of $\mathbf{B}$ are refined by the least squares method.

Not only do these components give information on the thermal motion which may be useful in deriving potential functions or vibrational frequencies, but they also aid in correcting bond lengths to obtain something closer to the equilibrium bond length than is the quantity directly obtained from the diffraction experiment:

$$R_0 = |\langle\mathbf{r}_1\rangle - \langle\mathbf{r}_2\rangle| \tag{2-64}$$

As we have seen in Section 1-3, we may be more interested in the mean bond length

$$\bar{R} = \langle|\mathbf{r}_1 - \mathbf{r}_2|\rangle \tag{2-65}$$

A good and extreme example is an atom (1) freely rotating about another atom (2) in the plane (see Figure 2-8). Note that $\langle\mathbf{r}_1\rangle = \langle\mathbf{r}_2\rangle$, and therefore $R_0 = 0$. A more interesting quantity is the radius of the circle $\bar{R} = \langle|\mathbf{r}_1 - \mathbf{r}_2|\rangle$. As we have previously noted, this requires knowledge of the two-particle density function, which is not given by the diffraction experiment. By

---

[16] The coordinates x_1, x_2, x_3 refer to displacements from the mean position and are conveniently assembled into the matrix $\mathbf{r}$. The transpose of the matrix $\mathbf{r}$ is denoted by $\mathbf{r}'$.

[17] This follows from the fact that the scattering factor $f(\mathbf{H})$ is the Fourier transform of the scattering density $\rho(\mathbf{r})$. The Fourier transform of a Gaussian function is again a Gaussian function. In the present notation it is easy to show that

$$\mathbf{B} = 2\pi^2\mathbf{U}^{-1}$$

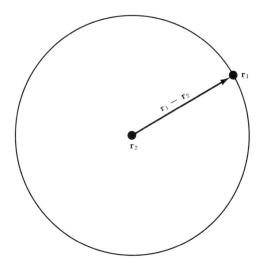

Figure 2-8 *An atom at position* r_1, *freely rotating about another atom at position* r_2. *The constant bond length is* $r_1 - r_2$. *The difference between the mean positions of the two atoms is zero, since the mean value of* r_1 *is* r_2.

assuming various models of the thermal motion one can, however, arrive at corrected bond lengths which may be good approximations to $\bar{R}$. A sound treatment of this problem has been given by Busing and Levy (1964). The essential results are as follows.

Let us denote by w_B^2 and w_A^2 the mean square components of thermal motion in a plane perpendicular to the direction of the bond for atoms B and A, respectively.[18]   Then an approximate value for $\bar{R}$, the mean bond length, may be obtained from the uncorrected value R_0 by

$$\bar{R} = R_0 + \frac{w^2}{2R_0} \tag{2-66}$$

with w^2 being defined in terms of w_B^2 and w_A^2 in a way that depends on the model assumed for the correlated motion of the two atoms.

The most commonly used model is the "riding" model in which it is assumed that the group A—B is vibrating as a whole but that atom B is executing an independent motion which is superimposed on the motion of

---

[18] That is, if the bond is in the z direction, and the deviations of atom A from its mean position are Δx, Δy, and Δz, we define

$$w_A^2 = E\{\Delta x^2\} + E\{\Delta y^2\} \equiv E\{\Delta r^2\} - E\{\Delta z^2\}$$

For an isotropic (spherical) atom,

$$w_A^2 = \tfrac{2}{3}\{\Delta r^2\}$$

the group. This model should be suitable for a light atom forming a single bond to a much heavier ion or molecule. Good examples would be non-hydrogen-bonded OH^- ions or H_2O molecules in a crystal. The model would not be expected to be as good for hydrogen-bonded water molecules but is often assumed in the absence of anything better. For this model, the estimated bond length is obtained by defining

$$w^2 \text{ (riding)} = w_B^2 - w_A^2 \qquad (2\text{-}67)$$

Another model frequently used, and one that may be especially appropriate for nonbonded atoms on different molecules, is based on the assumption that the two atoms are moving completely independently. Then the interatomic distance corrected for thermal motion is given by defining

$$w^2 \text{ (independent)} = w_A^2 + w_B^2 \qquad (2\text{-}68)$$

The minimum correction is obtained when the two atoms are moving completely in phase, the component of motion of atom A being parallel to the component of motion of atom B but perhaps with a different amplitude. In this case

$$w_{\min}^2 = [(w_B^2)^{1/2} - (w_A^2)^{1/2}]^2 \qquad (2\text{-}69)$$

The maximum correction is obtained in the opposite extreme, when the two atoms are moving strictly out of phase; when atom A moves left, atom B always moves right. The correction in this case is given by using

$$w_{\max}^2 = [(w_B^2)^{1/2} + (w_A^2)^{1/2}]^2 \qquad (2\text{-}70)$$

To give some idea of the possible magnitude of the effect, consider the case of $Ca(OH)_2$, which has a nonhydrogen-bonded OH^- ion. The mean O—H separation is 0.936 A with an estimated standard deviation of 0.003 A. The lower bound for the length corrected for thermal motion is 0.956 A, the length assuming the "riding model" is 0.983 A, and the maximum correction brings the length to 1.051 A. One can see that in the absence of knowledge of the complete potential function it is impossible to determine a true mean bond length to the accuracy that the estimated standard deviation of 0.003 implies. In this particular case, since the H atom is not involved in a hydrogen bond, the riding model is probably a very close approximation to the truth. A strong point must be made that even when the model assumed for the corrections is meaningful, the magnitude of the correction is dependent on the thermal parameters derived from the experiment, and these quantities are very sensitive to systematic errors in the data.

A further uncertainty in the meaning of bond lengths derived from diffraction data arises because the stretching motion of a bond is not harmonic; that is, the potential function is not a parabola but an asymmetric function such as a Morse function (Figure 2-9). It is r_e, the minimum point on the potential function curve, which is perhaps best called *the* bond length. This is the equilibrium value in the classical case. Because of the asymmetry of the potential curve and the fact that the first vibrational level lies above the bottom of the well because of zero-point energy, the mean bond length is greater than r_e. Ibers (1959) has shown that the difference between r_e and the mean bond length is typically as great as 0.02 A for A—H bonds. The difference is four to six times as great as the precision with which the average separation can be determined in a good neutron diffraction study. Again, if the potential function is not known completely, it is impossible to relate the mean separation back to an equilibrium bond length.

The point of all the preceding discussion is that the precision with which bond lengths are often quoted should not be taken seriously by theoreticians, or even by the experimenters themselves, as implying that the *accuracy* of the measurement is really that high. It would seem unrealistic to attach an accuracy of greater than about 0.02 to 0.03 A to O—H bond lengths as determined by neutron diffraction.

Another problem connected with thermal motion in diffraction studies is related to the anharmonicity discussed above. Practically all studies carried out to date have assumed harmonic motion—the ellipsoidal approximation (2-62) for the atomic shapes. Anharmonicity along the bond direction is one kind of departure from this approximation. Librational or other complex modes of motion may also render the approximation invalid. Figure 2-10 indicates the shapes that the atoms may have for libration and for anharmonic bond stretching. The refinement of the structure, using the

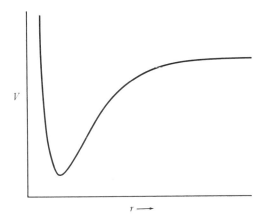

Figure 2-9 *A typical anharmonic potential function for atomic vibrations: the Morse function. V is the potential energy, and r is the internuclear distance.*

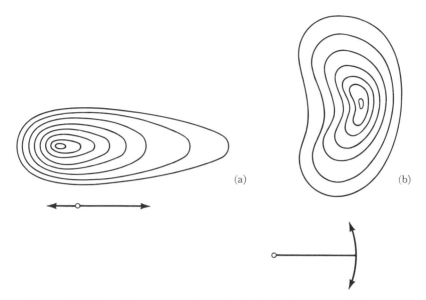

Figure 2-10 *Two of the many types of scattering density distributions possible for atoms undergoing anharmonic motion. The first might arise from an anharmonic stretching vibration described by a Morse function (Figure 2-9). The second could result from an atom undergoing a partial rotation about a fixed center.*

ellipsoidal approximation to these shapes, will not only give unrealistic descriptions of the thermal motion, but the use of an incorrect model may, because of correlation between the thermal motion parameters and the positional parameters, give rise to incorrect values for the positional parameters. This of course causes further uncertainties in the bond lengths which may not be reflected in the estimated standard deviations from the least squares refinements.

With better diffraction data becoming available through the use of computer techniques and automated diffractometers, it seems possible that more structures will be refined using more sophisticated models for thermal motion than the usual harmonic approximation. One such application has been suggested by Willis (1965), who has proposed a vibration of the F atom in CaF_2 and of the O atom in UO_2 which has tetrahedral symmetry. A least squares refinement of the data, based on such a model, has been carried out by Dawson (1966).

Improper Model for Atomic Scattering

One great advantage of the neutron diffraction method is that for all but a very few elements the atomic scattering factor is a well-known constant,

independent of scattering angle or state of chemical bonding. This is not
true for x-ray diffraction. The x-ray scattering factors used almost univer-
sally in crystal structure refinements are those which have been calculated
from the free atom wave functions. There are certainly changes in the
wave functions in going from free atoms to molecules or solids. The wave
function of a molecule is more than a simple superposition of the wave
functions for nonreacting spherical atoms. Bonding effects will be particularly important for bonds including a hydrogen atom. Since the valence
electrons are the electrons affected most strongly by bonding and since the
only electron on the hydrogen atom is the valence electron, we may expect
the relative departure from spherical symmetry to be greatest for the hydrogen
atom. The center of gravity of the electron distribution may be somewhat
removed from the nuclear position. Thus the refinement of the hydrogen
atom position, using a spherical hydrogen atom in the calculation, may lead
to results which are not necessarily simply related to the nuclear position.
In the course of many x-ray structural studies a number of O—H, N—H,
and C—H distances have been determined. Naturally there is wide variation among these distances owing to the limited accuracy obtainable and to
the diverse experimental conditions employed. Nevertheless the trend for
these apparent interelectron-cloud distances to be 0.05 to 0.20 A shorter than
the internuclear distances determined spectroscopically or by neutron diffraction is obvious. [Various tabulations of such distances are available.
See, for example, Tomiie (1958) and, more recently, Table VI of Stewart,
Davidson, and Simpson (1965).] Tomiie (1958) has presented a semiempirical quantum mechanical calculation which tends to support these
anomalously short distances as arising from the shift of the K electron toward
the heavier atom on bonding. Since in electron diffraction studies it is the
separation of potential that is determined, a question may be asked concerning the relation of distances determined by electron diffraction to spectroscopic ones. A calculation (Ibers, 1961) suggests that a K electron shift
would result in electron diffraction distances that are long in comparison
with spectroscopic values. The effect here would be difficult to detect owing
to the limited accuracy of such studies.

The effects of this interaction have been demonstrated by Jensen and
Sundaralingam (1964), who found that the isotropic thermal parameters
for hydrogen atoms in several structures are abnormally low if the scattering

factor for the isolated hydrogen atom is assumed. These authors have recommended a modified scattering factor for hydrogen which is still spherical, but which is for an electron distribution which represents the best fit in a least squares sense to the proper three-dimensional electron distribution. Stewart, Davidson, and Simpson (1965) have presented a quantum mechanical justification for this for scattering from the hydrogen molecule. They have taken one of the best molecular electronic wave functions available for the hydrogen molecule and obtained from it a molecular scattering factor. Then they have asked the question, What superposition of spherical hydrogen atoms gives the best fit to the calculated molecular scattering factor? They have found that a superposition of two spherical hydrogen atoms separated by a distance which is 0.14 A less than the internuclear distance is the most suitable. For O—H, C—H, and N—H bonds, similar calculations suggest that a least squares refinement using the free atom scattering factor for hydrogen will result in a value of the internuclear distance that is 0.09 A too short and a thermal parameter B that is 2.3 A^2 too small. Although such calculations make plausible the short internuclear distances often found by x-rays for bonds involving hydrogen, it is clearly not an adequate treatment of the problem since it introduces an effective electron distribution which does not have cusps at the nuclear positions— an impossible situation.

In view of the discussion of thermal motion earlier in this chapter it is apparent that it is difficult to assess these effects in relation to a possible aspherical distribution. Thus if those distances involving hydrogen that have been found could be corrected for the effects of thermal motion it is possible that the discrepancies with spectroscopically determined values would disappear or, perhaps, become much smaller. The difficulty here, in addition to that involving the proper choice of model for thermal correction, is that for the most part there have not been data sets of sufficient accuracy to allow a meaningful anisotropic refinement of the thermal parameters for the hydrogen atom. Without such a refinement, even the approximate corrections for thermal motion may be grossly in error. In a very recent study of deuterated and normal oxalic acid dihydrate, Delaplane and Ibers (1966) obtained results which may be pertinent to this problem of anomalously short distances. The data set, which was obtained by counter methods and was corrected for absorption and, eventually, for extinction, showed remarkably good internal consistency among equivalent reflections. The four independent heavy atoms along with the three independent hydrogen atoms refined smoothly anisotropically to give a final value of the residual $\Sigma||F_0|^2 - |F_c|^2|/\Sigma|F_0|^2$ of 5.6 % for the D compound and 4.1 % for the H compound, pleasingly low values by current standards. In these

Table 2-5 *Bond Lengths (in A) in Normal and Deuterated Oxalic Acid Dihydrate*

	Uncorrected[a]	Riding model	Independent model
O—H$_1$	0.934 (0.024)	—[b]	1.05
O—H$_2$	0.823 (0.027)	0.86	0.98
O—H$_3$	0.821 (0.028)	0.90	1.02
O—D$_1$	0.914 (0.022)	0.92	1.04
O—D$_2$	0.822 (0.023)	0.86	0.99
O—D$_3$	0.793 (0.031)	0.85	0.98

[a] The values in parentheses are estimated standard deviations. These are not given for the corrected distances because of the uncertainty of the correction.

[b] Not applicable since $w_0{}^2$ is greater than $w_H{}^2$. (See Equation 2-67.)

calculations, the modified hydrogen atom scattering factor derived by Stewart, Davidson, and Simpson (1965) was used. Nevertheless, as the data of Table 2-5 indicate, the uncorrected O—H distances are considerably shorter than the value 1.00 A found in a neutron diffraction study of ice (Peterson and Levy, 1957). Note, however, that the corrections for thermal motion improve the situation considerably. Although the use of the independent model of thermal motion leads to O—H distances that are in good agreement with one another and in satisfactory agreement with the expected value, this model would not appear to be as realistic as the riding model. These results suggest that at least part of the difficulty in past determinations of anomalously short distances involving hydrogen atoms arose from the necessarily unrealistic thermal refinement of the hydrogen atom positions with consequent inability to correct distances involving hydrogen atoms for thermal motion.

Without question, a neutron diffraction study of these two crystals would yield valuable information on this problem.

Anomalous Scattering

In normal x-ray scattering, the scattering factor f_0 is the transform of the electron density of the atom. This is true only if the energy of the x-radiation is far greater than any transition energy between electronic levels in the scattering atom. When this condition is not satisfied, the atomic scattering factor may be expressed in general as

$$f = f_0 + \delta f' + i\delta f'' \qquad (2\text{-}71)$$

The additional terms, both $\delta f'$ and $\delta f''$, are referred to as anomalous scattering contributions since they would not be present for scattering from classical electrons. It is particularly important in calculating structure factors to include the imaginary term $i\delta f''$. Although the inclusion of these effects in the calculated structure factors is not difficult (Ibers and Hamilton, 1964), the results may be less than satisfactory because the values of $\delta f'$ and $\delta f''$ are not known with much accuracy.

It is especially important to include these effects when the substances under investigation crystallize in a polar space group. (A polar space group is a noncentrosymmetric space group in which the origin is not defined by symmetry.) Ueki, Zalkin, and Templeton (1966) and Cruickshank and McDonald (1967) have demonstrated that if these effects of anomalous scattering are neglected, or if the incorrect absolute configuration is chosen, then bond distances involving the anomalously scattering atoms may be incorrect by 10 or more times the apparent standard deviations of these distances.

It was first shown experimentally by Peterson and Smith (1961) that neutrons also exhibit anomalous scattering. The scattering factor always includes an imaginary component $i\delta f''$ if the atom is a strong absorber for the incident radiation. For neutron scattering from most elements, the absorption and hence the imaginary component of the scattering factor are small, and these effects are of little importance. They thus do not present additional sources of error in the model. However, they can be used, at least in principle, as an aid to the solution of the phase problem, especially since the anomalous terms show a rapid dependence on neutron wavelength. Thus one may be able to obtain absolutely isomorphous derivatives simply by changing the neutron wavelength. This technique may become very important in the solution of large, complex structures.

A interesting example of the use of anomalous scattering of neutrons to establish an absolute configuration of a complex molecule is provided by the work of Johnson and co-workers (1965).

Absorption

If there are processes other than the Bragg scattering process which cause an attenuation of the radiation as it passes through the crystal, we say that the radiation is absorbed. If the intensity of a Bragg reflection is I_h in the absence of absorption, and if the total path length of the incident and scattered beams is T, the observed intensity will be

$$I_{\text{obs}} = I_h e^{-\mu T} \tag{2-72}$$

where μ is the *linear absorption coefficient*. The linear absorption coefficient is related to the absorption cross sections σ_i of the atoms in the crystal by

$$\mu = V_{\text{cell}}^{-1} \sum_i \sigma_i \qquad (2\text{-}73)$$

where the summation is over all atoms in the cell. In a crystal of arbitrary shape, there will be many different path lengths T corresponding to the same Bragg reflection. For the crystal as a whole, then, the observed intensity is

$$I_{\text{obs}} = I_h \int_{\text{all paths}} e^{-\mu T(p)} \, dp \qquad (2\text{-}74)$$

where p is a set of parameters that defines the path through the crystal.

Absorption errors in the data can be corrected for by numerical methods if (i) the shape of the crystal and its dimensions are accurately known and (ii) the absorption coefficient of the crystal for the x-rays used is known. Neither the crystal shape nor the linear absorption coefficient is generally known with enough accuracy to make this correction with an accuracy of better than about 2%. For this reason, whenever possible, the conditions of crystal size and radiation used must be chosen so that the absorption correction is minimized.

It is sometimes stated that as long as μT, the product of the linear absorption coefficient μ and the path length T, is small, 0.3 for instance, absorption errors can be neglected. This is fallacious, as a simple example will illustrate. Suppose for a given reflection μT is 0.1, while for another reflection it is 0.25. This situation invariably arises in diffraction from crystals which are much longer than they are wide, for example. Then the correction for the first reflection is 1.11; for the second it is 1.28. Clearly if the absorption correction is neglected the systematic error introduced into the data set far exceeds the apparent precision with which intensities can be measured with the use of counter methods.

Failure to correct for absorption in a real crystal structure determination will have several effects. First, high accuracy in the parameter determination will not be achieved. More serious, however, will be the fact that the estimated standard deviations in the derived parameters may be too low. These standard deviations are meaningful if the data are subject only to random errors. The presence of systematic errors makes the interpretation of the estimated parameter variances much less certain. Finally, neglect of absorption corrections will prevent the definition of the finer details of the structure determination, such as meaningful anisotropic thermal parameters for the heavier atoms and probably the positional parameters themselves for the lighter atoms, including hydrogen. In short, if one is interested in reliable thermal parameters and reliable positions for the light atoms, then the importance of properly taking into account the effects of absorption cannot be overemphasized.

Extinction

The intensity of an x-ray reflection may be reduced to less than its ideal value not only by absorption but also by the scattering process itself. This process is known as *extinction*. For most x-ray problems, extinction is important for only a few percent of the very strongest reflections, and for these it is usually sufficient to consider that the extinction is an effective absorption with an empirically determined absorption coefficient. This single parameter approach is probably not extremely realistic, although experience indicates that it may not introduce errors much more severe than those caused by the inaccuracy of the absorption correction. As with absorption, knowledge of the exact shape of the crystal is important in applying the extinction correction (Hamilton, 1957). Zachariasen (1964) has recently emphasized that proper account must be taken of the polarization of the x-rays in applying this correction. A more general treatment of extinction must consider not only the loss in intensity in the incident beam due to scattering out and the increase in intensity due to the scattering of a diffracted beam into the incident beam but also the possible anisotropy of the extinction effects. This anisotropy can be as large as a few percent. Even in data taken from a spherical cyrstal, where the absorption and extinction effects are independent of the orientation of the crystal in the simple theory, one can see differences as great as a few percent between the intensities of the reflections h_1, h_2, h_3 and $-h_1$, $-h_2$, $-h_3$.[19] The cause of some of these discrepancies can be labeled *crystal imperfection* to cover up our lack of knowledge concerning the detailed mosaic structure of the crystal.

Multiple and Simultaneous Diffraction

Simultaneous reflection can be important only if the crystal is large enough for extinction to be important. In addition to loss of intensity in the incident beam because of the intensity gain in the diffracted beam of interest, it is possible that other reflections will be occurring simultaneously with the one of interest but diffracting in a different direction. If these simultaneous reflections are strong, the loss in intensity in the incident beam due to one reflection will also cause a diminution of the intensity of the other reflection.

The effect of multiple Bragg scattering—the Renninger effect—can be important even when extinction is not severe. A diffracted ray from a strong reflection can be rescattered in a direction corresponding to a very weak or

[19] This is true even for centrosymmetric crystals where the effects of anomalous scattering cannot be the source of the discrepancy.

absent reflection and give a false impression of strength.   These effects are probably more important than is commonly realized in x-ray diffraction experiments and they are very noticeable in neutron diffraction work.

2-8 CONCLUSIONS

In this chapter we have outlined some of the elements of diffraction theory and have emphasized the intrinsic errors and difficulties in the determination of the crystal structure.   We would be amiss if we failed to emphasize the more positive side of such a determination.

We may consider the types of errors involved in diffraction studies to be of two kinds—those which involve the interpretation of the diffraction data and the solution of the approximate structure and those which are due to random and systematic errors in the data and model.   The first group, which we might term mistakes, are far less common in diffraction experiments than in most of the other fields of molecular structure determination.   The Patterson function summarizes all the information available from the usual diffraction experiment.   The abstraction of a scattering density function from the Patterson function is not unique, but in most cases the imposition of rather general restrictions on the model is sufficient to lead to a unique solution.   For example, we know that an acceptable model must contain atoms that are no closer together than about 1 A, that nonbonded atoms in the structure must be separated approximately by the usual van der Waals distances, and so on.   With such chemical and physical information there will rarely be any ambiguity in the interpretation of the Patterson function. That is not to say that incorrect structures have never been reported, but rather that if the difference between observed and calculated structure factors is about 10% or less, then one may usually be confident that the major details of the structure determination are correct.

Although we have emphasized the fact that neutron diffraction provides the best method for hydrogen atom location, there are valid reasons for studying hydrogen bonding by x-ray diffraction.   The first reason is that it is often possible from the positions of the heavy atoms to infer the positions of the hydrogen atoms even if these cannot be located directly; much of the interest in hydrogen-bonded crystals lies in the effect that the hydrogen bonds have on the geometry of the heavy atom positions, particularly the molecular packing.   Much of our understanding of the general features of hydrogen-bonded structures has come from crystal structure investigations which make no pretense at explicit hydrogen atom location.   There will continue to be many such structures of interest, and since modern x-ray techniques can be accurate enough for at least the approximate location of all the hydrogen atoms in most structures, these techniques will continue to be widely applied in the study of hydrogen bonding in complex crystals.

One of the major difficulties in the interpretation of diffraction data is in the elucidation of the precise nature of disordered structures. The diffraction data can be ambiguous, and it is for this reason that the combination of diffraction and spectroscopic data can often give far more insight into the nature of the disorder than can either method alone. In the next chapter, we shall discuss spectroscopic methods and the combined application of the two methods.

REFERENCES

American Crystallographic Association (1965), Proceedings of the Symposium on Accuracy in X-Ray Intensity Measurement, *Trans. Am. Cryst. Assoc.* **1**, 1–112.

American Crystallographic Association (1966), Proceedings of the Symposium on Machine Interpretations of Patterson Functions and Alternative Direct Approaches, *Trans. Am. Cryst. Assoc.* **2**, 1–78.

Busing, W. R., and Levy, H. A. (1964), The Effect of Thermal Motion on the Estimation of Bond Lengths from Diffraction Measurements, *Acta Cryst.* **17**, 142.

Cowley, J. M., and Ibers, J. A. (1956), The Structures of Some Ferric Chloride-Graphite Compounds, *Acta Cryst.* **9**, 421.

Cruickshank D. W. J., and McDonald, W. S. (1967), Parameter Errors in Polar Space Groups, Caused by Neglect of Anomalous Scattering, *Acta Cryst.*, **23**, 9.

Dawson, B. (1966), Antisymmetric Aspects of Atomic Charge Density in Diamond and Fluorite Lattices, *Acta Cryst.* **21**, A5.

Delaplane, R. G., and Ibers, J. A. (1966), Direct Determination of the Effect of Isotopic Substitution on Bond Lengths in Solid Oxalic Acid Dihydrate. *J. Chem. Phys.* **45**, 3451.

Hamilton, W. C. (1957), The Effect of Crystal Shape and Setting on Secondary Extinction, *Acta Cryst.* **10**, 629.

Hamilton, W. C. (1964), *Statistics in Physical Science*. Ronald Press, New York.

Hamilton, W. C., and La Placa, S. J. (1967), Neutron and X-Ray Diffraction Studies of the Anti-Leukemia Agent, Methylglyoxal Bisguanylhydrazone Dihydrochloride Monohydrate, *Acta Cryst.*, in press.

Ibers, J. A. (1959), Anharmonic Oscillations of Nuclei, *Acta Cryst.* **12**, 251.

Ibers, J. A. (1961), Effects of Bonding on Electron Diffraction Values of Bond Distances Involving Hydrogen Atoms in Solids, *Acta Cryst.* **14**, 853.

Ibers, J. A., and Hamilton, W. C. (1964), Dispersion Corrections and Crystal Structure Refinements, *Acta Cryst.* **17**, 781.

International Tables for X-Ray Crystallography, Vol. 3 (1962). Kynoch Press, Birmingham, England.

Jensen, L., and Sundaralingam, M. (1964), Hydrogen Atom Thermal Parameters, *Science* **145,** 1185.

Johnson, A. W. S. (1966), An Electron Diffraction Study of Some Lamellar Graphite Compounds. Thesis, Physics Department, University of Western Australia.

Johnson, C. K., Gabe, E. J., Taylor, M. R., and Rose, I. A. (1965), Determination by Neutron and X-ray Diffraction of the Absolute Configuration of an Enzymatically Formed α-Monodeuterioglycolate, *J. Am. Chem. Soc.* **87,** 1802.

Karle, I. L., and Karle, J. (1963), An Application of a New Phase Determination Procedure to the Structure of Cyclo(hexaglycyl)hemihydrate, *Acta Cryst.* **16,** 969.

La Placa, S. J., and Ibers, J. A. (1965), The Crystal Structure of *tris*-(Triphenylphosphine)Rhodium Carbonyl Hydride, *Acta Cryst.* **18,** 511.

Patterson, A. L. (1934), A Fourier Series Method for the Determination of the Components of Interatomic Distances in Crystals, *Phys. Rev.* **46,** 372.

Peterson, S. W., and Levy, H. A. (1957), A Single Crystal Neutron Diffraction Study of Heavy Ice, *Acta Cryst.* **10,** 70.

Peterson, S. W., and Smith, H. G. (1961), Anomalous Neutron Diffraction in α-CdS, *Phys. Rev. Letters* **6,** 7.

Sayre, D. (1952), The Squaring Method: A New Method for Phase Determination, *Acta Cryst.* **5,** 60.

Stewart, R. F., Davidson, E. R., and Simpson, W. T. (1965), Coherent X-Ray Scattering for the Hydrogen Atom in the Hydrogen Molecule, *J. Chem. Phys.* **42,** 3175.

Tomiie, Y. (1958), The Electron Distribution and the Location of the Bonded Hydrogen Atom in Crystals, *J. Phys. Soc. Japan* **13,** 1030.

Ueki, T., Zalkin, A., and Templeton, D. H. (1966), Crystal Structure of Thorium Nitrate Pentahydrate by X-Ray Diffraction, *Acta Cryst.* **20,** 836.

Willis, B. T. M. (1965), The Anomalous Behaviour of the Neutron Reflexions of Fluorite, *Acta Cryst.* **18,** 75.

Zachariasen, W. H. (1952), A New Analytical Method for Solving Complex Crystal Structures, *Acta Cryst.* **5,** 68.

Zachariasen, W. H. (1964), The Secondary Extinction Correction, *Acta Cryst.* **16,** 1139.

Spectroscopic and Diffraction Studies of Hydrogen-Bonded Systems

In studies of the hydrogen bond, diffraction and spectroscopic methods are complementary. Diffraction methods reveal the position of the atoms in a crystal structure and on occasion lead to some understanding of the thermal vibrations that these atoms undergo; spectroscopic methods yield information on the energy levels of the system, and for especially simple systems this may lead to some understanding of potential functions for the hydrogen bond.

In diffraction studies there is an excess of observations over parameters needed for the description of the structure. In such overdetermined problems there are many built-in checks that lead to answers and interpretations that are generally unequivocal. The diffractionist can usually say, "The atoms in this structure are here." In spectroscopic studies generally there are fewer observations than are needed in the most general description of the vibrations. In such underdetermined problems various approximations are necessary and the answers and interpretations are usually equivocal. The spectroscopist should say, "Here is the spectrum of the material. I believe that this spectrum may best be interpreted in the following way, although this interpretation is by no means unique." Nevertheless, the spectroscopist can record and examine hundreds of well-defined spectra while the diffractionist is solving a single crystal structure. In this sense also the two methods are complementary: diffraction methods yield more certain results at a slower rate; these results often are the basis for interpretations of spectroscopic data, and the abundance of these data enables one, at least qualitatively, to extend his knowledge of related systems with minimum effort in minimum time.

In this chapter we discuss some general aspects of spectroscopic methods. We also discuss potential functions for hydrogen bonding. We then illustrate the applications of spectroscopic and diffraction methods to some simple hydrogen-bonded systems. The examples we take are few, compared with those available, and they reflect our own interests as well as the complementary nature of diffraction and spectroscopic methods.

3-1 GENERAL ASPECTS OF SPECTROSCOPIC METHODS

Harmonic and Anharmonic Oscillators

The traditional spectroscopic methods for the detection and study of hydrogen bonding are infrared and Raman spectroscopy. More recently, NMR (nuclear magnetic resonance) methods have also been used. Readily available commercial instruments make studies by spectroscopic methods both rapid and easy, and as a result not only have hundreds of papers on the subject appeared, but also several very useful books. In particular, the book by Pimentel and McClellan (1960) is encyclopedic in its coverage of the literature up to about 1956. The book provides a useful description of the applications of infrared and Raman spectroscopy to studies of hydrogen bonding, and does this in far greater detail than is necessary here. Nevertheless, we feel that it is worthwhile to provide some background for these studies.

The absorption of radiation may bring about a transition within a molecular system to an excited vibrational level. The energy required to excite such a transition usually falls within the infrared region of the spectrum. Consider a description of the vibrational motion of a diatomic molecule, A—B. The potential energy for such a molecule is conveniently assumed to be that of a harmonic oscillator:

$$2V(x) = kx^2 \qquad (3-1)$$

where x is a displacement coordinate along the A—B bond. In (3-1), k is called the "force constant," since the restoring force F acting to return the vibrating system to equilibrium is, in this approximation, proportional to the displacement x from equilibrium and is given by

$$F = kx \qquad (3-2)$$

Thus the force constant provides some measure of the strength of the A—B bond.   It is shown in most elementary books on quantum mechanics that the energy levels of this linear harmonic oscillator are

$$E_v = (v + \tfrac{1}{2})h\nu \tag{3-3}$$

where v is the quantum number or running index of the energy levels, with the ground state corresponding to $v = 0$, where h is Planck's constant, and where ν, the fundamental frequency (frequency for the transition from the ground state to the first excited state), is given by

$$\nu = \left(\frac{1}{2\pi}\right)\left(\frac{k}{\mu}\right)^{1/2} \tag{3-4}$$

In (3-4) μ, the reduced mass, is equal to $(m_A{}^{-1} + m_B{}^{-1})^{-1}$.   The wave function for $v = 0$ in terms of a *normal coordinate* ξ has the form

$$\psi(\xi) = N \exp\left[-\alpha\xi^2/2\right] \tag{3-5}$$

where $\alpha = 4\pi^2\nu/h$ and N is a normalizing constant.   In Fig. 3-1, we sketch the energy levels, wave functions, and probability distributions for the harmonic oscillator for the states $v = 0$ through $v = 3$.

If we analyze the spectrum obtained from a diatomic gaseous molecule, we conclude that the energy levels are not equally spaced as shown in Figure 3-1, but rather that generally they converge as v increases.   This is because the molecule is undergoing anharmonic, rather than harmonic, motion. The anharmonic oscillator may be described by a potential of the form

$$2V = kx^2 + k'x^3 + k''x^4 + \cdots \tag{3-6}$$

The deviations from harmonic oscillation that occur in molecules are generally small.   For this reason the harmonic oscillator description remains a very useful one.   The anharmonic oscillator is usually treated as a perturbation of the harmonic oscillator since the wave functions and energy levels of the general anharmonic oscillator cannot be expressed in closed form.

Let us now consider the problem of small, harmonic vibrations of a polyatomic molecule of N atoms.   We may express the kinetic energy T and the potential energy V of this polyatomic system in terms of the displacements x_i of the nuclei from their equilibrium positions:

$$2T = \sum_{i=1}^{3N} m_i \dot{x}_i{}^2 \qquad 2V = \sum_{i,j=1}^{3N} k_{ij} x_i x_j \tag{3-7}$$

The rotations and translations of the molecule are not of interest to us, and by suitable choice of a moving coordinate system we need only $3N - 6$ coordinates, or degrees of freedom, to describe the positions of the nuclei in

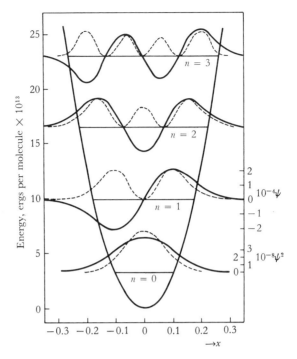

Figure 3-1 *Energy levels, wave functions (solid curves), and probability distributions (dashed curves) for the harmonic oscillator.*   *The wave functions are calculated for a hydrogen nucleus vibrating against a much larger mass.*   (From Brand and Speakman, 1960.)

space.[1] The vibrations of a polyatomic molecule are not chaotic or random. Rather the displacements of the nuclei from their equilibrium positions are the sums of displacements associated with $3N$ special vibrations, the normal vibrations or normal modes. A normal mode of vibration has the characteristic that the motion of each atomic coordinate has the same frequency and phase. As a result each atom reaches its position of maximum displacement at the same time, and each atom passes through its equilibrium position at the same time. In mathematical terms, if Q_i is a normal coordinate and $\dot{Q}_i$ its time derivative, then the kinetic and potential energies of the system are given by

$$2T = \sum_{i=1}^{3N} \dot{Q}_i{}^2 \quad \text{and} \quad 2V = \sum_{i=1}^{3N} \lambda_i Q_i{}^2 \tag{3-8}$$

where

$$\lambda_i = 4\pi^2 \nu_i{}^2 \tag{3-9}$$

[1] For a linear molecule, $3N - 5$ coordinates are required.

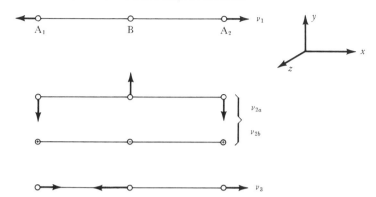

Figure 3-2 *A schematic drawing of the normal vibrations of the linear symmetric A—B—A molecule.*

and ν_i are the fundamental frequencies of vibration. (In this formulation there are six zero frequencies, corresponding to the rotations and translations of the molecule.) Quantum-mechanically the polyatomic vibrational problem is formulated as the combination of vibrations of harmonic oscillators. The wave function for the molecule is written as a product of harmonic oscillator wave functions. In effect one is assuming that there is no coupling or interaction between the normal modes. That is, the extension of a given bond does not change the force constant of a second bond.

The various techniques for describing the normal modes of vibration are adequately described elsewhere (Wilson, Decius, and Cross, 1955) and here we simply illustrate the results for the symmetric, linear triatomic molecule A—B—A. We choose this example because of its importance in later discussions of the O—H—O bond. This linear system has $3 \times 3 - 5 = 4$ normal modes; these are illustrated in Figure 3-2. Normal mode 1 is usually called the symmetric stretching mode; normal mode 2 the bending mode; and normal mode 3 the antisymmetric stretching mode. Normal mode 2, with associated normal coordinates Q_{2a} and Q_{2b}, is doubly degenerate in that ν_{2a} and ν_{2b} are equal. The displacements of the three atoms along the coordinate axes illustrated in Fig. 3-2 may be expressed in terms of the normal coordinates:

$$x_1 = -\frac{Q_1}{(2\mu_1)^{1/2}} - \left(\frac{\mu_3}{2}\right)^{1/2} \frac{Q_3}{m_A}$$

$$y_1 = -\left(\frac{\mu_3}{2}\right)^{1/2} \frac{Q_{2a}}{m_A}$$

$$z_1 = -\left(\frac{\mu_3}{2}\right)^{1/2} \frac{Q_{2b}}{m_A}$$

$$x_2 = (2\mu_3)^{1/2} \frac{Q_3}{m_B}$$

$$y_2 = (2\mu_3)^{1/2} \frac{Q_{2a}}{m_B} \qquad (3\text{-}10)$$

$$z_2 = (2\mu_3)^{1/2} \frac{Q_{2b}}{m_B}$$

$$x_3 = \frac{Q_1}{(2\mu_1)^{1/2}} - \left(\frac{\mu_3}{2}\right)^{1/2} \frac{Q_3}{m_A}$$

$$y_3 = y_1$$

$$z_3 = z_1$$

where

$$\mu_1 = m_A \qquad \mu_3 = \frac{m_A m_B}{2m_A + m_B}$$

Let r_1 and r_2 be the instantaneous displacements from equilibrium of the A_1—B and B—A_2 bonds; that is, $r_1 = x_2 - x_1$ and $r_2 = x_3 - x_2$. It follows from (3-10) that

$$Q_1 = \left(\frac{\mu_1}{2}\right)^{1/2} (r_1 + r_2) \qquad Q_3 = \left(\frac{\mu_3}{2}\right)^{1/2} (r_1 - r_2) \qquad (3\text{-}11)$$

Thus the normal coordinate Q_1 is proportional to the change in the A—A bond length; the normal coordinate Q_3 is proportional to the deviation of the B atom in the direction of the bond from the center of the bond.

Complications in Infrared and Raman Spectra

In the usual infrared spectroscopic experiment one measures the percentage absorption through the sample of radiation as a function of its wavelength. Absorption occurs when the frequency of the radiation corresponds to certain transitions within the molecule. There are two selection rules for the absorption of infrared radiation. The first is that molecules will absorb infrared radiation as vibrational excitation energy only if there is a change in the dipole moment of the molecule as it vibrates. The second selection rule, strictly valid only in the harmonic oscillator approximation, is that with the absorption of radiation transitions may occur only between states separated by $v = 1$.

In the usual Raman experiment a monochromatic beam of light illuminates a sample and one observes the scattered light, usually at right angles to the incident beam. Two situations can occur. A quantum of light can collide with a molecule and be scattered with its frequency unchanged. This is called Rayleigh scattering.   It is also possible for the quantum of light to induce a transition within the molecule.   If this occurs, and the incident light is of frequency ν_0 and the transition of frequency ν_1, then the scattered light will be of frequency $\nu_0 - \nu_1$.   It is also possible for a molecule in an exicted state to collide with the incoming light and return to the ground state. Then the scattered light will have frequency $\nu_0 + \nu_1$.   The $(\nu_0 - \nu_1)$ lines are called Stokes lines; the $(\nu_0 + \nu_1)$ lines are called anti-Stokes lines.   For a vibration to be Raman active, there must be a change in polarizability during the vibration.

Except in the simplest cases, recourse is made to group theoretical methods (e.g., Wilson, Decius, and Cross, 1955) to decide if a given vibrational motion will lead to an observable band in the infrared or Raman or both. If a band occurs, the vibrational mode is said to be "active."   Since the selection rules are different, the two methods are frequently complementary in the study and characterizations of molecules and their symmetry.   For the linear system A—B—A discussed above, the symmetric stretching mode ν_1 is inactive in the infrared, but active in the Raman; the antisymmetric stretching mode ν_3 and the degenerate bending mode ν_2 are both active in the infrared but not in the Raman.   If the molecule possesses a center of symmetry, as does the linear symmetric triatomic molecule, then no given band is active in both the infrared and the Raman.

Now if we were to observe the infrared and Raman spectra from this hypothetical A—B—A molecule in the gas state, then bands in addition to ν_1, ν_2, and ν_3 would occur.   In particular, various combination bands with frequencies such as $\nu_1 - \nu_2$ or $\nu_2 + \nu_3$ would be found.   In addition, overtone bands, such as $2\nu_1$, would be observed, because such bands are strictly forbidden only if the harmonic oscillator approximation holds rigorously.   Since all molecular vibrations exhibit some anharmonicity, such overtone and combination bands will occur, though not precisely at the positions predicted for harmonic motion.   Bands might also occur that appear to be misplaced, owing to a phenomenon known as Fermi resonance. If two allowed anharmonic vibrations occur near the same frequency, then they can interact strongly through a quantum mechanical resonance effect, with the result that the observed position of one band is raised and the other is lowered.   Such an interaction can also bring about a dramatic increase in intensity in a band that otherwise might have been forbidden or very weak. Bands might also be missing, owing to degeneracies such as those for the bending mode above.   Moreover, any given instrument records spectra over a fixed range of frequencies, and so it is possible that various fundamental modes will be missed because they are outside the range of the instrument. To summarize, then, among the complicating features of the spectrum from an apparently simple gas molecule are (1) vibrational frequencies outside the range of the instrument; (2) degeneracies in certain bands; (3) the presence of overtones; (4) the presence of various combination bands; (5) possible presence of Fermi resonance;(6) general shifts resulting from the effects of anharmonicity.

Let us now consider the additional complications that arise when we record spectra from solid samples, rather than from gases. To begin with, Raman spectra can only be obtained from solids if Rayleigh scattering is kept to a minimum. Because of this, carefully grown single crystals of considerable size are often required. It is likely that the development of laser optics in combination with the relatively new commercial Raman instruments will bring about a considerable extension of Raman studies to systems that were unsuitable in the past. At present, however, most spectroscopic studies of hydrogen bonding in solids are based on infrared techniques. Such studies may be carried out in several ways. (1) A single crystal may be used if very thin samples of known orientation can be obtained. (2) The crystalline material may be carefully ground and dispersed in some type of carrier, usually a paraffin oil. The spectrum of the sample will then contain, in addition to those characteristic of the compound of interest, bands corresponding to the paraffin oil; in order to get a complete spectrum from the compound it may be necessary to make several runs with different carriers. (3) The material may be ground and intimately mixed with KBr or KCl and the mixture then pressed into a clear disk suitable for direct observation. A major disadvantage of this approach is that chemical reactions between sample and KBr may occur. Even when these various difficulties are overcome and a suitable spectrum has been recorded, the interpretation of the spectrum is complicated by all the features discussed above and by additional ones that we now consider. Various interactions in the solid state cause frequency shifts, intensity changes, and band splittings. In a crystalline solid there occur vibrations of one molecular or atomic group relative to one of a similar type elsewhere in the crystal. These lattice modes do not occur in a gaseous sample, since no fixed distance or orientation relationship between individual molecules exists in the gaseous state. If the unit cell of the solid contains more than one equivalent molecule, then interactions occur between those molecules within the same unit cell with resultant frequency shifts and splittings, so-called factor splittings. Of even more importance is the change in selection rules that can occur. Selection rules depend on symmetry relationships. For the gaseous molecule one uses the molecular symmetry to establish allowed bands; for a molecule in the solid state one must employ the crystallographic site symmetry of the molecule. This has important implications. First, bands that are forbidden in the gas state may occur in the solid, and various degeneracies may be removed. Second, complete analysis of the spectrum from even a simple substance

may rest largely on the assumed site symmetry or on knowing this symmetry as a result of prior diffraction studies.

Force Fields and the Assignment of Simple Spectra

In view of the features that complicate spectra from gases and solids,
can we generally account for the observed bands in such spectra and determine force constants? The answer is usually, "No," although for simple
molecules, especially in the gas phase, assignment of the bands and determination of force constants of a simplified force field (potential function)
are possible. If cubic and higher terms are neglected, then the potential
energy expression of (3-7) is general. For a completely unsymmetric
molecule there will be $(3N - 5)(3N - 6)/2$ independent force constants
in this expression. If the molecule possesses symmetry elements, then this
number will be smaller. Nevertheless, the number of force constants is
always larger than the number of fundamental frequencies, namely $3N - 6$,
except for a few highly symmetric configurations, such as the symmetric
linear triatomic molecule. In order to make assignments of bands and
determination of force constants practical, in general it is necessary to reduce
the number of terms in the potential energy expression. Three commonly
used force fields that accomplish this are (1) the central force field, (2) the
valence force field, and (3) the Urey-Bradley force field.

The assumption that the forces holding atoms in their equilibrium positions act only along the lines joining pairs of atoms leads to the central force
force field: $2V = \Sigma_i k_{ii}(\Delta r_i{}^2)$, where the sum extends over all interatomic
distances r_i. The central force field has not been especially successful for the
calculation of frequencies. To take but one example, this force field is
completely unrealistic for the symmetric triatomic molecule. For small
displacements, the bending mode with coordinate Q_2 does not change any
interatomic distances; thus there would be no quadratic term in the central
force potential energy that would resist this motion, and the frequency ν_2
would be predicted to be zero.

The valence force field is more reasonable chemically, and it has been
applied extensively. Here the forces considered are those which resist the
changes in the lengths of the valence bonds, together with those that oppose
the bending or torsion of the bonds. Forces between nonbonded atoms are
not considered directly. As an example, consider the tetrahedral XY_4
molecule. The valence force field will include two types of terms:

$$f_1(r_1{}^2 + r_2{}^2 + r_3{}^2 + r_4{}^2)$$
$$f_2(\alpha_{12}^2 + \alpha_{13}^2 + \alpha_{14}^2 + \alpha_{23}^2 + \alpha_{24}^2 + \alpha_{34}^2)$$

$$(3\text{-}12)$$

where r_i is the extension of an X—Y bond and where α_{ij} is the distortion of the valence angle between bonds i and j. In this example there are two force constants to be determined from the four fundamental frequencies. Since the problem is overdetermined it is possible to assess the reliability of the procedure. It is generally found that the valence force field leads to calculated frequencies that are within about 10% of those observed. (In making such comparisons it should be remembered that in applying normal coordinate theory one is almost always attempting to fit the *observed* frequencies. These are not the harmonic or "mechanical" frequencies that would be observed in the absence of anharmonicities. Thus the error of fit between calculated and observed frequencies reflects both the inadequacies in the simplification of the quadratic potential function and the importance of the anharmonic terms that were omitted from this function in the first place.)

Of the many other approximate force fields that have been proposed, the Urey-Bradley (1931) mixed field is perhaps the most popular. This is essentially a valence force field with inclusion of additional central force terms between nonbonded atoms. By adding such terms one attempts to take into account the van der Waals forces between atoms. The Urey-Bradley potential for the tetrahedral XY_4 molecule includes, in addition to the terms given in (3-12), terms of the type

$$f_3(r_1 + r_2 + r_3 + r_4)$$
$$f_4(q_{12} + q_{13} + q_{14} + q_{23} + q_{24} + q_{34}) \qquad (3\text{-}13)$$
$$f_5(q_{12}^2 + q_{13}^2 + q_{14}^2 + q_{23}^2 + q_{24}^2 + q_{34}^2)$$

where q_{ij} is the extension of the $Y_i \cdots Y_j$ "bond". Although the force field as formulated here involves five force constants, the number of independent force constants is four, the same as the number of fundamental frequencies. For more complicated molecules only a limited number of central force terms are added, and the success of the potential is often dependent on guessing or determining which nonbonded interactions are important.

Once the form of the simplified potential is assumed, then it is possible to carry out a normal coordinate analysis. Particularly if data are available from isotopically substituted molecules it is sometimes possible to achieve an overdetermined problem and hence obtain both cross checks and a qualitative feeling for the reliability of the analysis. The procedures used, though often laborious, are reasonably straightforward.

Another alternative, which has been made possible primarily by the advent of high-speed computers, is to collect vibrational data on a series of closely related molecules and attempt to determine transferable force constants, that is, force constants that are applicable to all of the molecules in the series. To do this one generally starts with a Urey-Bradley potential with the central-force terms added by intuition or by experience during the calculations, and one carries out a nonlinear least squares fit to minimize the differences between observed and calculated frequencies. In this way the force field is determined from the combined data. (This method has the additional advantage of providing a powerful method of assigning the bands.) A classic example of this approach is the work on a series of n-paraffins, C_3H_8 through n-$C_{19}H_{40}$. (Snyder and Schachtschneider, 1963; Schachtschneider and Snyder, 1963). These authors were able to use a 35-term force field to fit 270 observed frequencies to an average error of 0.25%.

There is no *a priori* way to determine which simplified force field is best in a given case, and in general few authors have bothered to collect the vast amount of data, typified by the work cited above, that is necessary before the appropriate simplified force field can be determined. On the other hand, if force constants are obtained for a series of compounds of the same symmetry using the same force field, inadequate though it may be, then there is the expectation that differences in these force constants may serve as a measure of the relative strengths of bonds in these compounds.

An Example of a Normal Coordinate Analysis of a Hydrogen-Bonded System

To illustrate normal coordinate analysis in the study of hydrogen bonding we take monomeric formic acid (Nakamoto and Kishida, 1964) and

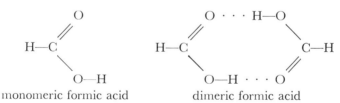

monomeric formic acid   dimeric formic acid

dimeric formic acid (Kishida and Nakamoto, 1964). For both of these molecules only the in-plane vibrations were considered in order to simplify the problem. For the monomer a simple Urey-Bradley force field was chosen as adequately representing the forces in the molecule. For the dimer it was necessary to introduce additional interaction terms, but the basic form of the force field is the same. With the use of the observed vibrational frequencies for the normal and deuterated molecules it was possible to determine the various force constants. Some of these results are given in Table 3-1. The most marked effect is the large decrease in the O—H stretching force constant. There is a normal mode which is almost entirely associated with the O—H stretching vibration; the frequency of this mode shifts from 3570 cm^{-1} in the monomer to 3109 cm^{-1} in the dimer. The corresponding shift in the deuterated compound is from 2632 cm^{-1} to 2251

Table 3-1 *Comparison of Bond Stretching Force Constants in Formic Acid and Formic Acid Dimer. The Units Are 10^5 dynes cm^{-1}*

	Monomer	Dimer
K_{OH}	6.90	4.70
$K_{C=O}$	11.20	10.00
K_{C-O}	4.60	5.50

cm^{-1}. Although the frequency shifts for the $C=O$ and $C-O$ stretching frequencies are less dramatic, examination of the force constants indicates that there is a considerable weakening of the $C=O$ bond and a strengthening of the $C-O$ bond on formation of the dimer. This is the direction to be expected. In a symmetrically hydrogen-bonded dimer the two force constants would be equal. The changes in the bending and repulsion force constants are much smaller and are not easily interpreted. A frequency at 237 cm^{-1} in the dimer is associated almost entirely with the $O \cdots H$ stretch; the associated force constant is 0.36×10^5 dynes cm^{-1}.

This work illustrates that very useful information on relative bond strengths can be obtained from spectroscopic studies of closely related molecules, even though simplified force fields of uncertain applicability are employed.

Complex Spectra and Group Frequencies

In a complex molecule the problem of determining force constants is often written off as intractable or possibly not even germane, and interest centers on possible assignments of the bands. In order to make plausible assignments one generally applies the concept of group frequencies. It is a matter of observation, for example, that $C-O$ stretching vibrations occur in the region of 1700 to 2200 cm^{-1} and that metal—C stretching occur in the region of 300 to 800 cm^{-1}. Such qualitative information, together with symmetry arguments, is often sufficient to enable one to decide with reasonable certainty between two possible structures for the molecule in question. When one applies this concept of group frequencies, one is assuming that the functional group absorbs in a particular region of the spectrum regardless of what is attached to it. This is not precisely true, of course, for the frequencies of the normal modes depend on the reduced masses for these particular vibrations and these in turn depend on the masses of other atoms in the molecule. Moreover, owing to coupling between various normal modes, overlap of bands, anharmonic effects, and many other complications, the entire concept of group frequencies may be of very limited use in sorting out complicated spectra.

If we now return our attention to spectroscopic studies of hydrogen bonding in solids we find that, despite all of the possible complications, infrared spectroscopy has provided a great deal of qualitative information on hydrogen bonding in solids.   In part this is because of the ability to provide extensive data in a short time.   Furthermore, within the group frequency concept, the A—H · · · B bond may be thought of as "triatomic" and thus not of extreme complexity.

3-2 SPECTROSCOPIC MANIFESTATIONS OF HYDROGEN BONDING

Hydrogen bonds may range from the symmetric F—H—F species to the bent A—H · · · B species.   Because the normal modes of the linear and slightly nonlinear Z—X—Y molecules are closely related to those depicted in Figure 3-2 for the symmetric linear Y—X—Y molecule, we find it convenient to employ the terms "symmetric stretch" and "antisymmetric stretch" to mean those modes most closely associated with ν_1 and ν_3 of Figure 3-2, even though the species we have in mind may not be symmetric and linear.   Thus these normal modes will be used as a basis for the discussion of the characteristic spectral changes that occur when hydrogen bonding takes place in any state of matter.   The following are the most pronounced changes that occur in the formation of the A—H · · · B bond:

(1) the A—H stretching frequency shifts to lower frequencies;
(2) the A—H bending frequency shifts to higher frequencies;
(3) the breadth of the A—H stretching frequency increases markedly, as does its intensity.

The resultant vibrations (Figure 3-2) of the A—H · · · B bond may be divided up roughly into the following categories[2]:

(1) A—H · · · B antisymmetric stretch

$$\overset{\leftarrow}{(A}\overset{\rightarrow}{-H}\overset{\rightarrow}{-B)}$$

3500 to 1700 cm^{-1};
(2) A—H · · · B bend

$$(A\overset{\uparrow}{-H}-B)$$
$$\downarrow \qquad \downarrow$$

1700 to 800 cm^{-1};

[2] These may not be descriptions of pure normal modes.

(3) A—H $\cdot$ $\cdot$ $\cdot$ B "symmetric" stretch

$$(\overset{\leftarrow}{A}\text{—}H\text{—}\vec{B})$$

600 to 50 cm^{-1};

(4) various torsional modes $\leqslant 500$ cm^{-1}.

Vibrations in categories (1) and (2) occur in the absence of hydrogen bonding as well. Nevertheless, one need not depend on the detection of the symmetric stretching frequency to characterize hydrogen bonding; the changes in the antisymmetic stretching frequency on hydrogen bonding are large enough to provide such characterization. For example, consider an isolated O—H group in the solid state. The stretching frequency for this group might occur at about 3500 cm^{-1} and be less than 10 cm^{-1} in breadth. Now let this group enter into a strong O—H $\cdot$ $\cdot$ $\cdot$ O bond. The antisymmetric stretching frequency may now occur at about 1700 cm^{-1} and be several hundred cm^{-1} in breadth. Its intensity will also have increased markedly. At the same time there will have occurred a somewhat smaller shift of the bending vibrational frequency toward higher frequencies.

It has been shown by several groups of workers (Rundle and Parasol, 1952; Lord and Merrifield, 1953; Nakamoto, Margoshes, and Rundle, 1955; Pimentel and Sederholm, 1956) that the shift of frequency of the antisymmetric stretching mode correlates modestly well with the A—H $\cdot$ $\cdot$ $\cdot$ B bond length. Typical curves are presented in Figure 3-3. These correlations are generally useful for the prediction of bond distances. Qualitatively the trends seem reasonable: A lowering of the vibrational frequency corresponds to a lowering of the force constant for the bond, which in turn is consistent with a weaker (and hence longer) bond. As we have noted in Section 2-5, neutron diffraction results confirm that the O—H bond length increases as the O $\cdot$ $\cdot$ $\cdot$ O bond length decreases. However, these correlations are not applicable in the region of very strong hydrogen bonds where there occur both symmetric A—H—A bonds and asymmetric A—H $\cdot$ $\cdot$ $\cdot$ A bonds with the same A $\cdot$ $\cdot$ $\cdot$ A distance, but with widely differing antisymmetric stretching frequencies (see Section 3-4).

It is fair to say, however, that of those perturbations of the stretching frequency that are so characteristic of hydrogen bond formation, namely frequency shift, increase in breadth, and enhancement of intensity, there is no clear consensus of opinion on the origin of the latter two effects. There are at least three apparently different explanations for the width of the stretching band:

(1) The width of the band is the result of extreme anharmonicity in the vibration with the result that in a strong hydrogen bond all combination levels lying in the region of the excited hydrogen stretching levels mix with

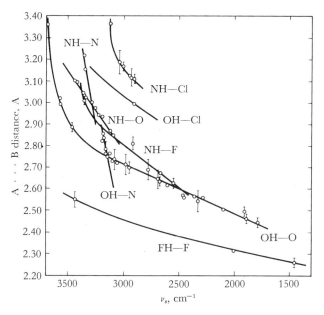

Figure 3-3 *A—H stretching frequency ν_s versus the A · · · B bond distance in the A—H · · · B bond in solids.* (*From Pimentel and McClellan, 1960; adapted from Nakamoto, Margoshes, and Rundle, 1955.*)

the corresponding hydrogen stretching levels. Thus the simple hydrogen band is replaced in the infrared by a group of bands (Bratož and Hadži, 1957).

(2) The width of the band may be explained in terms of combination bands. It is assumed that a number of low-frequency modes modulate the stretching mode (the so-called "frequency modulation" theory) (Batuev, 1949).

(3) There is a continuous sequence of energetically unstable states for the excitation of the stretching mode. This is the so-called "predissociation theory" of Stepanov (1946).

Although Bratož and Hadži (1957) have argued convincingly that explanation (1) should be accepted and that (2) is but a rough approximation to (1), it seems obvious to us that more definitive data are needed before one can even be certain that there is a single explanation that will fit all situations. In particular, there is little known about the temperature dependence of many of these strong hydrogen bonding modes, and the isotope effects are poorly understood.

The origins of the extreme intensity of the stretching band are even more poorly understood.

It is reasonable to say, in summary, that although the spectroscopic manifestations of hydrogen bonding are well known and generally agreed upon, there is remarkable lack of agreement and understanding on what these manifestations tell one about the nature of the hydrogen bond. However current theoretical work–including quantum-mechanical treatments of both the electronic wave function and the vibrational wave function–is beginning to clarify the problem.

3-3　APPLICATIONS OF NMR TO THE SOLID STATE

In view of the extensive and important applications of NMR to studies of hydrogen bonding in the liquid state, it may come as a surprise to learn that such applications to the study of hydrogen bonding in the solid state are severely limited, despite the fact that excellent commercial instrumentation is available. To understand the limitation in the solid state it is necessary to review qualitatively the theory behind NMR.

Consider an isolated nucleus, made up of protons and neutrons of spin quantum number $\frac{1}{2}$. If the nucleus has resultant net spin, then the total nuclear spin quantum number I will be nonzero. The presence of an unpaired spin imparts a nuclear magnetic moment to the nucleus. The nuclear spin angular momentum quantum number m may take on any of the $(2I + 1)$ values in the series $I, I - 1, I - 2, \ldots, -(I - 1), -I$. The value of this quantum number indicates the orientation of the nuclear magnetic moment vector in an external magnetic field $\mathbf{H}_0$. Thus for $I = 1$, m has the values 1, 0, and -1 and these correspond to alignments with, perpendicular to, and opposed to the field. Whereas these states are degenerate in the absence of a magnetic field, when a steady magnetic field is applied the degeneracy is removed and there result $(2I + 1)$ equally spaced energy levels, the separation between successive levels being $\mu H_0/I$, where μ is an experimentally derived quantity called the magnetic moment. This energy separation is frequently written as $g\mu_0 H_0$, where $g = \mu/(\mu_0 I)$ is the splitting factor or "g-factor" and where μ_0 is the nuclear magneton. The energy separation $\mu H_0/I$ is in general very small compared with thermal energies. As a result the first excited state is nearly as well populated as the ground state through thermal excitation. For example, for the proton $(I = \frac{1}{2})$ the excess in the lower energy state $(m = +\frac{1}{2})$ over the upper energy state $(m = -\frac{1}{2})$ at a field of 10^4 G (gauss) is about 7 per million.

A nucleus with a magnetic moment can be treated in a manner completely analogous to a classical magnetic dipole (e.g., a bar magnet) in a magnetic field. The interaction of the magnetic moment with the external field produces a torque that in turn interacts with the angular momentum and causes the magnetic moment vector to precess about the field vector $\mathbf{H}_0$. The rate of precession is given by the well-known Larmor angular frequency

$$\omega_0 = \gamma H_0 \qquad (3\text{-}14)$$

where γ is the gyromagnetic ratio for the dipole. The gyromagnetic ratio is a constant for a given nucleus.

In an NMR experiment a strong homogeneous field $\mathbf{H}_0$ is applied to a sample. The magnetic moment vector begins to precess. Then electromagnetic radiation with an energy comparable to the energy level separations of the system is applied. When the applied frequency is equal to the Larmor frequency the two are said to be in resonance and energy may be transferred to and from the sample and the transmitter. Transitions between various states are allowed for m that changes by ± 1. Accordingly in this resonance condition some nuclei are excited to higher states by absorption of energy from the source at a frequency equal to the Larmor frequency. A detector in the experimental arrangement is used to observe the frequency at which there is a loss of energy from the source. We are doing nothing more than conventional spectroscopy, although the frequency range is different. The frequency may be calculated from the relations

$$h\nu_0 = \frac{h\omega}{2\pi} = \frac{\mu H_0}{I} = g\mu_0 H_0 = \frac{h\gamma H_0}{2\pi} \qquad (3\text{-}15)$$

The gyromagnetic ratio of the proton has been determined experimentally to be $2.67530 \times 10^4 \text{ sec}^{-1} \text{ G}^{-1}$. Thus in a typical field of 10^4 G the resonance frequency is 42.6 Mc sec^{-1}, and is in the radio frequency region. The appropriate experimental conditions are obtained in commercially available NMR spectrometers either by holding the field constant and sweeping in frequency or, more commonly, by holding the frequency constant and sweeping in field.

The absorption of energy from the source puts the system into an energy state that is not at equilibrium upon removal of the source. There are several ways in which the excited nuclei can return or "relax" to the ground state without emitting radiation. These include spin-lattice and spin-spin relaxation processes. The return to equilibrium through interaction with the lattice[3] is a thermal process; as such, equilibrium is approached exponentially with a characteristic time T_1, called the spin-lattice relaxation time. In mathematical terms, let n be the excess number of nuclei in the lower

---

[3] The term lattice here is most unfortunate, for a lattice is properly a mathematical concept (see Section 2-1). The term, as used here, is firmly implanted in the NMR literature and means simply the rest of the system, comprising for example the solvent, the other electrons of the system, or other kinds of atoms or ions in the system.

state per cubic centimeter of a sample, and let n_0 be the value of n when the spin system is in thermal equilibrium with the lattice. Then the approach of the system to equilibrium is given by

$$\frac{dn}{dt} = \frac{(n_0 - n)}{T_1} \tag{3-16}$$

and this may be taken as a definition of T_1. In the phenomenological equations for the description of magnetic properties of collections of nuclei in external magnetic fields Bloch (1946) found it convenient to introduce a characteristic time T_2, the spin-spin relaxation time, which applies to spin-spin interactions in which a nucleus in a high energy state imparts energy to another nucleus in a low energy state.

Consider now the NMR absorption in a rigid solid that contains two identical nuclei of spin $\frac{1}{2}$ and no unpaired electrons. The classical potential energy V_{ij} of magnetic interaction between two magnetic dipoles of moment $\mathbf{\mu}_i$ and $\mathbf{\mu}_j$ joined by vector $\mathbf{r}_{ij}$ of length r is

$$V_{ij} = \frac{\mathbf{\mu}_i \cdot \mathbf{\mu}_j}{r^3} - \frac{3(\mathbf{\mu}_i \cdot \mathbf{r}_{ij})(\mathbf{\mu}_j \cdot \mathbf{r}_{ij})}{r^5} \tag{3-17}$$

If we write $\mathbf{\mu} = \gamma \hbar \mathbf{I}$ for this system of identical nuclear magnetic dipoles (3-17) becomes

$$V_{ij} = \gamma^2 \hbar^2 r^{-3}[\mathbf{I}_i \cdot \mathbf{I}_j - 3(\mathbf{I}_i \cdot \mathbf{P}_{ij})(\mathbf{I}_j \cdot \mathbf{P}_{ij})] \tag{3-18}$$

where $\mathbf{P}_{ij}$ is the unit vector parallel to $\mathbf{r}_{ij}$. It has been shown by Pake (1948) that when this expression is expanded in a spherical polar coordinate system, the energy levels perturbed by this dipole-dipole interaction are those shown

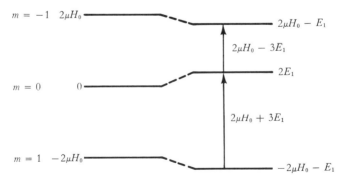

Figure 3-4 *The unperturbed energy levels for the two-spin system together with those obtained from the perturbing effect of the dipole-dipole interaction; E_1 represents $\mu^2 r^{-3}$ $(3 \cos^2 \theta - 1)$. (From Pake, 1948.)*

in Figure 3-4.   Resonance absorption occurs for the perturbed system when

$$h\nu = 2\mu H_0 \pm 3\mu^2 r^{-3}(3\cos^2\theta - 1) \qquad (3\text{-}19)$$

where θ is the angle between $\mathbf{H}_0$ and $\mathbf{r}_{ij}$.   Substitution of $h\nu = 2\mu H$ yields the resonance value of the external field as

$$H_0 = H \pm \tfrac{3}{2}\mu r^{-3}(3\cos^2\theta - 1) \qquad (3\text{-}20)$$

(With the exception of the factor $\tfrac{3}{2}$ this is the expression that one would derive from classical considerations where spin exchange is ignored.)

In Figure 3-5 we plot some results obtained by Pake (1948) for $CaSO_4 \cdot 2H_2O$.   From these spectra it is possible to derive not only the internuclear separation between the protons in the (assumed) isolated water molecule, but also the orientation of the dipole with the field and hence with the external faces of the crystal.

Many examples of what might be called the "Pake method" may be found in the literature.   El Saffar (1966) has considered the case of single crystals of $BaCl_2 \cdot 2H_2O$ and has resolved a conflict between earlier NMR studies (Silvidi and McGrath, 1960) and a neutron diffraction study (Padmanabhan, Busing, and Levy, 1963).   El Saffar has pointed out that the NMR method is rather crude when applied to complicated hydrates because of (1) the difficulty of orienting the crystal precisely in the magnetic field, (2) the low signal-to-noise ratio, (3) overlap of the resonance lines, and (4) the effects of thermal motion on the simple theory just described.   Nevertheless these crude data may often be of considerable value to neutron diffraction studies of such substances, expecially if x-ray data are not available for an attack on the phase problem.

It is possible to carry out more precise determinations of interproton distances in single crystals, using the NMR technique, provided that such materials are very simple.   This may be illustrated by the work of Pedersen (1966) on the H—H distances in potassium and rubidium oxalate monohydrates.   These substances are ideal for this application, owing to their simplicity: The water molecules are located on twofold axes and are all equivalent with all intramolecular proton-proton vectors parallel; the water molecules are well separated from one another; the compounds contain no other nuclei with large magnetic moments; the crystals may be grown large.   Pedersen has given some discussion in this and an earlier paper (Pedersen, 1964) of proper approaches to the problems of magnetic coupling of separated water molecules and to thermal motions.   The problem of thermal motions was treated somewhat earlier in detail by Ibers and Stevenson (1958) for the ammonium ion.   In effect, one must obtain averages over thermal vibrations of terms of the type $(3\cos^2\theta - 1)r^{-3}$ and to do this one must understand the normal vibrations of the system.   Only in this way may one derive an accurately defined proton-proton distance. Pedersen has offered an approximate model for thermal motion which led him to "equilibrium" distances r_e for the H—H interactions in these two compounds. These are found to be significantly different at 1.534 A for the K salt and 1.547 A (both ± 0.003 A) for the Rb salt. Yet Pedersen has not investigated the effects on these standard deviations of various assumptions in his model, such as the harmonic approximation. It seems more likely that this difference in "equilibrium" distances is not significant.

Because of the very low signal-to-noise ratio large single crystals are required in the method just described. It is therefore far more convenient to employ a polycrystalline (powder) sample. Then the average over all orientations must be carried out. Let $\beta = H_0 - H$. Then the contribution to the normalized line shape function of each of the two component lines for a single crystal to the spectrum for polycrystalline material is

$$g(\beta) = \frac{1}{2} \frac{d(\cos \theta)}{d\beta} \tag{3-21}$$

where θ is the angle between $\mathbf{H_0}$ and $\mathbf{r}_{ij}$, since the fraction of pairs for which θ lies in $d\theta$ is $d(\cos \theta)$. From (3-20) and (3-21) it follows that

$$g(\beta) = (6 \sqrt{3} \, \mu r^{-3})^{-1} \left[1 \pm \frac{\beta}{(\frac{3}{2}\mu r^{-3})} \right]^{-\frac{1}{2}} \tag{3-22}$$

where

$$-\tfrac{3}{2}\mu r^{-3} < \beta < 3\mu r^{-3}$$

for the positive value of the sign and

$$-3\mu r^{-3} < \beta < \tfrac{3}{2}\mu r^{-3}$$

for the negative value.

The line shape is plotted in Figure 3-5 as the broken curve. The actual experimental curve is broadened out somewhat, primarily from interactions with neighboring nuclei, which have been neglected in this two-spin case, and from the effects of thermal motion. When this is taken into account the full curve shown in Figure 3-5 results. From the shape of the curve and the separation of the humps the interproton distance in the water molecules can be found, but all information on the orientations of these proton pairs with respect to the crystal axes has been lost.

As the number of nuclei with spins increases, the interpretation of the experiment, based on the shape of the absorption line, becomes difficult, if not impossible. However, Van Vleck (1948) has shown that the second moment of the absorption spectrum may be interpreted in terms of structurally significant parameters. The second moment of the absorption line

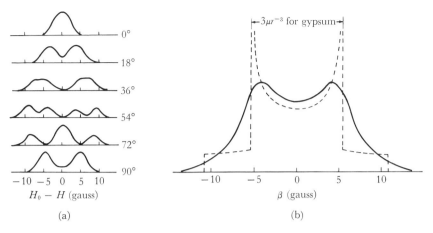

Figure 3-5 *Resonance absorption spectra for gypsum, CaSO$_4$·2H$_2$O.   (a) Spectra for various directions of the applied field H$_0$ in the (001) plane of a single crystal.   The angle between H$_0$ and the [100] direction is given with each spectrum.   (b) The broken curve is the theoretical line shape obtained when only nearest-neighbor interactions are considered [equation (3-22)]; the full curve results when all interactions are considered.   (From Pake, 1948.)*

is defined as

$$S = \frac{\int_{-\infty}^{\infty} (H_0 - H)^2 I(H) \, dH}{\int_{-\infty}^{\infty} I(H) \, dH} \tag{3-23}$$

where $I(H)$ is the observed intensity of the line.   Van Vleck has shown that the second moment of the resonance absorption spectrum for nuclei of type j may be calculated from the expression

$$S_j = \tfrac{3}{4}(I_j)(I_j + 1) \left(\frac{h\nu_j}{H_0}\right)^2 \sum_j (3 \cos^2 \theta_{jj'} - 1)^2 r_{jj'}^{-6}$$

$$+ \tfrac{1}{3} \sum_l (I_l)(I_l + 1) \left(\frac{h\nu_l}{H_0}\right)^2 (3 \cos^2 \theta_{jl} - 1)^2 r_{jl}^{-6} \tag{3-24}$$

In (3-24) nucleus j has resonance frequency ν_j at field H_0.   The first summation is over like nuclei; the second sum is over different nuclei.   If there are crystallographically nonequivalent nuclei of type j in the unit cell, then S_j is evaluated for each of these in turn and the weighted average is formed to yield the calculated second moment.

For reasons already discussed above it is usual to employ a polycrystalline sample; under these conditions the terms $(3 \cos^2 \theta - 1)^2$ average to $\tfrac{4}{5}$. Thus the NMR experiment on a polycrystalline sample yields, in general, a structureless absorption spectrum from which a single quantity, the second moment, is usually derived.[4] This quantity, on the other hand, is related to a summation over all spin-spin interactions in the entire crystal. Thus the NMR experiment will yield useful results when only a very few (ideally one) structural parameters are unknown in an otherwise thoroughly characterized structure. (An example of the use of the technique is given in Section 3-7.) But high accuracy may not be achieved, for as we have indicated one must understand the normal vibrations of the particular system in order to apply appropriate corrections for the effects of thermal motion. Such an understanding of the vibrational problem is only possible in the very simplest of systems.

3-4 QUALITATIVE POTENTIAL FUNCTIONS

Let us describe some simple potential function models for the bond A—H · · · B. When A and B are different species, then the one-dimensional potential function along the A—B bond may be represented qualitatively as in Figure 3-6. (For the sake of simplicity we neglect possible nonlinearities in the A—H · · · B bond.) Thus if A and B are different, then it is chemically reasonable and invariably the case that H is associated more closely with A than with B (or the reverse).

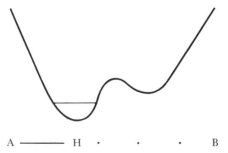

A ———— H ·   ·   · B

Figure 3-6 *Qualitative potential function along the AB direction for the asymmetric A—H · · · B bond.*

---

[4] Note from (3-23) that the contributions to S from large values of $(H_0 - H)$ are important. Yet for large values of $(H_0 - H)$ the function $I(H)$ is poorly defined because of the difficulties of separating signal from noise. The observed moment may not be determined very accurately as a consequence. Van Vleck (1948) has also shown that the fourth moment of the resonance line may be expressed in terms of structurally interesting parameters. Yet the difficulties of obtaining experimentally a reliable fourth moment are such that the quantity is hardly ever employed.

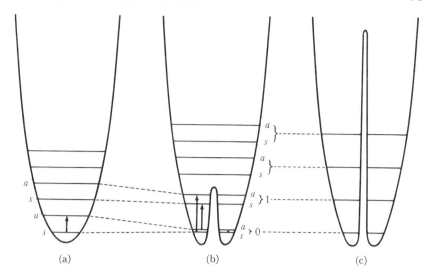

Figure 3-7 *Qualitative potential functions and energy levels for the AHA bond as a function of the height of the barrier. Note the very low frequency transition between 0_s and 0_a in (b).*

Now consider the AHA bond. Further assume that the chemical environments about both A nuclei are identical. Then the potential functions illustrated in Figure 3-7 are possible. In Figure 3-7 we also illustrate in a very qualitative way how the various energy levels change as a function of the height of the barrier and we show the allowed transitions for infrared absorption. The potential with a very high barrier implies that the AHA bond is asymmetric and that the actual bonding in the solid can be represented by equal probability of A—H $\cdots$ A and A $\cdots$ H—A. As the barrier decreases the rate of interconversion of these two species increases; the splitting of the ground state is often taken as a measure of the "tunneling frequency" through the barrier, that is, the frequency of interconversion. As the barrier disappears altogether, or at least goes below the ground state, the A—H—A bond is said to be symmetric, in that the H atom is situated symmetrically between the two A atoms.

Now let us ask if it is possible to determine the form of the potential function from spectroscopic measurements. The answer, as we shall discuss in greater detail, is that it is possible to single out the asymmetric case shown in Figure 3-6, but that it is extremely difficult to distinguish between the functions shown in Figure 3-7a,b. Of course, these differ only in the height of the barrier and it is not surprising that certain intermediate cases can exist. The allowed spectroscopic transitions shown in Figure 3-7b should all be infrared active, but there are problems in their detection. Thus the transition 0_s-0_a may occur beyond the range of far infrared instruments. Moreover the two high frequency transitions 0_s-1_a and 0_a-1_s may be relatively close together. Since these bands are usually of great breadth it will be difficult, if not impossible, to determine in the region from 1900 to 1500 cm^{-1} (for O—H—O) whether or not there is a single band corresponding to Figure 3-7a or whether there are in fact two superimposed bands (as would arise from Figure 3-7b). The relative intensities of these two high frequency bands will shift with temperature, but if the splitting of the ground state is sufficiently small it will not be possible to observe the change since the populations in the two ground levels will vary little with temperature.

Isotopic substitution of D for H has been a standard and very powerful method for checking spectroscopic assignments. Thus take, for example, the linear, symmetric AHA bond. The reduced mass of the antisymmetric stretching vibration is $(m_H m_A)/(2m_A + m_H)$ (3-10). Hence substitution of D for H ought to bring about a lowering of the harmonic frequency by the factor

$$\left[\frac{m_D(2m_A + m_H)}{m_H(2m_A + m_D)}\right]^{1/2} \approx \left(\frac{m_D}{m_H}\right)^{1/2} = \sqrt{2}$$

The bending mode should show a similar shift. However, as we shall indicate in the next section, there are anomalous isotope effects that preclude the use of these simple relationships just where it is difficult to discern the symmetry of the potential function.

In answer to the question of whether or not diffraction measurements can be used to distinguish the various potential functions, the same remarks may be made. It is possible to single out the asymmetric case, but to distinguish between the functions shown in Figure 3-7a and 3-7b requires, even in extremely simple systems, a knowledge of the vibrations of the system.

Blinc, Hadži, and Novak (1960) have discussed the symmetries of these qualitative potential functions as determined from a combination of infrared and NMR studies on OHO systems. They suggest the same types of potential functions, but they subdivide the double-minimum symmetric functions into those with low barriers and those with high barriers. They suggest that the resultant four types may be distinguished with some reliability on the basis of the observed infrared frequencies, and in particular, on the temperature dependence of the tunneling frequency as determined from NMR studies on double-minimum system. They argue that if the potential is of a single-minimum type or is a double-minimum type with low barrier, then the tunneling frequency is essentially temperature independent.

There are probably semantic difficulties in these discussions, for clearly there is some point at which a high barrier becomes a low barrier and a further point at which a low barrier is below the ground state vibrational level with the result that the potential could well be called a single-minimum type.   In any event these authors have presented interesting experimental evidence that bears on the relationship between the shift in the stretching frequency and the A—B distance discussed earlier.   In Figure 3-8 their histogram curves are reproduced.   In particular we note that for O—O distances less than 2.60 A the resultant frequencies fall into two distinct groups.   The first group, (A), ascribed to the symmetric single-minimum function, has an average O—H stretching frequency of 1694 cm^{-1} and an average O—D stretching frequency of 1367 cm^{-1} for a H/D ratio of 1.24.   The second group, (B), which they subdivide into three subgroups, is

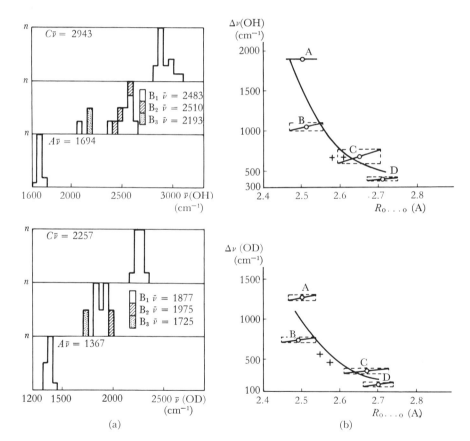

Figure 3-8 (a) *The distributions of OH (upper) and OD (lower) stretching frequencies with respect to the number of substances in a given range of frequencies for the main types of hydrogen bonds.* (b) *The centers of gravity and standard deviations of the shifts of the stretching frequency from that in the free OH ion as a function of the O · · · O distance for the OHO bond (upper) and ODO bond (lower).*   (From Blinc, Hadži, and Novak, 1960.)*

ascribed to double-minimum functions with low barriers; these have average O—H stretching frequencies which lie between 2193 and 2510 cm^{-1} and a H/D ratio of about 1.27. Note, however, that in both of these groups there is a large variation of O—O distance with the same stretching frequency. The range of frequencies in each group is much smaller than the range of distances. Clearly then the early correlations of frequency shift versus distance (Section 3-2) must be considered gross approximations. These authors consider this problem in some detail and present some criteria for measuring the degree of variability. Their data for O—O distances above 2.7 A also fall into two distinct classes. The first, ascribed to the double minimum with high barrier, has average frequencies of 2943 and 2257 cm^{-1} for H and D for a ratio of 1.31; the second, ascribed to the asymmetric function, has average frequencies of approximately 3200 and 2350 cm^{-1} for H and D for a ratio of 1.36. Again the variation of frequency seems somewhat less than that of distance.

Blinc, Hadži, and Novak suggest that their results are in general agreement with those crystallographic studies that have been carried out. In particular, those structures they ascribe to the symmetric single-minimum function are ones in which the H lies at a crystallographic symmetry center (and thus the chemical environments of both oxygen atoms are identical). Moreover, these are structures in which there is no need to postulate cooperative motions between pairs of protons, such as those discussed by Coulson (1959). Yet the requirement of a symmetry center is precisely the main difficulty in the accurate location of the hydrogen by diffraction methods. It is impossible, as we shall illustrate for the FHF ion, to tell from diffraction methods alone whether or not a hydrogen atom (or any other atom, for that matter) is precisely on a symmetry element.

The arguments of Blinc, Hadži, and Novak would seem to imply that if an OHO bond is formed from two oxygen atoms that have different chemical environments, then the bond will not be of the symmetric single-minimum type. Yet this appears to be the case in potassium hydrogen chloromaleate, where there is a slight change in the chemical environment. Ellison and Levy (1965) have carried out a neutron diffraction study of this structure, where the introduction of the chlorine has destroyed the symmetry center present in potassium hydrogen maleate itself. Ellison and Levy found (Figure 3-9) that the O—O distance is shorter than in the parent salt (2.403 ± 0.003 versus 2.437 ± 0.004 A) and that the *refined* position of the hydrogen is essentially at the center of the O—O bond, the two O—H distances being 1.206 and 1.199 ± 0.005 A, and the O—H—O angle being 175.4 ± 0.4°. Even though no symmetry center is present, one cannot be certain that the potential function for this hydrogen is a symmetric single-minimum one without taking into consideration the thermal motions of the nuclei. (See the discussion of the FHF ion (Section 3-7) for an illustration of this point.) Ellison and Levy did consider the implications of the thermal motions they found in a manner similar to that employed by McGaw and Ibers (1963) for $NaHF_2$-$NaDF_2$. If we subtract the oxygen atom motion from the motion of the hydrogen atom, we find that the mean square amplitude of hydrogen thermal motion along the O—H—O line is 0.017 A^2. The infrared spectrum of potassium hydrogen maleate is insensitive to deuterium substitution at frequencies above 1600 cm^{-1}. This suggests that the O—H stretching frequency is below 1600 cm^{-1}; this in itself suggests a symmetric hydrogen bond. If the hydrogen atom is moving as a harmonic oscillator, the minimum mean square displacement for a frequency of 1600 cm^{-1} is 0.010 A^2. Although the vibration amplitude from the neutron diffraction study is greater than this, the difference of 0.007 A^2 is not sufficient to account for the equivalent motion which would be expected from a static disorder in a double-minimum potential. That is to say, the bump in the double-minimum potential, if any, must be so small that it is comparable in height to the zero-point level. Hence a description in terms of static disorder would be meaningless.

The mean square amplitude of vibration perpendicular to the bond is greater than that parallel to the bond. This is further evidence that the equilibrium position is truly in the center of the bond.

In these discussions we have ignored small deviations from a symmetric double minimum. Suppose, for example, that the double minimum is only "slightly" asymmetric. Then what do we expect? A suggestion of an answer may be found in some model calculations of Somorjai and Hornig (1962). They have found that in order to detect slight asymmetry we need to look at the intensities of the bands as well as the frequencies of all levels up

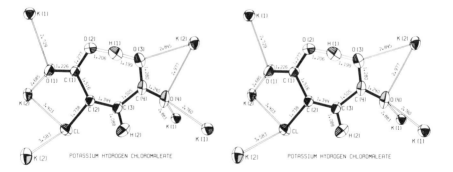

Figure 3-9 *Structure of potassium hydrogen chloromaleate as determined by neutron diffraction (Ellison and Levy, 1965). The hydrogen atom lies at the midpoint of the bond, although it is not required by crystallographic symmetry to do so.*

to and above the barrier. Clearly this is not an easy task. They have suggested additional tests including temperature studies (the symmetric double minimum should be more temperature dependent) and correlated infrared and Raman studies (the asymmetric double minimum should have identical frequencies in both methods). It would be fair to say that Somorjai and Hornig have succeeded in providing through model calculations an indication of how difficult it is to apply spectroscopic methods to the determination of potential function shapes and symmetry. Clearly it is always possible to propose a degree of asymmetry that will be undetectable. This is completely analogous to another unanswerable question in spectroscopy: how far does my molecule have to differ from idealized symmetry before I see "forbidden" bands? There is no generally useful quantitative answer to this question.

3-5 SEMIEMPIRICAL POTENTIAL FUNCTIONS FOR HYDROGEN BONDING

Numerous attempts have been made to develop semiempirical potential functions for hydrogen bonding that will explain a number of observations, including the variation of the A—H length with the A—A length in the AHA bond and the effects of isotopic substitution (Section 3-6). We choose in this section to discuss only those semiempirical potential functions that are closely related to the Lippincott-Schroeder potential. We do this primarily because this simple potential has had the widest applications. The development of this potential is based on the assumption that the A—H—A bond is linear. Departures from linear hydrogen bonding are rather common (Chapter 6) and it is important to realize that this potential model cannot be used to explain these departures. The assumption of linearity is probably a desirable simplification, since one cannot expect semiempirical potential functions to do much more than suggest qualitative explanations for observed phenomena.

Lippincott (1957) has shown that a potential curve of the form

$$U_{(r)} = D_0 \left(1 - \exp\left[-\frac{n(\Delta r)^2}{2r} \right] \right) \qquad (3\text{-}25)$$

is a very satisfactory function for diatomic molecules. Here D_0 is the dissociation energy from the equilibrium configuration, r is the interatomic distance, and $\Delta r = r - r_e$ is the stretching or compression of the bond from its equilibrium length r_e. The quantity n is given by

$$n = \frac{k_0 r_e}{D_0} \qquad (3\text{-}26)$$

where k_0 is the force constant.

Lippincott and Schroeder (1955) used a combination of curves of form (3-25) to represent the O—H $\cdot$ $\cdot$ $\cdot$ O bond. They did this with one for O—H and the other for H $\cdot$ $\cdot$ $\cdot$ O. Their potential was of the form

$$V = U_{(r)} + U'_{(R-r)} + W_{(R)} \qquad (3\text{-}27)$$

where W takes account of O—O interaction at distance R. The functions U and U' are similar, but U uses the dissociation energy of the isolated molecule and U' uses a dissociation energy that has been adjusted empirically.

This model has been extended by Reid (1959). In particular, Lippincott and Schroeder used the same dissociation energy for U' for all bonds. Reid introduced an adjustment factor that was a function of the bond length, going from 1.0 for symmetric bonds to 0.0 for no hydrogen bonding. The final form of Reid's potential is

$$V(r, R) = D_0 \left[1 - \exp \left(\frac{-n(r - r_e)^2}{2r} \right) \right]$$
$$+ CD_0 \left[1 - \exp \left(\frac{-n(R_e - r - r_e)^2}{2C(R_e - r)} \right) \right] + \frac{259.5}{R_e^6} - 4.55 \times 10^6 e^{-4.8R_e}$$

$$(3\text{-}28)$$

where R_e is the equilibrium O—O distance. The constant C is adjusted to give the correct equilibrium bond length. The W term has both repulsive and electrostatic contributions and is based on the "most probable" empirical values.

The potential function is shown in Figures 3-10 and 3-11. Using this potential model, Reid has suggested explanations for various phenomena and made some predictions. In particular his model shows great sensitivity of the shape of the potential curve to the equilibrium O—O distance and at approximately 2.51 A the curve is flat bottomed with a single minimum. This is approximately what we expect, since many of the O—H—O bonds with O—O bond length less than 2.5 A are probably symmetric. As was pointed out in Section 3-4, however, single-minimum potential functions occur for widely different O—O distances. Reid's potentials also suggest that the O—H bond length should vary little with O—O distance for very strong and very weak hydrogen bonds; this conclusion is certainly borne out by the diffraction data on the weak bonds (and also by intuition), but there

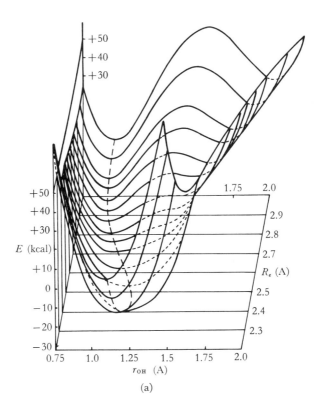

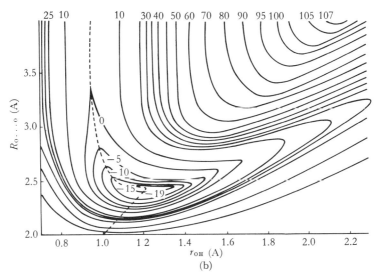

Figure 3-10 (*a*) *Potential function for the H-bonded proton constructed from an array of potential curves each referring to a bond with fixed equilibrium* $O \cdots O$ *distance* R_e. $r_{OH} =$ *distance of proton from the oxygen to which it was originally bound.* (*b*) *The corresponding surface expressed by potential contours.* (*From Reid, 1959.*)

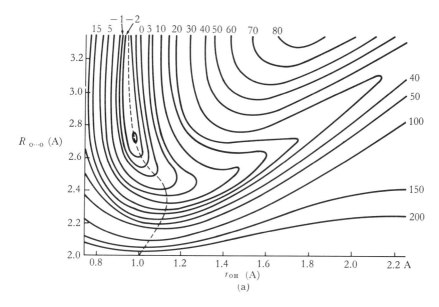

(a)

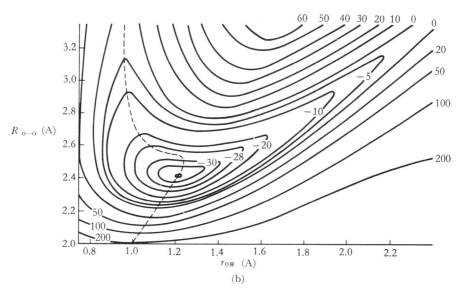

(b)

Figure 3-11 *Potential surface for the H-bonded proton in an equilibrium O · · · O bond of length (a) 2.72 and (b) 2.42 A. Both the O · · · O and O—H bond lengths are allowed to vary. (From Reid, 1959.)*

is little evidence for strong hydrogen bonds, since usually their symmetry is in doubt. Reid suggested that in the intermediate region the motions of the O—H and O—O are strongly coupled and that this is the explanation for the extreme breadth and intensity of the O—H stretching band. (This explanation is not completely convincing, for why then is the F—H stretching band in the very strong F—H—F ion broad?) Reid also suggested an explanation for the effect of isotopic substitution on O—O bond length, a topic to be discussed next.

Although these semiempirical potential functions usefully provide an overall view of the hydrogen-bonding potential, they are indeed semi-empirical and as new and better data are obtained on hydrogen bonding it is probable that gross adjustments will have to be made in such potential functions.

3-6 ISOTOPE EFFECTS IN HYDROGEN BONDING

The substitution of D for H in principle yields valuable information on the potential function for hydrogen bonding. Ubbelohde and co-workers were the first to study such effects in solids. Their results, together with those of later investigators, are given in Table 3-2. In all cases the primary measured quantities are the lattice constants; these can be measured with little difficulty to 0.1 % or better. The assumption is then made that the effects of deuteration are confined to the bond of interest, and from a knowledge of the orientation of this bond with respect to the unit cell and from the changes in the lattice constants the difference in hydrogen and deuterium bond lengths is obtained. This procedure seems justifiable in extremely simple systems where there is only one hydrogen bond in the asymmetric unit (e.g., $NaHF_2$ and $HCrO_2$). It was only recently (Delaplane and Ibers, 1966a) that this assumption was checked for a case in which there are different, independent bonds in the cell. Consider, for example, oxalic acid dihydrate. This compound was studied by Robertson and Ubbelohde (1939), who determined the directions and magnitudes of minimum and maximum expansion, shown in Figure 3-12. These authors argued in favor of the total expansion being confined to the short bond, with little or no change in the longer bonds. This was in part based on the fact that one of the long bonds was in the direction of minimum expansion. Nevertheless, the complete structure determinations of normal and deuterated oxalic acid dihydrate (Figure 3-12) have shown that deuteration lengthens all three bonds, with the short bond showing the intermediate expansion. On this basis one can ignore the data of Table 3-2 insofar as it provides information on changes in bond lengths, except where there is but one kind of hydrogen bond in the cell ($NaHF_2$, $HCoO_2$, $HCrO_2$).

If one now considers cases such as $HCoO_2$ and $HCrO_2$, where there is only one independent molecule in the unit cell, then it is reasonable to assume that the lattice expansion is indeed a direct consequence of the change in the OHO bond on deuteration. How does one explain the direction of this isotope effect and its magnitude? The effect is generally explained on the basis of the different H bond energy and amplitude of vibration implied by the fact that D must lie lower in the potential well than H. This is presumed to result in greater "overlap" in the H bond (Ubbelohde and Gallagher, 1955; Nordman and Lipscomb, 1951). Such an explanation is also implicit in Reid's semiempirical potential function (Section 3-5) for he found that

Table 3-2 *Isotope Effects on Hydrogen Bond Lengths in Solids*[a]

Crystal	r_{AA} (A)	$(r_D - r_H)$ (A)	Reference[b]
KHF_2	2.277	-0.0024	1, 2
$NaHF_2$	2.264	-0.0046	3, 4
$NH_4H_2PO_4$	2.49	0.010	5
Oxalic acid dihydrate	2.49	0.040_5	6
$HCrO_2$	2.49	0.06	7, 8
KH_2PO_4	2.48	0.0097	2
KH_2AsO_4	2.49	0.0080	9
Acetylene dicarboxylic acid dihydrate	2.56	0.034	10
Succinic acid	2.64	≈ 0.018	6
Resorcinol (α, β)	2.70, 2.75	No measurable effect	6
Ice (0°)	2.76	0.001_5	11
Urea	2.99	Slightly negative	2
$HCoO_2$	2.48	0.07	12

[a] r_{AA} is the distance between the two heavy atoms in the A—H—A hydrogen bond. $r_D - r_H$ is the difference between the values of r_{AA} for the deuterated and undeuterated compounds.

[b] (1) Ibers (1964a); (2) Ubbelohde (1939); (3) McGaw and Ibers (1963); (4) Ibers (1964b); (5) Ubbelohde and Woodward (1942); (6) Robertson and Ubbelohde (1939); (7) Snyder and Ibers (1962); (8) Hamilton and Ibers (1963); (9) Dickson and Ubbelohde (1950); (10) Gallagher, Ubbelohde, and Woodward (1954); (11) Megaw (1934); (12) Delaplane and Ibers (1966b).

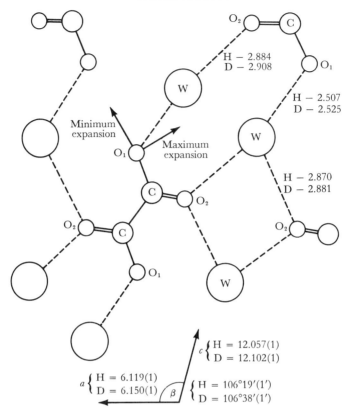

Figure 3-12 *Part of the structure of oxalic acid dihydrate projected onto the a-c plane. There is a symmetry center midway along C—C. The independent O—H—O and O—D—O bond lengths are shown. Each has an estimated standard deviation of 0.002 A. Standard deviations of the lattice parameters are shown in parentheses. The directions of minimum and maximum expansion are from Robertson and Ubbelohde (1939). (From Delaplane and Ibers, 1966a.)*

for an estimated decrease in O—D over O—H bond length of 0.01 A the O—O distance should increase by about 0.02 A.

Rundle (1964) suggested a somewhat different explanation, although it again is both qualitative and to some extent an extension of the above explanations. He suggested that as two oxygens of the O—H—O hydrogen bond approach one another the potential energy curve should have a symmetric double well of the type obtained by adding two Lippincott potentials (Section 3-5) for single O—H bonds. The height of the barrier should then decrease rapidly as the O—O distance decreases. At the same time the number of vibrational levels below the barrier will decrease, and the separation of symmetric and antisymmetric levels will increase. At sufficiently short O—O distances there will be at most one symmetric (and possibly one antisymmetric) vibrational level below the barrier. This level will lie lower for D than for H, and the various distributions as a function of O—O distance will resemble those illustrated in Figure 3-13. (These calculations have been made for a potential of the form $V(x) = -Ax^2 + Bx^4$.) Note that as the lowest H level approaches the top of the barrier the differences between the D and H distributions become marked, so that the hydrogen has considerably more density than deuterium in the center of the double well. Rundle then asserted that regardless of what sort of interaction is assumed between H and O the hydrogen density at the center will attract both oxygens and lead to a shortening of the bond, while deuterium will have lower density in the center of the bond and less effect. Hence it is in just that region where the difference in hydrogen and deuterium density differs most that the abnormal

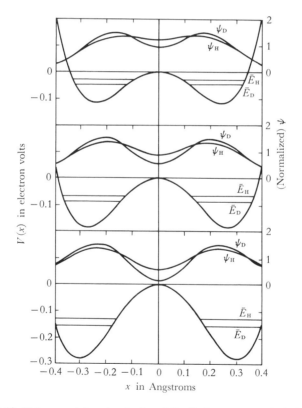

Figure 3-13 *Hydrogen and deuterium levels and distributions in symmetric double well. V is assumed to have the form $-Ax^2 + Bx^4$. From top to bottom the curves represent approximately the expected potential curves for bond lengths 2.50, 2.55, and 2.60 A. (From Rundle, 1964.)*

isotope effect should be greatest, with the O—H—O distance smaller than the O—D—O distance. The readjustments of the distances will provide a lower barrier for hydrogen, a still higher barrier for deuterium, enhancing still further the difference in H and D density in the center of the bond. We add, parenthetically, that if this difference becomes great enough then it would seem reasonable to believe that H could be in a symmetric potential and D in a double-minimum potential as the evidence for chromous and cobaltous acids suggests (see Section 3-7). Rundle made some attempts to put this explanation on a semiquantitative basis, but owing to his untimely death this was never brought to fruition.

3-7 SOME EXAMPLES

We now present a few examples that illustrate both the complementary nature of spectroscopic and diffraction methods and the difficulties of defining reliably the potential function for hydrogen bonding.

A Strong Hydrogen Bond: The Bifluoride Ion

The bifluoride ion has been extensively studied by a variety of techniques, primarily because it is an example of a very strong hydrogen bond. In fact, the F—H—F distance is about 0.5 A shorter than twice the van der Waals radius of F^-.

The first infrared study of the bifluoride ion was carried out by Ketelaar (1941) on KHF_2, KDF_2, and $RbHF_2$. He observed two bands in KHF_2 that he believed were fundamentals: one at 1450 cm^{-1} and the other at 1225 cm^{-1}. He assumed that the latter was too high for the bending mode and he ascribed both fundamentals to the two components of the antisymmetric stretch, illustrated earlier in Figure 3-7b. Thus Ketelaar concluded that FHF is asymmetric.

Pitzer and Westrum (1947) concluded from thermodynamic measurements that the FHF potential function could not have a high barrier. They suggested that Ketelaar's assignment was incoreect, and that the 1450 cm^{-1} band is the antisymmetric stretching frequency and the 1225 cm^{-1} band is the bending mode. A later infrared study by Coté and Thompson (1951) and further measurements by Ketelaar and Vedder (1951) confirmed this suggestion. In order to explain the divergence of their vibrational energy levels, Coté and Thompson alluded to a suggestion of Pitzer and Westrum that the potential function for the antisymmetric stretching mode approaches that of a quartic oscillator (that is, the dominant term is $kQ_3{}^4$).

The hydrogen bond in KHF_2 was one of the first subjects of study using broad line NMR techniques. Waugh, Humphrey, and Yost (1953) determined the second moments of the proton and fluorine magnetic resonance absorption lines in a polycrystalline sample of KHF_2. They attempted to make some allowance for the effects of thermal motion, but their calculations are not described precisely. They did conclude that the H atom is centered to within ± 0.06 A. It is probable that because of various uncertainties in the thermal corrections their estimate of centering was somewhat optimistic. Even if account is taken of the amplitudes of the normal modes, there is insufficient data available on KHF_2 to allow a proper account to be taken of the anharmonicities in these modes (Ibers and Stevenson, 1958).

Potassium bifluoride was also the subject of one of the first applications of neutron diffraction to single crystals (Peterson and Levy, 1952). These data have been reanalyzed by Ibers (1964a). We discuss this reanalysis and neutron diffraction results on $NaHF_2$ and $NaDF_2$ (McGaw and Ibers, 1963), for they illustrate well some of the points to which we have alluded. The basic problem in both of these studies is uncertainty about zero-point motional amplitudes. Thus McGaw and Ibers were able to obtain equally good agreement with their data over a wide range of displacements of the H from the center, provided that suitable adjustments were made in the amplitude of vibration of the H along the bond. Let us describe $NaHF_2$ (and $NaDF_2$) in terms of the triply primitive hexagonal cell with constants a and c. Then Na is at the origin, and F is at $\pm (0, 0, z_F)$. If the FHF bond is symmetric, then H is at $(0, 0, \frac{1}{2})$. If F—H $\cdots$ F and F $\cdots$ H—F occur with equal probability, then there are half H's at $\pm (0, 0, z_H)$. (See also Figure 3-20.) Let $\langle u_\perp{}^2 \rangle$ and $\langle u_\parallel{}^2 \rangle$ be the mean square amplitudes of vibration normal to and along the FHF bond. Then the structure factor expression is

$$F(hkl) = b_{Na}T_{Na} + 2b_F T_F \cos 2\pi l z_F + b_H T_H \cos 2\pi l z_H \qquad (3\text{-}29)$$

where the b's are neutron scattering amplitudes and where

$$T_i = \exp\left(-2\pi^2 \left[\left(\frac{4}{3a^2}\right)(h^2 + hk + k^2)\langle u_\perp{}^2 \rangle_i + \left(\frac{1}{c^2}\right) l^2 \langle u_\parallel{}^2 \rangle_i \right]\right) \qquad (3\text{-}30)$$

This form is general if the assumption of harmonic vibrations is made. What then is the relation between a small change dz_H from the value $z_H = \frac{1}{2}$ corresponding to centering that may be compensated for by a small change $d\langle u^2 \rangle$ in $\langle u_\parallel{}^2 \rangle$? Expansion of the cosine and exponential terms with retention of first terms only leads to the expression

$$d\langle u^2 \rangle = -(c\,dz_H)^2 = -r^2 \qquad (3\text{-}31)$$

where r is the distance of H from the center. If this expression is obeyed, then little or no change in F_c (and hence in agreement between F_c and F_o)

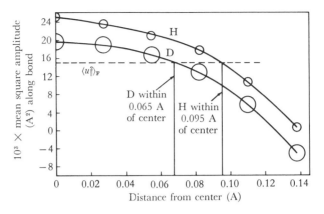

Figure 3-14 *The variation of $\langle u_\parallel{}^2 \rangle$ for H and D with distance of H and D from the center of the bond. The circles represent the estimated standard deviations in $\langle u_\parallel{}^2 \rangle$. (From McGaw and Ibers, 1963.)*

will result. Figure 3-14 shows the values of the mean square amplitudes of D or H along the bond versus assumed distance of the half-hydrogen atom from the center. The data of Figure 3-14 all give equally good agreement with observation, even when the mean square amplitude of vibration along the bond of the hydrogen is negative, and hence physically impossible. This is illustrated in another way in Figure 3-15 where the density from two half-deuterium atoms has been added to yield a total density that is indistinguishable from that obtained from a centered model. A similar ambiguity exists in the interpretation of the neutron diffraction data from KHF_2 (Ibers, 1964a).

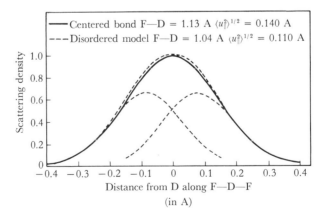

Figure 3-15 *An illustration of the equivalence in scattering density of FDF bonds obeying the potential functions of Figures 3-7a and 3-7c. The dotted line that nearly superimposes on the solid line is the sum of the two half-deuterium peaks. (From McGaw and Ibers, 1963.)*

However, at this point it is possible to combine spectroscopic and diffraction data. The thermal vibrational motions from neutron diffraction data are the sum of all motions undergone by these atoms. In the absence of a complete analysis of the vibrations in the crystal it is an impossible task to calculate these amplitudes from theory, and yet without these, as we have seen, it is impossible to distinguish a symmetric from an asymmetric potential for FHF. However, if one makes the reasonable assumption that the vibrational amplitude of H (or D) along the bond must be greater than that of F, then certain restrictions can be put on the lack of centering; specifically D must be within 0.065 A and H within 0.085 A of the center (Figure 3-14). Moreover, if the motions of F and H are assumed to be harmonic then the differences in amplitudes of H and F along the bond arise only from those motions in which the H and F do not move together, that is, only from the symmetric and antisymmetric stretching vibrations. Suppose that an atomic displacement coordinate x_i is given by

$$x_i = \sum_j c_{ij} Q_j \tag{3-32}$$

where Q_j are normal coordinates. Then

$$\langle x_i{}^2 \rangle = \sum_j c_{ij}^2 \langle Q_j{}^2 \rangle = \sum c_{ij}^2 \left(\frac{h}{8\pi^2 \nu_j} \right) \tag{3-33}$$

since from (3-5) it follows that $\langle \xi^2 \rangle$ (and hence $\langle Q^2 \rangle$) is given by $\frac{1}{2}\alpha$. If we apply (3-33) to the x_1 and x_2 coordinates of (3-10) we find immediately that

$$\langle x_F{}^2 \rangle = \frac{h}{8\pi^2} \left[\frac{1}{2\mu_1 \nu_1} + \frac{\mu_3}{2m_F{}^2 \nu_3} \right]$$

$$\langle x_H{}^2 \rangle = \frac{h}{8\pi^2} \left[\frac{2\mu_3}{m_H{}^2 \nu_3{}^2} \right] \tag{3-34}$$

and hence

$$\langle x_H{}^2 \rangle - \langle x_F{}^2 \rangle = \frac{h}{16\pi^2 m_F} \left[\frac{2m_F - m_H}{m_H \nu_3} - \frac{1}{\nu_1} \right] \tag{3-35}$$

With the values $\nu_3(H) = 1577$ and $\nu_3(D) = 1150$ and $\nu_1(H) = \nu_1(D) = 600$ cm^{-1} we obtain for the differences in mean square amplitudes of vibration along the bond 0.0097 and 0.0062 A^2 for H and for D. These are plotted in Figure 3-16. It is seen that the agreement between the calculated values (where a linear symmetric bond is assumed) and those obtained from the neutron data is excellent at $z_H = z_D = \frac{1}{2}$. This agreement, which can only be obtained from a combination of spectroscopic and diffraction data, provides the

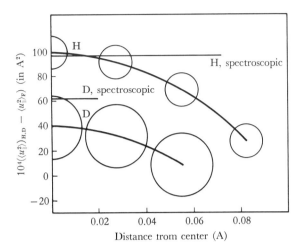

Figure 3-16 *The difference in mean square amplitude of vibration along the bond of H or D and F versus the distance of H or D from the center of the bond. The circles represent the estimated standard deviations of the ordinate. (From McGaw and Ibers, 1963.)*

most powerful evidence that the F—H—F and F—D—F bonds are symmetric. A similar argument has been applied to the data from KHF$_2$, although here the limits of error are larger, since KHF$_2$ involves additional thermal parameters because of its lower symmetry.

The isotope effect on the FHF ion is small. Ubbelohde's data on KHF$_2$ suggest that F—H—F is longer than F—D—F by not more than 0.0024 A while for NaHF$_2$ this quantity is 0.0046 ± 0.0005 A. The question then arises as to the source of this isotope effect. We pointed out earlier that the normal coordinate Q_1 is proportional to the change in the F · · · F length and the normal coordinate Q_3 is proportional to the deviation of the H atom from the center of the bond. A simple potential function of the form of (3-8), namely

$$2V = \lambda_1 Q_1{}^2 + \lambda_3 Q_3{}^2 \tag{3-36}$$

correctly leads to $\langle Q_3 \rangle = 0$ (and hence a centered bond), but it also leads to $\langle Q_1 \rangle = 0$, and hence no change of the F · · · F distance with isotopic substitution. In order to account for the observed isotope shift an additional term must be added to (3-36). In particular, a term of the type $Q_1 Q_3{}^2$ will lead to a value of $\langle Q_1 \rangle$ that is nonzero and isotopically dependent. Yet addition of such a term still leaves $\langle Q_3 \rangle = 0$, as required for a symmetric bond. Moreover, it is possible to evaluate the contribution of this assumed cross term directly from the isotopic data. This work is discussed in more detail elsewhere (Ibers, 1964b), but it suffices to say that using the isotopic data and the known spectroscopic frequencies and the single cross term enables us to get a reasonably good fit to the observed data. This illustrates two points: It is sometimes possible to determine potential constants from diffraction data; more important, the potential functions (3-8) we have been discussing are sometimes too simple and occasionally coupling between normal modes and other anharmonicities must be taken into account.

The Bichloride Ion

In view of the extensive literature on the bifluoride ion it is surprising that so little is known about the analogous bichloride and bibromide ions.

In a brilliant series of papers, Kaufler and Kunz (1909a,b) reported preparing a number of bichlorides and bibromides. Their work seems to have been largely overlooked until recently. Herbrandson, Dickerson, and Weinstein (1954) appear to be the first of many authors who have suggested that certain organo-nitrogen bases form complexes of the type $R_4N^+HCl_2^-$. Peterson and Williams (1966), in the only diffraction study of a related compound, have found that $CH_3CN \cdot 2HCl$ does not contain the bichloride ion, but rather is the compound

$$\left[\begin{array}{c} \underset{\displaystyle Cl}{\overset{\displaystyle CH_3}{\diagdown}} \; C \!-\! N \underset{\displaystyle H}{\overset{\displaystyle H}{\diagup}} \end{array} \right]^+ \quad Cl^-$$

There has also been recent interest in $CsHCl_2$ and related compounds (West, 1957; Vallée and McDaniel, 1962; Maki and West, 1963; Schroeder and Ibers, 1966).

Waddington (1958) reported the infrared spectrum of tetramethyl-ammonium bichloride and on the basis of the similarity of this spectrum with that of a typical bifluoride he suggested that the bichloride ion is linear and symmetric. Extensive infrared and Raman data on dihalide ions have recently been presented in two papers by Evans and Lo (1966a,b). They point out that the spectrum of the $ClHBr^-$ ion, which cannot be symmetric, is also very similar in the midinfrared region to the spectrum of the bifluoride ion, and they suggest that Waddington's argument should not be taken too seriously. Evans and Lo obtained very curious results in their study of the bichloride ion. They found two types of salts that exhibit distinctly different infrared and Raman spectra. Type I salts, which include those of cesium, tetramethylammonium, tetrabutylammonium, and hexadecyltrimethylam-monium, are characterized by two broad, strong bands in the infrared, one in the 1520–1670 cm^{-1} region and another near 1200 cm^{-1}, and by a weaker band near 220 cm^{-1}. Evans and Lo conclude that their evidence does not support the linear, symmetric, single-minimum model or the linear, symmetric, double-minimum model for the bichloride anion in these type I salts. Rather they conclude that the anion in these salts deviates from the symmetrical structure, probably because the two chlorine atoms are not equivalent crystallographically. Type II salts, which include those of tetraethylammonium, tetrapropylammonium, and tetrapentylammonium, are characterized by very broad, asymmetric absorptions extending between about 600 and 1300 cm^{-1}, which appear to consist of a main, broad band centered in the 700–800 cm^{-1} region and a slightly weaker, broad band near 1000–1050 cm^{-1}. Evans and Lo conclude tentatively that the bichloride anion in type II salts has the linear, symmetric, single-minimum potential, as does the bifluoride ion. It is reasonable to suppose that in some crystal structures the two chlorines of the bichloride ion might be independent crystallographically, whereas in other structures they might be equivalent. It is far from obvious that the two cases should be distributed in an apparently random way among the cations given under type I and type II. But even granting that this should be the case, it is surprising that nonequivalence of the two chlorine atoms would necessarily have such a pronounced effect on the spectrum. Yet it is difficult to argue with experimental facts, and it is clear that diffraction data on bichloride ion systems are badly needed, especially data on a typical type I and type II salt.

The only definitive structural data on a bichloride salt are from the structure of CsCl·$\frac{1}{3}$(H$_3$O$^+$HCl$_2^-$) (Schroeder and Ibers, 1966). Part of this structure is shown in Figure 3-17. The bichloride ions occur as strings, Cl—H—Cl $\cdots$ Cl—H—Cl $\cdots$, parallel to the hexagonal axis in the structure. The Cl—H—Cl distance is 3.14 ± 0.02 A, compared with the Cl $\cdots$ Cl distance of 3.62 A, a normal van der Waals Cl $\cdots$ Cl distance. No evidence for the proton positions was found in this x-ray study. The Cl—H—Cl distance provides no evidence for the symmetry of the anion. Yet since the Cl atoms are crystallographically equivalent,[5] this should be a type II salt in the notation of Evans and Lo. Attempts to obtain good infrared spectra of this compound were not successful, owing mainly to its rapid decomposition in mull liquids. It is interesting that the observed shortening of 0.48 A from a van der Waals Cl $\cdots$ Cl distance is just about the shortening observed in going from a van der Waals F $\cdots$ F distance to the F—H—F distance in the bifluoride ion.

[5] Because of this equivalence a potential neutron diffraction study of this compound may not be able to distinguish the single minimum potential from the symmetric double minimum potential. See the discussion in the preceding section on the bifluoride ion.

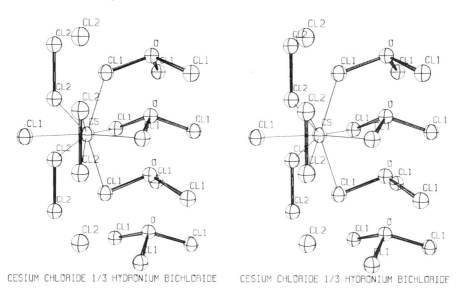

CESIUM CHLORIDE 1/3 HYDRONIUM BICHLORIDE   CESIUM CHLORIDE 1/3 HYDRONIUM BICHLORIDE

Figure 3-17 *Part of the structure of CsCl·$\frac{1}{3}$(H₃OHCl₂).   The c axis is vertical in the figure. The heavier lines represent probable hydrogen bonds.   (See Schroeder and Ibers, 1966.)*

The Bibromide Ion

The compound CsBr·$\frac{1}{3}$(H₃O⁺HBr₂⁻) has been prepared and its structure determined (Schroeder and Ibers, 1967).   The structure is completely analogous to that depicted in Figure 3-17 for the chloride compound.   The Br—H—Br distance is 3.35 ± 0.02 A.   No other bibromide distance appears to be available in the literature for comparison.   The Br · · · Br distance in this compound is 3.73 A, somewhat shorter than that of 3.90 A expected from the usual van der Waals radii tables, but comparable with several nonbonded Br · · · Br distances in the literature.

The Hydronium Ion

The hydronium (or oxonium) ion, H₃O⁺, has been studied by a number of techniques and hence is a useful example to discuss.

It was first suggested by Volmer (1924) on the basis of the similarity of x-ray powder patterns of NH₄ClO₄ and HClO₄ · H₂O that the acid hydrate was really H₃O⁺ClO₄⁻.

This suggestion was confirmed in two independent NMR studies. Richards and Smith (1951) studied a number of acid hydrates and concluded that they contained the hydronium ion.   They determined the H—H distance to be approximately 1.72 A.   In order for the ion to be planar, an an O—H distance of 0.993 A would be required.   Richards and Smith felt that it was more reasonable to expect the ion to be a relatively flat pyramid. An O—H distance of 1.02 A would lead to an H—O—H angle of 115°; an O—H distance of 1.04 A to an angle of 110°. Kakiuchi and co-workers (1952) reached similar conclusions in their study of hydronium perchlorate.

Subsequent infrared studies (Bethell and Sheppard, 1953; Ferriso and Hornig, 1955; Taylor and Vidale, 1956) led to the assignments of the fundamentals of the hydronium ion and left little doubt that the ion is a relatively flat pyramid.

Structural data on the hydronium ion began with Luzzati's (1953) study of $HNO_3 \cdot 3H_2O$, which turns out to be $H_3O^+NO_3^- \cdot 2H_2O$. This work provided no direct evidence on the geometry of the hydronium ion, as the hydrogen atoms were not located with any accuracy. Yoon and Carpenter (1959) in an x-ray study of $HCl \cdot H_2O$ confirmed that this substance is actually H_3OCl. They found the H_3O^+ ion to be a relatively flat pyramid, with a crystallographically required threefold axis and H—O—H angle of approximately 117°. The O—H $\cdots$ Cl hydrogen bonds are 2.95 A in length, and the Cl—O—Cl angles are 110°. The same O $\cdots$ Cl geometry occurs in $CsCl \cdot \frac{1}{3}(H_3O^+HCl_2^-)$ (Schroeder and Ibers, 1966; Figure 3-17); in this study the hydrogen positions were not located. Lee and Carpenter (1959) studied perchloric acid hydrate at room temperature and found it to be hydronium perchlorate. In a somewhat more accurate study Nordman (1962) studied the low-temperature phase of hydronium perchlorate. He found the hydronium ion to be pyramidal with an H—O—H angle of 112°.

Thus the history of the structural characterization of the hydronium ion in acid hydrates illustrates the close interaction of structural methods. The original structural evidence came from an x-ray study; the existence of the ion was proven by NMR studies; the probable geometry was deduced from infrared studies and confirmed, at least approximately, from x-ray diffraction studies. A neutron diffraction study of an ordered hydronium salt would, of course, provide the most definitive information on the geometry of this ion.

Higher Protonated Water Species

The hydronium ion may be thought of as the first member in the series of cations of general formula $H(H_2O)_n^+$. Evidence for the existence of higher members in this series in various solutions has been available for years, but it is only very recently that definitive structural evidence for their existence in the solid state has been obtained. For the second member in the series, $H_5O_2^+$, there are three current reports: The ion occurs in hydrogen chloride dihydrate (Lundgren and Olovsson, 1967a), in hydrogen chloride trihydrate (Lundgren and Olovsson, 1967b), and in the compound $(Co(en)_2Cl_2)Cl \cdot HCl \cdot 2H_2O$ (en = ethylenediamine) (Williams, 1967). Evidence for the existence of the $H_5O_2^+$ ion in this latter compound was originally obtained in an x-ray study (Nakahara, Saito, and Kuroya, 1952), and it has been confirmed by Williams' neutron diffraction study. The O—H—O bond lengths of the $H_5O_2^+$ ion in these compounds are 2.41, 2.43, and 2.50 A.

Structural evidence for the species with n of 3 and 4 has been obtained from x-ray studies of the higher hydrates of various simple acids (Olovsson, 1967).

Hydrogen Bonding in Orthoboric Acid

Zachariasen (1934) determined in an x-ray study the B and O positions in orthoboric acid (H_3BO_3). Owing to the limited accuracy obtainable at that time, he was unable to place the hydrogen atoms, except through chemical arguments. The structure of orthoboric acid consists of layers of hydrogen-bonded molecules (Figure 3-18) that are only very weakly bound together. Because of this it is possible to obtain very thin crystals of orthoboric acid suitable for electron diffraction investigation, and Cowley (1953) carried out such a study. He found an interesting type of disorder of the layers. As noted in Section 2-3, this disorder should be of value in reducing the electron scattering problem to one of kinematic scattering. Cowley was able to handle the disorder problem and to derive the structure of the idealized hexagonal layer. This layer closely resembled the layer found by Zachariasen (1934). Surprisingly, however, the hydrogen atoms were not found along the O · · · O bonds, but rather were significantly displaced off these bonds in the manner shown in Figure 3-19. This placement of the hydrogen atoms was not confirmed in a redetermination of the structure of orthoboric acid using x-ray methods (Zachariasen, 1954). Rather, Zachariasen found the hydrogen atoms to lie along the lines shown in Figure 3-18, with an approximate O—H separation of 0.88 A.

Kume and Kakiuchi (1960) determined the second moment of the

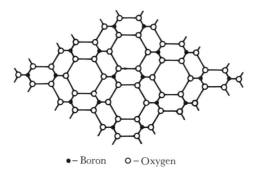

•– Boron   O– Oxygen

Figure 3-18 *The structure of a boric acid layer, according to Zachariasen. The longer lines indicate hydrogen bonds. (From Cowley, 1953.)*

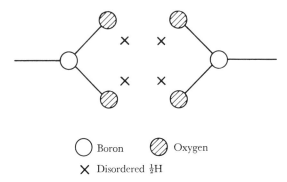

○ Boron   ⊘ Oxygen

✗ Disordered ½H

Figure 3-19 *The arrangement of the half-hydrogen atoms in the boric acid layer, according to Cowley (1953).*

proton magnetic resonance absorption line in polycrystalline orthoboric acid, and they concluded on the basis of their derived H—H interactions that the H atoms must be off axis in the manner suggested by Cowley. A subsequent recalculation (Ibers and Holm, 1961) indicated that if proper account is taken of the magnetic contributions of the boron atoms, then the NMR results do not require Cowley's structure, but rather are in reasonable agreement with the one proposed by Zachariasen (1954). Owing to the complexity of the structure (six independent hydrogen and boron atoms) and a lack of knowledge of zero-point motions, it is not possible to interpret the single value of the proton second moment in terms of a unique model, and hence the O—H distance cannot be determined.

Definitive evidence on this problem has been obtained in a neutron diffraction study of $D_3{}^{11}BO_3$ by Craven and Sabine (1966). (The use of ^{11}B is necessary because of the extremely high absorption cross section for thermal neutrons of ^{10}B.) These authors found that the O—D—O bonds are essentially linear, in agreement with Zachariasen's (1954) result. The O—D distance was found to be 0.97 ± 0.01 A, again about 0.1 A longer than the x-ray result (see page 64).

Both from the x-ray and neutron results it is found that the layers are not strictly planar, but that some tilts occur between the individually coplanar molecules. Craven and Sabine have suggested that this occurs in order that stronger hydrogen bonds can be formed within the layers. Thus if the structure consisted of layers of coplanar molecules with trigonal symmetry with each molecule having the same geometry as observed in the crystal structure, and if the hydrogen bonds were equivalent with an O · · · O distance of 2.71 A, then the hydrogen atoms would be displaced by 0.11 A from the line of centers in each bond while the angle O—D—O would be 170° and the acceptor angle D · · · O—B would be 116°. These conditions for hydrogen bonding would not seem to be as favorable as the ones actually found in the distorted layers.

It is not clear why the electron diffraction results differ from the x-ray and neutron diffraction results. It may be that in very thin crystals the layers are strictly coplanar. However, it seems more likely that the complicated disorder problem, coupled with the difficulties of interpretation of electron diffraction intensities, was sufficient to prevent Cowley from determining the hydrogen positions accurately. This still does not explain the obvious and systematic deviation from the hydrogen positions found in the x-ray and neutron diffraction studies (but see Section 2-7).

Chromous Acid, $HCrO_2$—$DCrO_2$, and Cobaltous Acid, $HCoO_2$—$DCoO_2$

The chromous acid system has been studied by a variety of methods and illustrates some interesting limitations on these methods. The questions of interest in these studies are: (1) Are the O—H—O and O—D—O bonds symmetric? (2) How can one account for the large isotope effects (Table 3-2)?

$HCrO_2$ has the $NaHF_2$ structure and is illustrated in Figure 3-20. A helpful property of this system is that there is only one $HCrO_2$ unit in the trigonal unit cell, and this greatly simplifies interpretation of physical measurements, particularly the spectroscopic measurements. The Cr is fixed at the origin, the O atoms, assuming the cell has a center of symmetry, are fixed by a single parameter, and the H either is centered at $z = \frac{1}{2}$, or is disordered and fixed by another parameter. The isotope effect is large and unambiguous (Table 3-2). The O—H—O distance is approximately 2.48 A. The $HCrO_2$-$DCrO_2$ system has been studied by NMR techniques, by neutron diffraction, and by infrared spectroscopy.

The NMR study (Ibers, Holm, and Adams, 1961) was complicated by the paramagnetism of the material. However, it was possible to derive the usual paramagnetic independent second moment for $HCrO_2$. Interpretation of this moment would appear to be simple, for one can calculate it as a function of the H position. However, as we have emphasized earlier, the nuclear position of H is smeared out by thermal motion, and it proved impossible, in the absence of specific information on the thermal motions, to decide between a centered and a disordered model.

Neutron diffraction studies on $HCrO_2$ and $DCrO_2$ (Hamilton and Ibers, 1963) were necessarily carried out on polycrystalline samples, as no single crystals were obtainable. The overlapping powder data were refined by the least squares technique, using a variety of positional and thermal models. This study showed unambiguously that in $DCrO_2$ the O—D—O bond is not centered, but that the disordered arrangement of 50% O—D $\cdots$ O and 50% O $\cdots$ D—O exists (Figure 3-7c). The neutron diffraction study of

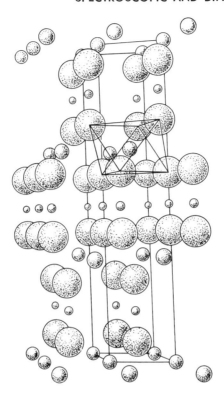

Figure 3-20 *The atomic arrangement in HCrO$_2$: Perspective view along the line ($x = \frac{1}{4}y$, $z = \frac{1}{2}$). Four hexagonal unit cells are shown. The largest spheres are oxygen atoms; those of intermediate size are chromium; and the smallest are hydrogen, shown in the central position of the O—H—O bond. One of the CrO$_6$ octahedra is outlined. The NaHF$_2$ structure is the same, with Na in place of Cr, and F in place of O (From Hamilton and Ibers, 1963).*

HCrO$_2$ is less definitive, in part because of the interference of the high spin-incoherence of the hydrogen scattering; no conclusion could be reached concerning the symmetry of the O—H—O bond.

An infrared study of HCrO$_2$ and DCrO$_2$ (Snyder and Ibers, 1962) revealed some unexpected effects and provided the most information on the nature of the potential function in this system. Representative spectra are shown in Figure 3-21. These spectra have been reproduced by Benoit (1963) and by Rush and Ferraro (1966). A comparison of the infrared spectrum of HCrO$_2$ with that of DCrO$_2$ leads to the conclusion that the differences between the spectra cannot be explained solely on the basis on the mass change. Thus it is found that (1) the O—H stretching band in HCrO$_2$ occurs at about 1640 cm^{-1}. Making a generous allowance for anharmonicity one would expect the O—D stretching band in DCrO$_2$ to be in the region

1300–1200 cm⁻¹. No strong bands are observed in this region. Instead strong bands are observed near 1750 cm⁻¹. (2) The band in the spectrum of HCrO₂ assigned to the O—H stretching vibration is a singlet, whereas the O—D stretching band in DCrO₂ is a doublet. (3) The ratio of the frequency of the OHO bending mode of HCrO₂ to that of the ODO bending mode of DCrO₂ is 1.441 at 24°C and 1.487 at −196°C. This ratio in other strongly hydrogen-bonded systems is usually around 1.34 to 1.38.[6] (4) There are two bands in the lattice-mode region (700–300 cm⁻¹) of the spectrum of HCrO₂, but there are six bands in the same region in the spectrum of DCrO₂.[7] The interpretation of these results rests on different potential functions for the two substances. These are illustrated in Figure 3-22. It is assumed that there is a high barrier in DCrO₂ (in agreement with the neutron diffraction results)

[6] This ratio is less than the harmonic value because of the presence of anharmonicity.
[7] Rush and Ferraro (1966) found no additional bands for either of these substances between 300 and 20 cm⁻¹.

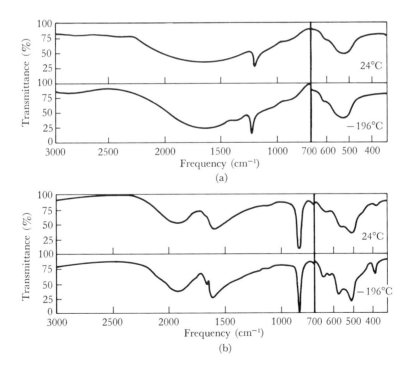

Figure 3-21 (a) Infrared spectrum of HCrO₂ at 24° and at −196°C (in 1 inch KBr disks). (b) Infrared spectrum of DCrO₂ at 24° and at −196°C (in 1 inch KBr disks). (From Snyder and Ibers, 1962.)

while the barrier, if any, in $HCrO_2$ is below the ground state.   Thus the differences noted above in the spectra can be explained: (1) If the shape of the potential energy curve changes, then the ratio ν_{OH}/ν_{OD} would not be expected to have the harmonic value.   In fact it can be seen from Figure 3-22 that the transition which results in ν_{OD} is not between the same levels as those involved in the transition which results in ν_{OH}.   (2) The high barrier between potential minima in the ODO potential results in two sets of closely spaced levels. The separation of the two lowest levels must be very small, ≈ 10 cm^{-1}, since the spectrum is insensitive to temperature in the range 24°C to 4°K, and the separation of the next two levels must be ≈ 310 cm^{-1}.   The allowed transitions between these levels (Figure 3-22) give rise to the observed doublet in the O—D stretching region of $DCrO_2$.   The first vibrational levels for O—H stretching in $HCrO_2$ are well separated and only one band appears.   (3) As we have pointed out (Section 3-2), the hydrogen bending mode increases in frequency as the stretching mode decreases.   If the hydrogen bond in $DCrO_2$ is weaker than the one in $HCrO_2$ (O—D—O longer than O—H—O), then the ratio of the OHO bending frequency to the ODO bending frequency will be larger than that permitted by mass effects alone.   (4) As a result of the low barrier in $HCrO_2$ the H is effectively centered and the selection rules must be based on D_{3d} symmetry.   On the other hand the deuterium in $DCrO_2$ is tunneling through the barrier at about the frequency equivalent of 10 cm^{-1}.   In effect D is not at a center of symmetry and all nine funda-

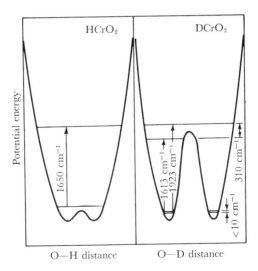

Figure 3-22 *Potential energy curves for the hydrogen bond of HCrO₂ and DCrO₂.   (From Snyder and Ibers, 1962).*

mentals should be active. Instead of just two lattice modes, as predicted and found for $HCrO_2$, all six lattice modes should be active. These are actually observed.

These models for the potential curves in $HCrO_2$ and $DCrO_2$ were supported in part by model potential function calculations. Snyder and Ibers assumed a potential of the form $V(x) = -Ax^2 + Bx^4$, since this is the simplest two-constant potential function that has the general form shown in Figure 3-22. In order to determine the potential constants the position and splitting of the first level in $DCrO_2$ were chosen. Harmonic oscillator wave functions were chosen as a basis set and the matrix elements in the Hamiltonian were computed numerically. The Hamiltonian was truncated at order 20 and diagonalized to yield the energy levels and wave functions. [See Swalen and Ibers (1962) for more details.[8]] By successive approximations it was found that the first four levels were at -1773, -1760, -173, and $+177$ cm^{-1} relative to the top of the barrier for a barrier height of 2860 cm^{-1} and a separation of minima of 0.56 A. These results are encouraging, for with somewhat inaccurate input data and a potential function which is certainly too simple, a zero splitting of 13 cm^{-1}, versus a guess of 10 cm^{-1}, and a separation of minima which corresponds to an O—D distance of about 0.96 A, versus the neutron diffraction results of 0.96 ± 0.04 A, were obtained. When Snyder and Ibers assumed that the potential functions for $HCrO_2$ and $DCrO_2$ were the same and took account of the mass change they obtained energy levels for the O—H—O bond in complete disagreement with observation. No single set of potential function constants will fit both the O—D—O and O—H—O bonds.

The system $HCoO_2$-$DCoO_2$ behaves in a completely analogous manner (Benoit, 1963). Recently (Delaplane et al., 1967) these systems have been studied by infrared techniques, and by elastic and inelastic neutron scattering. The infrared spectra of these substances between 4000 and 30 cm^{-1} are completely analogous to those described for the $HCrO_2$-$DCrO_2$ systems, except that the corresponding bands all occur at slightly higher frequencies. The O—H—O distance in $HCoO_2$ is found to be 2.49 ± 0.02 A, a more normal value than that of 2.36 A originally reported from an x-ray study (Kondrashev and Federova, 1954). The Co—O distance is 1.90 A, compared with a Cr—O distance of 1.97 A, and thus the shift of the bands to higher frequencies seems reasonable: The cobalt compounds are more tightly bound than the chromium compounds. The fact that the cobalt compounds behave in exactly the same way as the chromium compounds eliminates one other possible explanation for some features of the infrared spectra: namely the possible presence of impurities.

[8] This same approach was used by Somorjai and Hornig (1962); see Section 3-4.

3-8 CONCLUDING REMARKS

We have attempted in this chapter to illustrate the complementary nature of diffraction and spectroscopic techniques in the study of the hydrogen bond, and to introduce the simple concepts of potential functions for the hydrogen bond. It should be obvious that even in these simple systems there are many unanswered questions and that much experimental and theoretical work needs to be done. It should also be obvious that no single method provides all of the data that are needed. In fact we eagerly anticipate the development of new methods for the study of the hydrogen bond. We need all the help we can get! In the next chapter we discuss such a new method: neutron inelastic scattering.

REFERENCES

Batuev, M. I. (1949), Chastotno-Modulyatsionnaya Teoriya Vodorodnoi Svyazi, *Zh. Fiz. Khim.* **23,** 1399.

Benoit, A. (1963), Spectres infra-rouges de Substances solides renfermant des Liaisons hydrogène très courtes: $HCrO_2$-$DCrO_2$ et $HCoO_2$-$DCoO_2$, *Spectrochim. Acta* **19,** 2011.

Bethell, D. E., and Sheppard, N. (1953), The Infrared Spectrum of the H_3O^+ Ion in Acid Hydrates, *J. Chem. Phys.* **21,** 1421.

Blinc, R., Hadži, D., and Novak, A. (1960), Relation between the Bridge Length of Short Hydrogen Bonds, the Potential Curve, and the Hydroxyl Stretching Frequency, *Z. Elektrochem.* **64,** 567.

Bloch, F. (1946), Nuclear Induction, *Phys. Rev.* **70,** 460.

Brand, J. C. D., and Speakman, J. C. (1960), *Molecular Structure.* E. Arnold, London.

Bratož, S., and Hadži, D. (1957), Infrared Spectra of Molecules with Hydrogen Bonds, *J. Chem. Phys.* **27,** 991.

Coté, G. L., and Thompson, H. W. (1951), Infrared Spectra and the Solid State. III. Potassium Bifluoride, *Proc. Roy. Soc. London* **A210,** 206.

Coulson, C. A. (1959), The Hydrogen Bond, in *Hydrogen Bonding* (D. Hadži, ed.), p. 339. Pergamon Press, New York.

Cowley, J. M. (1953), Structure Analysis of Single Crystals by Electron Diffraction. II. Disordered Boric Acid Structure, *Acta Cryst.* **6,** 522.

Craven, B. M., and Sabine, T. M. (1966), A Neutron Diffraction Study of Orthoboric Acid $D_3{}^{11}BO_3$, *Acta Cryst.* **20,** 214.

Delaplane, R. G., Ferraro, J. R., Ibers, J. A., and Rush, J. J. (1967), unpublished results.

Delaplane, R. G., and Ibers, J. A. (1966a), Direct Determination of the Effect of Isotopic Substitution on Bond Lengths in Solid Oxalic Acid Dihydrate, *J. Chem. Phys.* **45,** 3451.

Delaplane, R. G., and Ibers, J. A. (1966b), Studies of the $HCoO_2$-$DCoO_2$ System, unpublished results.

Dickson, D. H. W., and Ubbelohde, A. R. (1950), The Hydrogen Bond in Crystals. VIII. The Isotope Effect in KH_2AsO_4, *Acta Cryst.* **3,** 6.

Ellison, R. D., and Levy, H. A. (1965), A Centered Hydrogen Bond in Potassium Hydrogen Chloromaleate: A Neutron Diffraction Structure Determination, *Acta Cryst.* **19,** 260.

El Saffar, Z. M. (1966), Nuclear Magnetic Resonance in $BaCl_2 \cdot 2H_2O$, *Acta Cryst.* **20,** 310.

Evans, J. C., and Lo, G. Y.-S. (1966a), Vibrational Spectra of the Hydrogen Dihalide Ions. I. ClHCl and ClDCl, *J. Phys. Chem.* **70,** 11.

Evans, J. C., and Lo, G. Y.-S. (1966b), Vibrational Spectra of the Hydrogen Dihalide Ions. II. ClHBr and ClDBr, *J. Phys. Chem.* **70,** 20.

Ferriso, C. C., and Hornig, D. F. (1955), Infrared Spectra of Oxonium Halides and the Structure of the Oxonium Ion, *J. Chem. Phys.* **23,** 1464.

Gallagher, K. J., Ubbelohde, A. R., and Woodward, I. (1954), Hydrogen Bonds in Crystals. IX. The Isotope Effect in Acetylenedicarboxylic Acid Dihydrate, *Proc. Roy. Soc. London* **A222,** 195.

Hamilton, W. C., and Ibers, J. A. (1963), Structures of $HCrO_2$ and $DCrO_2$, *Acta Cryst.* **16,** 1209.

Herbrandson, H. F., Dickerson, R. T., Jr., and Weinstein, J. (1954), The Bichloride Ion, *J. Am. Chem. Soc.* **76,** 4046.

Ibers, J. A. (1964a), Refinement of Peterson and Levy's Neutron Diffraction Data on KHF_2, *J. Chem. Phys.* **40,** 402.

Ibers, J. A. (1964b), Potential Function for the Stretching Region in Potassium Acid Fluoride, *J. Chem. Phys.* **41,** 25.

Ibers, J. A., and Holm, C. H. (1961), The O—H $\cdots$ O Bond in Orthoboric Acid, *J. Phys. Soc. Japan* **16,** 839.

Ibers, J. A., Holm, C. H., and Adams, C. R. (1961), Proton Magnetic Resonance Study of Polycrystalline $HCrO_2$, *Phys. Rev.* **121,** 1620.

Ibers, J. A., and Stevenson, D. P. (1958), Motional Corrections to Distances Derived from NMR Data: NH_4Cl, NH_4F, and $N_2H_6F_2$, *J. Chem. Phys.* **28,** 929.

Kakiuchi, Y., Shono, H., Komatsu, H., and Kigoshi, K. (1952), Proton Magnetic Resonance Absorption in Hydrogen Perchlorate Monohydrate and the Structure of the Oxonium Ion, I, *J. Phys. Soc. Japan* **7,** 102.

Kaufler, F., and Kunz, E. (1909a), Über saure Haloidsalze, *Chem. Ber.* **42,** 385.

Kaufler, F., and Kunz, E. (1909b), Über saure Haloidsalze, II, *Chem. Ber.* **42,** 2482.

Ketelaar, J. A. A. (1941), Investigations in the Infrared. I. The Absorption and Reflection Spectra of KHF_2, KDF_2 and $RbHF_2$ in Relation to the Constitution of the Bifluoride Ion, *Rec. Trav. Chim.* **60,** 523.

Ketelaar, J. A. A., and Vedder, W. (1951), The Infrared Spectrum of KHF_2, *J. Chem. Phys.* **19,** 654.

Kishida, S., and Nakamoto, K. (1964), Normal Coordinate Analyses of Hydrogen Bonded Compounds. II. Dimeric Formic Acid and Acetic Acid, *J. Chem. Phys.* **41**, 1558.

Kondrashev, Y. D., and Federova, N. N. (1954), Kristallcheskaya Struktura $CoHO_2$, *Dokl. Akad. Nauk SSSR* **94**, 229.

Kume, K., and Kakiuchi, Y. (1960), Proton Magnetic Resonance in Hydrogen Bonded Dimers in Solids, *J. Phys. Soc. Japan* **15**, 1277.

Lee, F. S., and Carpenter, G. B. (1959), The Crystal Structure of Perchloric Acid Monohydrate, *J. Phys. Chem.* **63**, 279.

Lippincott, E. R. (1957), Derivation of an Internuclear Potential Function from a Quantum-Mechanical Model, *J. Chem. Phys.* **26**, 1678.

Lippincott, E. R., and Schroeder, R. (1955), One-Dimensional Model of the Hydrogen Bond, *J. Chem. Phys.* **23**, 1099.

Lord, R. C., and Merrifield, R. E. (1953), Strong Hydrogen Bonds in Crystals, *J. Chem. Phys.* **21**, 166.

Lundgren, J.-O., and Olovsson, I. (1967a), Hydrogen Bond Studies. The Crystal Structure of Hydrogen Chloride Dihydrate, *Acta Cryst.* in press.

Lundgren, J.-O., and Olovsson, I. (1967b), Hydrogen Bond Studies. The Crystal Structure of Hydrogen Chloride Trihydrate, *Acta Cryst.* in press.

Luzzati, V. (1953), Structure Cristalline de $HNO_3 \cdot 3H_2O$. II. Localisation des Atomes d'Hydrogène; Discussion des Erreurs; Description de la Structure, *Acta Cryst.* **6**, 157.

Maki, A. G., and West, R. (1963), The Nature of the Compound Obtained from Aqueous Cesium Chloride Solution and Hydrogen Chloride, *Inorg. Chem.* **2**, 657.

McGaw, B. L., and Ibers, J. A. (1963), Nature of the Hydrogen Bond in Sodium Acid Fluoride, *J. Chem. Phys.* **39**, 2677.

Megaw, H. D. (1934), Cell Dimensions of Ordinary and "Heavy" Ice, *Nature* **134**, 900.

Nakahara, A., Saito, Y., and Kuroya, H. (1952), The Crystal Structure of Trans-dichloro-diethylenediamine-cobalt-(III)-Chloride Hydrochloride Dihydrate, $(Coen_2Cl_2)Cl \cdot HCl \cdot 2H_2O$, *Bull. Chem. Soc. Japan* **25**, 331.

Nakamoto, K., and Kishida, S. (1964), Normal Coordinate Analyses of Hydrogen-Bonded Compounds. I. Monomeric Formic Acid and Acetic Acid, *J. Chem. Phys.* **41**, 1554.

Nakamoto, K., Margoshes, M., and Rundle, R. E. (1955), Stretching Frequencies as a Function of Distances in Hydrogen Bonds, *J. Am. Chem. Soc.* **77**, 6480.

Nordman, C. E. (1962), The Crystal Structure of Hydronium Perchlorate at $-80°C$, *Acta Cryst.* **15**, 18.

Nordman, C. E., and Lipscomb, W. N. (1951), Note on the Hydrogen-Deuterium Isotope Effect in Crystals, *J. Chem. Phys.* **19**, 1422.

Olovsson, I. (1967). Private communication.

Padmanabhan, V. M., Busing, W. R., and Levy, H. A. (1963), A Single-Crystal Neutron-Diffraction Study of $BaCl_2 \cdot 2H_2O$, *Acta Cryst.* **16**, A26.

Pake, G. E. (1948), Nuclear Resonance Absorption in Hydrated Crystals: Fine Structure of the Proton Line, *J. Chem. Phys.* **16**, 327.

Pedersen, B. (1964), NMR in Hydrate Crystals: Correction for Vibrational Motion, *J. Chem. Phys.* **41**, 122.

Pedersen, B. (1966), The Equilibrium Hydrogen-Hydrogen Distances in the Water Molecules in Potassium and Rubidium Oxalate Monohydrates, *Acta Cryst.* **20,** 412.

Peterson, S. W., and Levy, H. A. (1952), A Single Crystal Neutron Diffraction Determination of the Hydrogen Position in Potassium Bifluoride, *J. Chem. Phys.* **20,** 704.

Peterson, S. W., and Williams, J. M. (1966), Neutron-Diffraction Determination of the Structure of $CH_3CN \cdot 2HCl$, *J. Am. Chem. Soc.* **88,** 2866.

Pimentel, G. C., and McClellan, A. L. (1960), *The Hydrogen Bond.* W. H. Freeman, San Francisco.

Pimentel, G. C., and Sederholm, C. H. (1956), Correlation of Infrared Stretching Frequencies and Hydrogen Bond Distances in Crystals, *J. Chem. Phys.* **24,** 639.

Pitzer, K. S., and Westrum, E. F. (1947), The Nature of the Hydrogen Bond in KHF_2, *J. Chem. Phys.* **15,** 526.

Reid, C. (1959), Semiempirical Treatment of the Hydrogen Bond, *J. Chem Phys.* **30,** 182.

Richards, R. E., and Smith, J. A. S. (1951), NMR Spectra of Some Acid Hydrates, *Trans. Faraday Soc.* **47,** 1261.

Robertson, J. M., and Ubbelohde, A. R. (1939), Structure and Thermal Properties Associated with Some Hydrogen Bonds in Crystals. I. The Isotope Effect, *Proc. Roy. Soc. London* **A170,** 222.

Rundle, R. E. (1964), On Symmetrical OHO Hydrogen Bonds, *J. Phys.* **25,** 487.

Rundle, R. E., and Parasol, M. (1952), OH Stretching Frequencies in Very Short and Possibly Symmetrical Hydrogen Bonds, *J. Chem. Phys.* **20,** 1487.

Rush, J. J., and Ferraro, J. R. (1966), Neutron and Infrared Spectra of $HCrO_2$, and $DCrO_2$, *J. Chem. Phys.* **44,** 2496.

Schachtschneider, J. H., and Snyder, R. G. (1963), Vibrational Analysis of the *n*-Paraffins. II. Normal Co-ordinate Calculations, *Spectrochim. Acta* **19,** 117.

Schroeder, L. W., and Ibers, J. A. (1966), Geometry of the Bichloride Ion. Preparation and Crystal Structure of Cesium Chloride·$\frac{1}{3}$ Hydronium Bichloride, *J. Am. Chem. Soc.* **88,** 2601.

Schroeder, L. W., and Ibers, J. A. (1967), The Bihalide Ions ClHCl and BrHBr: Crystal Structure of Cesium Chloride $\frac{1}{3}$ Hydronium Bichloride and Cesium Bromide $\frac{1}{3}$ Hydronium Bibromide, *Inorg. Chem.*, in press.

Silvidi, A. A., and McGrath, J. W. (1960), Proton Magnetic Resonance Study of the Structure of Barium Chloride Dihydrate, *J. Chem. Phys.* **32,** 924.

Snyder, R. G., and Ibers, J. A. (1962), O—H—O and O—D—O Potential Energy Curves for Chromous Acid, *J. Chem. Phys.* **36,** 1356.

Snyder, R. G., and Schachtschneider, J. H. (1963), Vibrational Analysis of the *n*-Paraffins. I. Assignments of Infrared Bands in the Spectra of C_3H_8 through *n*-$C_{19}H_{40}$, *Spectrochim. Acta* **19,** 85.

Somorjai, R. L., and Hornig, D. F. (1962), Double-Minimum Potentials in Hydrogen-Bonded Solids, *J. Chem. Phys.* **36,** 1980.

Stepanov, B. I. (1946), Interpretation of the Regularities in the Spectra of Molecules Forming the Intermolecular Hydrogen Bond by the Predissociation Effect, *Nature* **157,** 808.

Swalen, J. D., and Ibers, J. A. (1962), Potential Function for the Inversion of Ammonia, *J. Chem. Phys.* **36,** 1914.

Taylor, R. C., and Vidale, G. L. (1956), The Vibrational Spectrum of the Hydronium Ion in Hydronium Perchlorate, *J. Am. Chem. Soc.* **78,** 5999.

Ubbelohde, A. R. (1939), Structure and Thermal Properties Associated with Some Hydrogen Bonds in Crystals. III. Further Examples of the Isotope Effect, *Proc. Roy. Soc. London* **A173,** 417.

Ubbelohde, A. R., and Gallagher, K. J. (1955), Acid-Base Effects in Hydrogen Bonds in Crystals, *Acta Cryst.* **8,** 71.

Ubbelohde, A. R., and Woodward, I. (1942), Structure and Thermal Properties Associated with Some Hydrogen Bonds in Crystals. IV. Isotope Effects in Some Acid Phosphates, *Proc. Roy. Soc. London* **A179,** 399.

Urey, H. C., and Bradley, C. A., Jr. (1931), The Vibrations of Pentatomic Tetrahedral Molecules, *Phys. Rev.* **38,** 1969.

Valleé, R. E., and McDaniel, D. H. (1962), Cesium Salts Containing the $ClHCl^-$ Species. *J. Am. Chem. Soc.* **84,** 3412.

Van Vleck, J. H. (1948), The Dipolar Broadening of Magnetic Resonance Lines in Crystals, *Phys. Rev.* **74,** 1168.

Volmer, M. (1924), Über die Existenz des Oxenium perchlorats, *Ann. Chem.* **440,** 200.

Waddington, T. C. (1958), The Preparation of Tetramethylammonium Hydrogen Dichloride and the Structure of the Hydrogen Dichloride Ion, HCl_2^-, *J. Chem. Soc.,* 1708.

Waugh, J. S., Humphrey, F. B., and Yost, D. M. (1953), Magnetic Resonance Spectrum of a Linear Three-Spin System: The Configuration of the Bifluoride Ion, *J. Phys. Chem.* **57,** 486.

West, R. (1957), Evidence for the Hydrogen Dichloride Anion: The Compound $CsHCl_2$, *J. Am. Chem. Soc.* **79,** 4568.

Williams, J. M. (1967), The Diaquohydrogen Ion $(H_5O_2)^+$: A Neutron Diffraction Structure Investigation of trans-$(Co(en)_2Cl_2)^+Cl^-(H_5O_2)^+Cl^-$, *Inorg. Nucl. Chem. Letters,* **3,** 297.

Wilson, E. B., Jr., Decius, J. C., and Cross, P. C. (1955), *Molecular Vibrations.* McGraw-Hill, New York.

Yoon, Y. K., and Carpenter, G. B. (1959), The Crystal Structure of Hydrogen Chloride Monohydrate, *Acta Cryst.* **12,** 17.

Zachariasen, W. H. (1934), The Crystal Lattice of Boric Acid BO_3H_3, *Z. Krist.* **88,** 150.

Zachariasen, W. H. (1954), The Precise Structure of Orthoboric Acid, *Acta Cryst.* **7,** 305.

Rotational Motion in Solids and Neutron Spectroscopy

In many solids, molecules or atomic groups undergo hindered rotational motions or "jumps" about one or more molecular axes. This is a particularly common phenomenon when the groups are not tightly bound together, for example when only weak hydrogen bonding is involved. It is of interest in a book on hydrogen bonding to examine the nature of such rotational motions and the methods used in their detection. The frequency of such jumps or reorientations increases with temperature. It is usually assumed that these motions are controlled by an activated process, and one then writes

$$\nu = \nu_0 \exp\left(-\frac{E}{RT}\right) \tag{4-1}$$

where ν is the frequency of reorientation at temperature T and E is the barrier which hinders this reorientation. Let us consider benzene in the solid state and take as a likely motion the reorientation of individual molecules about their sixfold axes. If we carry out an x-ray diffraction study of solid benzene we find the expected electron density distribution, slightly broadened by the effects of thermal motion of the atoms. We do not find that this postulated reorientation motion has smeared out the electron density. This means that a given benzene molecule spends most of its time in an equilibrium configuration, and the time spent in the reorientation process is relatively small. But time relative to what? Clearly one must speak of such times relative to the time that the x-ray beam interacts with the molecule in question. The x-ray beam is traveling at 10^{10} cm sec^{-1} (10^{18} A sec^{-1}) and since the effective inter-action is of the order of an atomic dimension, the "time scale" or time of interaction of the x-ray experiment is of the order of 10^{-18} sec. Thus even if the reorientation of the benzene molecules occurs 10^{16} times per second, the benzene molecules will "look" stationary to the x-ray beam and the scattering will be barely affected by such motions.

Consider now an NMR experiment on solid benzene. How might these reorientations affect the spectrum? Clearly the interactions between nuclear magnetic dipoles on the rotating groups could be affected with a resultant effect on the spectrum. Loosely speaking one might say: If the spins are in rapid relative motion the local field seen by a given spin will fluctuate rapidly with time, and only its value averaged over a time long compared with the fluctuations will be observed. This average will be smaller than the instantaneous value of the local field, and hence the resonance line will be narrowed. What sorts of frequencies are involved here? One might guess that the average, reduced value of the local field will occur if the fluctuations of the local field are rapid compared with the resonance (or Larmor) frequency of the experiment. This turns out to be approximately correct, the more precise criterion being that motional narrowing will occur if

$$S^{1/2} \ll \nu \qquad\qquad (4\text{-}2)$$

where S is the second moment of the resonance line (in frequency units). Thus reorientations of the benzene molecules will have a pronounced narrowing effect on the spectrum if they occur at a rate of about 10^5 times per second or faster. While the benzene molecules in the solid state undergo various motions that are independent of the experiment, the deductions made concerning these motions will depend markedly on the time scale of the experimental method employed. Benzene molecules reorienting about their sixfold axes in the solid state at 10^{10} times per second will have essen-tially no effect on the x-ray diffraction pattern that would be obtained if the molecules were at rest, but the effect on the NMR absorption spectrum will be drastic. It is essential to discuss thermal motions in solids in relation to the time scale of the experiment. Time scales for various experimental methods are given in Table 4-1.

The detection of these rotational or reorientational motions depends, of course, not only on their frequencies being compatible with the time scales of the experimental methods employed, but also on a resultant change in an observable. Infrared and Raman techniques are not especially useful for the detection and characterization of rotational motions in solids. Such motions may cause splittings of the spectroscopic bands, but such splittings

Table 4-1 *Approximate Time Scales for Various Structural Techniques*[a]

Technique	Time scale (sec)
x-Ray and electron diffraction	10^{-18}
Ultraviolet	10^{-15}
Visible	10^{-14}
Infrared-Raman	10^{-13}
Neutron diffraction and neutron inelastic scattering	10^{-13}
Electron spin resonance[b]	10^{-4}–10^{-8}
Nuclear magnetic resonance[b]	10^{-1}–10^{-9}
Quadrupole resonance[b]	10^{-1}–10^{-8}
Mössbauer effect (Fe)	10^{-7}
Molecular beam	10^{-6}

[a] Adapted from a similar table of Muetterties (1965).
[b] Dependent on the particular chemical system.

are difficult to associate with motional effects rather than with, for example, interactions among neighboring molecules.   Thus for those nuclei with spins, the NMR method is generally the most sensitive one for the detection of motions of such nuclei in the solid state.   Of the other methods available, that of neutron inelastic scattering is also very useful; it has principally been applied to the detection of the motions of hydrogen nuclei in solids.   We limit our discussion in this chapter to these two techniques.

4-1   MOTIONAL EFFECTS ON NMR SPECTRA

We have already given a qualitative description of the narrowing of an NMR absorption spectrum if suitable molecular motions occur in the solid. Let us now confine ourselves to multispin systems and consider how the second moment (Section 3-3) of the absorption line will be modified by such motions, and whether or not changes in the second moment can be related to parameters of interest, such as the barrier hindering rotation.   One finds experimentally that the *measured* second moment is reduced through the effects of molecular motion.   This is illustrated in Figure 4-1, where the second moments of the proton resonance absorption lines in solid benzenes are displayed as a function of temperature (Andrew and Eades, 1953b). Below $90°K$ the second moment of C_6H_6 is constant at about $9.7 \ G^2$, a value that may be calculated from equation (3-24) and reasonable assumptions about C—H distances and the crystal structure of C_6H_6 at this temperature.

Above 120°K the second moment is constant at 1.6 G². Isotopic substitution studies (Andrew and Eades, 1953a,b) have shown that this reduction of the second moment in solid, polycrystalline benzene results from the reduction of both intra- and intermolecular terms to the second moment, and that the change in the intramolecular contribution is consistent with a model in which the benzene molecules are reorienting about their sixfold axes. Nevertheless, Andrew and Newing (1958) have shown that the second moment of the NMR absorption line is independent of any thermal motion occurring in the solid. The explanation for this apparent anomaly is that thermal motion causes the resonance absorption line to develop satellite peaks far out on the wings of the line. These satellite peaks are lost in the background noise; if they could be observed and measured, then the second moment would be found to be constant. Since they are not observed, the *measured* second moment is found to decrease with increasing thermal motion. Under these conditions the effects on the measured second moment can be estimated by replacing terms of the type $(r_{ij}^{-3}(3 \cos^2 \theta_{ij} - 1))^2$ in the expression (3-24) for the second moment by terms of the sort $(\langle r_{ij}^{-3}(3 \cos^2 \theta_{ij} - 1)\rangle_{\text{motion}})^2$. Suppose now that the two spins i and j belong to the same molecule, so that r_{ij} is independent of the motions of the molecule. Suppose further that the molecule is rotating around some axis OV which makes an angle θ' with the applied field and an angle ϕ with $\mathbf{r}_{ij}$. Then using the spherical harmonic addition theorem we find

$$\langle 3 \cos^2 \theta_{ij} - 1 \rangle = \tfrac{1}{2}(3 \cos^2 \theta' - 1)(3 \cos^2 \phi - 1) \qquad (4\text{-}3)$$

For a polycrystalline sample, all orientations of the axis OV with respect to the magnetic field are equally probable and the net effect of the reorientation

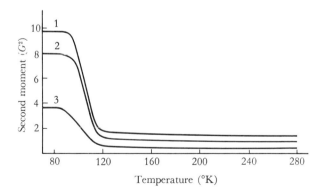

Figure 4-1 *Second moments of three isotopic species of benzene as a function of temperature. Curve 1 is for C_6H_6; curve 2 for C_6H_5D; curve 3 for 1,3,5-$C_6H_3D_3$. (From Andrew and Eades, 1953b.)*

on the intramolecular contributions to the second moment is to multiply them by the factor $(3 \cos^2 \phi - 1)^2/4$ (Gutowsky and Pake, 1950). For the intermolecular contributions the effects of such motions on the term r_{ij}^{-3} must also be considered, and no simple result may be obtained. Thus with rare exception the dependence of the observed second moment of a resonance line on temperature does not yield direct information about the thermal motions which are effective, nor does it lead to useful information on the barriers hindering such motions. One does learn from a study of the second moment as a function of temperature when such motions cease to be effective in reducing the second moment. Thus the information of Figure 4-1 must be obtained before it is safe to make deductions, based on the measured second moment, about the structure of solid benzene.

Attempts have been made to relate the narrowing of the resonance line with temperature to the barriers hindering reorientation. Such attempts are semiquantitative at best, owing mainly to uncertainties about true line shapes. For a change from a broad line to a narrower line the frequency width of the line $(\delta \nu)$ is given roughly as a function of ν by

$$(\delta \nu)^2 = B^2 + C^2 \left(\frac{2}{\pi}\right) \tan^{-1}\left(\alpha \left(\frac{\delta \nu}{\nu}\right)\right) \tag{4-4}$$

where B is the width of the narrow line, $(B^2 + C^2)$ is the width of the broad line, and α is a parameter which depends on the shape of the line (Gutowsky and Pake, 1950). If an idealized line shape is assumed, then from equations (4-4) and (4-1) and a study of line widths as a function of temperature it is possible to evaluate E and ν_0.

When absorption of energy occurs in the NMR experiment there is a transfer of nuclear spins in a lower energy level to an upper energy level. Thus the system is not in equilibrium with the lattice and there is a gradual return to equilbrium. This approach to equilibrium is exponential with a characteristic time T_1, called the spin-lattice relaxation time (Section 3-3). It has been shown by many workers (e.g., Gutowsky, Pake, and Bersohn, 1954) that reorientations of groups, such as the NH_4^+ ion, are effective in bringing about this return to equilibrium through the rapid variation of magnetic interaction between nuclear dipoles as the molecules which contain them reorient. Thus it is possible to infer something about reorientation motions from a study of T_1 as a function of temperature. The actual means of measuring T_1 are not germane to this discussion; it is sufficient to indicate that over certain ranges of times the newer pulsed methods are extremely useful.

The theory of spin-lattice relaxations has been treated by Bloembergen, Purcell, and Pound (1948), Kubo and Tomita (1954), and others, and summarized by Abragam (1961). Let us define a correlation time

$t_c = (2\pi\nu)^{-1}$, which is roughly speaking the time it takes the group to turn through a distance comparable with its dimensions. Then, in an analysis which is too complicated to present here, the dependence of T_1 on t_c, for a nonmetallic liquid, is given by

$$\frac{1}{T_1} = \frac{2}{5}\frac{\gamma^4\hbar^2}{b^6}(I)(I+1)\left[\frac{t_c}{1+\omega^2 t_c^2} + \frac{4t_c}{1+4\omega^2 t_c^2}\right] \qquad (4\text{-}5)$$

where γ is the gyromagnetic ratio, ω is the Larmor frequency in the experiment, and b is the interspin distance. If it is assumed that the relaxation time of a system of four spins of magnitude $\frac{1}{2}$, placed at the apices of a rotating tetrahedron, can be calculated by neglecting correlations existing between motions of the various spins, then one may write

$$\frac{1}{T_1} = \frac{9}{10}\frac{\gamma^4\hbar^2}{b^6}\left[\frac{t_c}{1+\omega^2 t_c^2} + \frac{4t_c}{1+4\omega^2 t_c^2}\right] \qquad (4\text{-}6)$$

where b is now the distance between two protons in the NH_4^+ ion. It is thus possible to evaluate t_c (and hence ν) as a function of T (temperature) from the variation of T_1 with T and hence to evaluate the barrier E. Such measurements have been carried out for several materials; in Figure 4-2 we illustrate the results of one such series of measurements for NH_4Br (Cooke and Drain, 1952). If $\log(1/T_1)$ is plotted against $1/T$, the slope is $+E/R$ for $\omega t_c \ll 1$ and is $-E/R$ for $\omega t_c \gg 1$.

The T_1 measurements have served as a basis for the interpretation of the much more rapid and easily made line-width narrowing measurements for

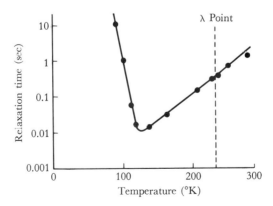

Figure 4-2 *Relaxation time T_1 versus temperature T for polycrystalline NH_4Br.* (*From Cooke and Drain, 1952.*)

the NH_4^+ salts. Suppose we rewrite equation (4-1) as

$$E = AT_t \qquad (4\text{-}7)$$

where A is a constant $[= R \ln(\nu_0/\nu)]$ and T_t is the line width transition temperature (Wert and Marx, 1953). Gutowsky, Pake, and Bersohn (1954) used this expression and the E value (from earlier T_1 measurements) and the observed T_t value for NH_4Cl to fix the constant A as 36.8 cal deg^{-1}, and on this basis derived E values for NH_4Br and NH_4I. (Another way of looking at this procedure is that from the T_1 measurements the line shape function α—equation (4-4)—is fixed and is assumed to be the same for all the NH_4^+ salts.) In later work Richards and Schaefer (1961) used the same procedure (and the same value of A) to derive barriers for a large number of ammonium salts. These range from around 5 kcal mole^{-1} for $(NH_4)_2SeO_4$ to an upper limit of 0.7 kcal mole^{-1} for the dichromate, persulfate, and stannibromate. There are many assumptions in this approach, and the actual derived barrier heights are not to be taken literally. (In fact barriers for NH_4I ranging from 1.7 to 2.9 kcal mole^{-1} have been derived by various workers who have assumed various potential forms.) The important point, however, is that there is a general sense to the results: intuitively one would expect the barriers in the ammonium halides to decrease in the order F, Cl, Br, and I, and this is what is observed. Moreover, there is a qualitative agreement between the NMR results and those from measurements of total cross-sections for neutron inelastic scattering. In fact in Figure 4-13 the results from these two measurements are displayed together. It seems evident that NMR is a very useful tool for the detection of rotational motion in solids, but it does not generally provide a very precise description of which motions are involved and what the barriers hindering these motions are. Increased application of T_1 measurements may improve our experimental knowledge of these motions and their barriers.

4-2 NEUTRON INELASTIC SCATTERING

In Chapter 3 we have discussed the information regarding hydrogen-bonded compounds that can be obtained by measurement of the transitions between the vibrational energy levels of these compounds. We have so far dealt entirely with transitions induced by the absorption or emission of electromagnetic radiation of appropriate frequencies. Any experimental method which can tell us something about the energy levels of the system can provide information pertinent to an understanding of the hydrogen bond. The inelastic scattering of slow neutrons is one such method.[1]

As we have discussed in Chapter 2 crystal and molecular structure can be determined by the elastic scattering of slow neutrons in the Bragg peaks. By *elastic* scattering, we mean that the scattered neutron has the same energy as the incident neutron; hence, by conservation of energy, the scattering system is in the same energy state after the scattering event as before. It is also possible for the neutron to interact with the scattering system in such a way that the energies of both are changed in the scattering process. This is *inelastic* scattering. The amount of energy which can be transferred between the neutron and the scattering system is governed by the energy level scheme of the scattering system. Transitions can only occur between stationary states of the system. The neutron can lose energy to the scattering system by inducing a transition from a lower energy state of the system to a higher energy state; an experiment in which such a process is the predominant one is called an *energy loss experiment*. (It is the neutron which has lost energy.) Alternatively, the neutron may gain energy by causing a transition of the system from a higher to a lower energy state. The neutron gains energy by depopulation of excited states of the scattering system, and an experiment in which this type of transition predominates is known as an *energy gain experiment*. The energy loss and energy gain experiments are thus analogous to Stokes and anti-Stokes lines in Raman spectroscopy.

The transitions between the vibrational energy states of molecular and crystal systems lie in energy ranges which are conveniently expressed in terms of millielectron volts (mV). One millielectron volt is equivalent to 8 cm^{-1} in terms of the frequency of the transition expressed in wave numbers. The mean translational energy of a neutron in thermal equilibrium at room temperature is about 25 mV. Thus the change in the energy of a neutron of near-thermal energy in an inelastic scattering process accompanied by a change in vibrational energy may be comparable to the incident energy of the neutron. Any device which is capable of measuring neutron energies with even moderate resolution is thus capable of measuring the transition energies of the system involved in the inelastic scattering process.

Cross Sections and Scattering Amplitudes

We shall neglect in this section the scattering of neutrons caused by the interaction between the magnetic moment of the neutron and the magnetic moments of unpaired electrons in the scattering systems. Although such scattering, both elastic and inelastic, has been of the greatest importance in the study of magnetic materials, it is generally unimportant in hydrogen-bonded systems, and its inclusion in the present discussion would lead to unnecessary complications.

[1] An extremely useful general reference is the book edited by Egelstaff (1965).

The differential scattering cross section $d\sigma/d\Omega$ is defined as the total number of scattered neutrons per second passing into the solid angle $d\Omega$, divided by the incident neutron flux in neutrons cm^{-2} sec^{-1}. For a single nucleus, the differential scattering cross section is given by

$$\frac{d\sigma}{d\Omega} = a^2 \tag{4-8}$$

where a is the scattering length for the nucleus.[2] Since the scattering length for slow neutrons is isotropic, integration over all solid angles results in

$$\sigma = \int \frac{d\sigma}{d\Omega} \, d\Omega = 4\pi a^2 \tag{4-9}$$

Each nuclear species has a specific value for the scattering length a which is characteristic of both the isotope and the nuclear spin state of that isotope (see Section 2-2).

Let us consider a neutron beam traveling in the positive z direction and described by the following wave equation:

$$\psi_0 = e^{ik_0 z} \tag{4-10}$$

The propagation vector $\mathbf{k}_0$ in the positive z direction is related to the neutron wave length λ and momentum $\mathbf{P}$ in the following way:

$$|\mathbf{k}_0| = k_0 = \frac{2\pi}{\lambda} \tag{4-11}$$

$$\mathbf{k}_0 = \frac{2\pi \mathbf{P}_0}{h} \tag{4-12}$$

where h is Planck's constant. The magnitude of the momentum P_0 is related to the incident energy E_0 and neutron mass m by

$$P_0 = (2mE_0)^{1/2} \tag{4-13}$$

In the inelastic scattering process the neutron will undergo both an energy and a momentum change.[3] Let us denote the wave vector and the energy of the scattered neutron by $\mathbf{k}_s$ and E_s, respectively. We define as in (2-25) the scattering vector

$$\mathbf{S} = \mathbf{k}_s - \mathbf{k}_0 \tag{4-14}$$

---

[2] We shall in this discussion always take a to be the *bound scattering length*, the scattering length when the nucleus is part of a massive scattering system, such as a crystal. The bound scattering length is related to the free atom scattering length a_f by $a = (m/\mu)a_f$, where m is the neutron mass and μ is the reduced mass of the neutron-nucleus system.

[3] In elastic scattering, only a change in the direction but not the magnitude of the momentum is involved.

such that the momentum change of the neutron is given by

$$\Delta \mathbf{P} = \mathbf{P}_s - \mathbf{P}_0 = \left(\frac{h}{2\pi}\right)\mathbf{S} \tag{4-15}$$

and the energy change by

$$\Delta E = E_s - E_0 = \left(\frac{h^2}{8\pi^2 m}\right)(k_s^2 - k_0^2) \tag{4-16}$$

Thus a positive ΔE corresponds to a gain in energy of the neutron and a loss in energy by the scattering system.

Let us now consider a scattering system which is composed of N atoms with position vectors

$$\mathbf{r}_i \qquad i = 1, \ldots, N \tag{4-17}$$

and scattering lengths

$$a_i \qquad i = 1, \ldots, N \tag{4-18}$$

If this system may be described before the scattering process by the wave function ψ_I and after the scattering process by the wave function ψ_F, it may be shown that the differential scattering cross section for the scattering process is

$$\frac{d\sigma_{\mathrm{IF}}}{d\Omega} = \frac{k_s}{k_0}|f_{\mathrm{IF}}|^2 \tag{4-19}$$

where the scattering amplitude f_{IF} is given by

$$f_{\mathrm{IF}} = \sum_{i=1}^{N} a_i \int \psi_I{}^*(\mathbf{r}_1, \ldots, \mathbf{r}_n)e^{i\mathbf{S}\cdot\mathbf{r}_i}\psi_F(\mathbf{r}_1, \ldots, \mathbf{r}_n)\, d\mathbf{r}_1, \ldots, d\mathbf{r}_n \tag{4-20}$$

The integral appearing in the equation above is conveniently written

$$M_i = \int \psi_I e^{i\mathbf{S}\cdot\mathbf{r}_i}\psi_F\, d\mathbf{r}_1\, d\mathbf{r}_2 \cdots d\mathbf{r}_N \tag{4-21}$$

so that we may write

$$f_{\mathrm{IF}} = \sum_{i=1}^{N} a_i M_i \tag{4-22}$$

The differential scattering cross section may then be expressed as

$$\frac{d\sigma_{\mathrm{IF}}}{d\Omega} = \frac{k_s}{k_0}\sum_{i=1}^{N}\sum_{j=1}^{N} a_i a_j M_i M_j{}^* \tag{4-23}$$

The preceding formulation must be extended somewhat if there are nuclei present in the system which have different isotope or spin states.

For example, the hydrogen nucleus with a spin of $\frac{1}{2}$ can couple with the spin of the neutron in two ways to give a total spin angular momentum of either 0 or 1 for the system neutron-proton. The scattering amplitudes are different for these two possible states and have been measured to be

$$a^- = 4.74 \times 10^{-12} \quad \text{cm}$$
$$a^+ = 1.076 \times 10^{-12} \quad \text{cm}$$
(4-24)

In the typical crystal or molecular aggregation, there will be complete disorder in the arrangement of the nuclei with various isotopes and spins. Thus we may expect a site in a crystal which is occupied by hydrogen to be randomly occupied by nuclei which will couple with the neutron to form the triplet state characterized by a^+ and the singlet state characterized by a^-. These will occur in the ratio 3:1. The expression for the scattering cross section must be averaged over all isotope and spin states which are possible for a given site. We need to determine [4]

$$\left\langle \sum_{i=1}^{N} \sum_{j=1}^{N} a_i a_j M_i M_j^* \right\rangle$$
(4-25)

We may write (4-25) as

$$\left\langle \sum_{i=1}^{N} a_i^2 M_i M_i^* \right\rangle + \left\langle \sum\sum_{i \neq j} a_i a_j M_i M_j^* \right\rangle$$

$$= \sum_{i=1}^{N} \langle a_i^2 \rangle M_i M_i^* + \sum\sum_{i \neq j} \langle a_i a_j \rangle M_i M_j^*$$

$$= \sum_{i=1}^{N} [\langle a_i^2 \rangle - \langle a_i \rangle^2] M_i M_i^* + \sum_{i=1}^{N} \sum_{j=1}^{N} \langle a_i \rangle \langle a_j \rangle M_i M_j^*$$
(4-26)

Let us define an *incoherent* nuclear scattering length for atomic species i as

$$a_{i(\text{inc})} = [\langle a_i^2 \rangle - \langle a_i \rangle^2]^{1/2}$$
(4-27)

and a *coherent* nuclear scattering length by

$$a_{i(\text{coh})} = \langle a_i \rangle$$
(4-28)

Then

$$\frac{d\sigma}{d\Omega} = \frac{k_s}{k_0} \sum_{i=1}^{N} a_{i(\text{inc})}^2 M_i M_i^* + \frac{k_s}{k_0} \sum_{i=1}^{N} \sum_{j=1}^{N} a_{i(\text{coh})} a_{j(\text{coh})} M_i M_j^*$$

$$\equiv \frac{d\sigma_{\text{inc}}}{d\Omega} + \frac{d\sigma_{\text{coh}}}{d\Omega}$$
(4-29)

[4] Average value is denoted as usual by the brackets $\langle \ \rangle$.

where (4-29) serves to define the incoherent and coherent scattering cross sections σ_{inc} and σ_{coh}. This separation into incoherent and coherent scattering cross sections would be entirely artificial for some systems but is convenient for an ordered system such as a crystal because the incoherent scattering cross section does not include *interference* effects which depend on the relative positions of the atoms, while the coherent scattering does exhibit such effects.

Before proceeding to a detailed discussion of inelastic scattering, it is instructive to consider the coherent and incoherent scattering terms for elastic scattering from a crystalline material. Let us write the position vector $\mathbf{r}_i$ of atom i as

$$\mathbf{r}_i = \mathbf{r}_i{}^0 + \Delta\mathbf{r}_i \tag{4-30}$$

where $\mathbf{r}_i{}^0$ is the mean position of the atom and $\Delta\mathbf{r}_i$ is the displacement of this atom from its mean position due to thermal motion. The temperature or Debye-Waller factor T_i is defined as

$$T_i(\mathbf{S}) = \langle \exp(i\mathbf{S} \cdot \Delta\mathbf{r}_i) \rangle \tag{4-31}$$

The structure factor may be written as

$$F(\mathbf{S}) = \sum_{\text{cell}} a_{i(\text{coh})} T_i(\mathbf{S}) \exp(i\mathbf{S} \cdot \mathbf{r}_i{}^0) \tag{4-32}$$

The differential scattering cross section per cell is then

$$\frac{d\sigma_{\text{coh}}}{d\Omega} = \frac{(2\pi)^3}{V_0} F^2(\mathbf{S}) \, \delta(\mathbf{S} - 2\pi\mathbf{H}) \tag{4-33}$$

where V_0 is the volume of the cell, $\mathbf{H}$ is a reciprocal lattice vector as defined in (2-5), and the multiplication by the δ function indicates that scattering fulfills the Bragg condition that[5]

$$\mathbf{S} = 2\pi\mathbf{H} \tag{4-34}$$

The elastic incoherent scattering cross section per cell is

$$\frac{d\sigma_{\text{inc}}}{d\Omega} = \sum_{\text{cell}} (a_{i(\text{inc})} T_i)^2 \tag{4-35}$$

There are no interference effects, and the incoherent scattering is just the sum of the incoherent scattering from all the atoms present, whether ordered or disordered.

As we have seen in equations (4-19) to (4-23), the quantitative evaluation of the scattering cross section demands a knowledge of the integrals M_i.

[5] The factor $(2\pi)^3/V_0$ disappears on integration of the δ function over Ω.

The evaluation of these integrals is in general difficult. In the first approximation, we may consider the crystal to be an assembly of harmonic oscillators. If this is so, the initial and final state wave functions of the crystal may be described as products of harmonic oscillator wave functions for the normal modes of the crystal. In this approximation, the most important inelastic scattering processes are those in which a single normal mode is excited or deexcited by the exchange of one quantum (phonon) of vibrational energy with the scattered neutron; this is called *one-phonon scattering*. For such scattering, the value of M_i will depend on the contribution of the motions of atom i to the normal mode involved in the scattering.

The displacement vector $\Delta \mathbf{r}_i$ of atom i from its mean position may be expressed in terms of the normal mode coordinates q_j, the atomic masses m_i, and the number of cells in the crystal N by

$$\Delta \mathbf{r}_i = (Nm_i)^{-1/2} \sum_j \mathbf{C}_{ij} q_j \tag{4-36}$$

where the normal mode displacement vectors $\mathbf{C}_{ij}$ have three components. These vectors are normalized so that for each mode the sum over the unit cell of the crystal gives

$$\sum_i |\mathbf{C}_{ij}|^2 = 1 \tag{4-37}$$

Calculation of M_i for the excitation of a single normal mode k gives rise to the result that the differential cross section for coherent, one-phonon scattering may be expressed as

$$\frac{d\sigma_{\text{coh}}}{d\Omega} = \frac{(2\pi)^3}{V_0} \frac{k_s}{k_0} \left| \sum_i \frac{a_i T_i(\mathbf{S})}{m_i^{1/2}} (\mathbf{S} \cdot \mathbf{C}_{ik}) \exp(i\mathbf{S} \cdot \mathbf{r}_i^0) \right|^2$$

$$\times \frac{n\hbar^2}{2|\Delta E|} \delta(\mathbf{S} - \mathbf{f} - 2\pi\mathbf{H}) \tag{4-38}$$

where n is the quantum number of the upper of the two states involved in the transition. There is, as for the Bragg scattering, a δ function which indicates that the scattering is observed only at specific points in reciprocal space—but not necessarily at reciprocal lattice points $2\pi\mathbf{H}$; the meaning of the vector $\mathbf{f}$ will be discussed in the following subsection.

For the incoherent one-phonon scattering, one obtains a similar expression:

$$\frac{d\sigma_{\text{inc}}}{d\Omega} = \frac{k_s}{k_0} \sum_i \left| a_{i(\text{inc})} \frac{T_i(\mathbf{S})}{m_i^{1/2}} (\mathbf{S} \cdot \mathbf{C}_{ik}) \right|^2 \frac{n\hbar^2}{2|\Delta E|} \tag{4-39}$$

Lattice Dynamics

In a crystal containing N unit cells with n atoms per unit cell, there will be $3Nn$ vibrational degrees of freedom. These may be analyzed in the following way:

Consider the $3n$ normal modes corresponding to the n atoms of a single unit cell. Corresponding to each of these, there are in the crystal N modes for which the normal mode amplitude vector for atom i in the unit cell with origin $\mathbf{R}_m$ is given by

$$\mathbf{C}_{ij}(\mathbf{R}_m) = \mathbf{C}_{ij}^0 e^{i\mathbf{f} \cdot \mathbf{R}_m} \tag{4-40}$$

where the vector $\mathbf{f}$ takes on the N values

$$\mathbf{f} = 2\pi \sum_{i=1}^{3} \left(\frac{n_i}{N_i} \right) \mathbf{a}_i^* \qquad n_i = 0, 1, \ldots, N_i - 1 \tag{4-41}$$

with $\mathbf{a}_i^*$ being the reciprocal lattice vectors of the crystal and N_i the number of unit cells in each direction. $\mathbf{C}_{ij}^0$ is independent of m. For $\mathbf{f} = 0$, the motions in all unit cells of the crystals are in phase; three of the modes (the translations) have zero frequency, and the remaining $3n - 3$ are the vibrational modes which may be studied by conventional infrared and Raman experiments (Section 3-1). For $\mathbf{f} \neq 0$,[6] we may still identify the modes as belonging to the same intracell vibrations, but there is a nonzero phase relationship between the motions in the various cells. The vector $\mathbf{f}$ is the *wave vector* of the normal mode. It is convenient and traditional to express the frequency ω of a normal mode q_j corresponding to a particular intracell motion as a function of $\mathbf{f}$,

$$\omega_j = \omega_j(\mathbf{f}) \tag{4-42}$$

There will be $3n$ such relations, one for each normal mode of the unit cell. Each such relation is known as a *dispersion relation;* the three corresponding to the modes with zero frequency for $\mathbf{f} = 0$ are known as the *acoustic branches*, the others as *optical branches*. A hypothetical set of dispersion curves for a crystal with three atoms in the unit cell is shown in Figure 4-3. In reality, since $\mathbf{f}$ is a vector, we deal with a three dimensional dispersion function of which one section is shown in the figure.

From equation (4-39) it is clear that $\omega(\mathbf{f})$ can in principle be determined for all the lattice modes in the crystal by a properly designed neutron scattering experiment. Such experiments have indeed yielded dispersion curves for a number of metallic crystals. The analysis of the lattice vibrations of molecular crystals, however, is considerably more difficult because of the

---

[6] Selection rules prohibit infrared absorption in this case.

great number of optical vibrational branches in such crystals. All that one can actually do in a neutron scattering experiment is to measure the scattering cross section as a function of the energy transfer and the position in reciprocal space. For any such set of experimental conditions, even given a perfect experiment, the information desired may be difficult to obtain. One must somehow resolve the incoherent scattering from the coherent scattering; one must estimate the amount of multiple transition (multiphonon) scattering that may be present; and one must always bear in mind that the intensities in inelastic scattering processes are inherently low. Furthermore, given a finite resolution in the measuring instrument, there may well be many normal modes contributing to scattering in the same energy and wave-vector interval. Nevertheless, slow neutron spectroscopy can be extremely valuable. It has already proved so in the measurement of the dispersion curves for simple crystals. Experiments are now beginning to show that much valuable information can be obtained for more complicated systems.

The basic formulas above for the coherent and incoherent scattering can obviously be integrated over all energies to obtain a total scattering cross section or over all crystalline orientations to obtain the scattering as a function of angle for a polycrystalline specimen. An average over all thermally excited initial states must also be taken.

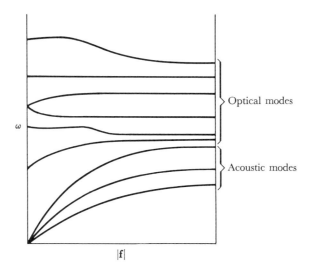

Figure 4-3 *Dispersion curves for a hypothetical crystal with three atoms in the unit cell. The frequency is plotted against the absolute value of the wave vector* **f** *in one direction of the reciprocal lattice. The curves would be different for different directions. If the dispersion curve for one of the optical modes is nearly flat, this means that there is very little intermolecular coupling.*

Application to Hydrogen-Containing Materials

Since the two spin states of hydrogen scatter in opposite directions, we can calculate for the bound scattering lengths

$$a_{coh} = -0.38 \times 10^{-12} \text{ cm}$$
$$a_{inc} = 2.52 \times 10^{-12} \text{ cm}$$
(4-43)

Thus hydrogen has an extremely large incoherent scattering cross section. Because of this large cross section, because of its small mass, and because hydrogen often contributes heavily to any normal mode in which it is involved, equation (4-39) shows that an examination of the energy spectrum of neutrons scattered from a hydrogen-containing system will reveal the vibrational spectrum of the crystal—with the modes involving hydrogen predominating. Neutron scattering is thus an ideal tool for the examination of hydrogen-bonded systems.

Experimental Neutron Scattering Techniques

Experiments for the study of neutron inelastic scattering are difficult. First of all, they require the use of the neutron beam from a nuclear reactor. The scattering cross sections are low. The need to measure extremely small effects means that the resolution cannot be equal to that found in the best optical experiments if adequate intensity is to be maintained. The lack of resolution means that the results are more difficult to interpret. The recent construction of several high-flux beam reactors, providing more intense neutron sources, will solve at least some of these difficulties.

The differences between neutron spectroscopy and optical spectroscopy make the interpretation of neutron spectra more difficult than that of infrared spectra—which is difficult enough. It is also true, however, that the neutron method can in principle provide more detailed information concerning the dynamics of solids and liquids than can optical spectroscopy.

ENERGY GAIN EXPERIMENTS. One technique that has been commonly used for the study of hydrogen-containing systems is the *energy gain* experiment in which the lattice is deexcited by the neutron, which thus gains energy. One prepares in some way a source of very low energy neutrons. These are scattered from a hydrogenous material, and the scattered neutrons which have gained energy are energy analyzed and counted—generally by a time-of-flight apparatus. A typical experimental arrangement is shown in Figure 4-4. A source of neutrons from a nuclear reactor may be further moderated by a cold moderator to increase the intensity of neutrons with very low energies. These neutrons then impinge on a beryllium filter which scatters out of the beam all neutrons with an energy greater than 5.2

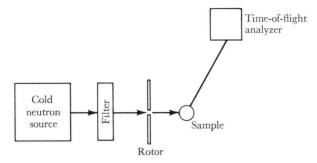

Figure 4-4 *An energy gain experiment. Neutrons from a cold moderator are passed through a beryllium filter, which passes neutrons with an energy less than 40 cm⁻¹. A rotating disk with a slit allows bursts of neutrons to impinge on the sample. The scattered neutrons are energy analyzed by measuring the time required for them to travel from the sample to the counter.*

mV (40 cm^{-1}). One effectively has then a source of neutrons with a mean energy of about 3.5 mV and an energy resolution of about 2 mV. These are allowed to hit the sample in bursts admitted by a "chopper." The neutrons scattered at some convenient angle are then energy analyzed by measuring the length of time required for them to reach a detector over a long flight path. The resulting time-of-flight spectrum is readily converted to an energy scale. Current developments in the use of phased chopper systems in connection with cold sources will soon provide incident neutron beams with an energy of 25 cm^{-1} and a resolution down to 1 cm^{-1}, thus making the resolution almost comparable with that of infrared spectra for low-energy transitions.

ENERGY LOSS EXPERIMENTS. The experiments of the type described above suffer from the fact that they require a population of excited states to be deexcited by the neutrons. This limits the experiments to relatively high temperatures and to small energy level spacings. An *energy loss experiment* in which energy is given up to the lattice should be preferable; the scattering cross section depends on the change in energy and momentum in the same way in both cases. One rather special type of energy loss experiment is in some ways the reverse of the energy gain experiment described above. An incident monochromatic neutron beam is scattered from the sample. The scattered beam is passed through a beryllium filter which allows only neutrons of essentially zero energy to pass (Figure 4-5). If the intensity of the neutrons passed through the filter is measured as a function of the incident energy, an energy loss spectrum will be obtained. This technique has not been widely used for studies of hydrogen-bonded systems, but such use should increase in the future.

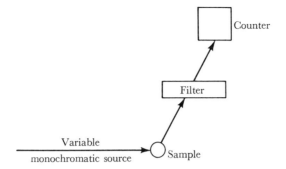

Figure 4-5 *An energy loss experiment.   Only neutrons which have lost most of their energy are detected.*

A MORE GENERAL INSTRUMENT.   The most versatile instrument is the three-axis spectrometer (Figure 4-6).   It can be used for both energy loss and energy gain studies.   A monochromatized neutron beam is allowed to fall on the crystal; the neutrons scattered from the crystal are reflected off a second monochromator in order to analyze their energy.   Proper choice of the angular settings of the various components of the instrument can lead to measurements for specific energy and momentum transfers.   Such instruments are more powerful than is necessary for the study of hydrogenous materials, since the incoherently scattered neutrons have a more or less isotropic distribution.   It is expected that such instruments may play an important part in the near future in the study of molecular dynamics; the study of single crystals of deuterated hydrogen-bonded substances is an attractive possibility.

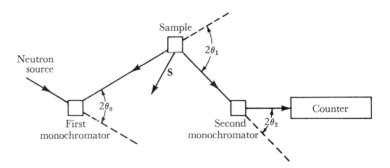

Figure 4-6 *A "three-axis spectrometer."   The energy of the incident beam is defined by diffraction from a monochromator crystal through an angle $2\theta_0$.   The neutron beam diffracted at the sample through an angle $2\theta_1$ is energy-analyzed by diffraction from a second monochromating crystal through an angle $2\theta_2$.*

Results of Neutron Scattering Experiments

We shall now consider some typical results, although we shall not attempt to give a complete review of all applications of inelastic scattering to hydrogen-bonded systems. These results are all from energy loss experiments.

The main differences in principle in the spectra observed by neutron scattering and in those observed by infrared spectroscopy are the following. First, with neutrons, transitions are observed for all values of the wave vector $\mathbf{f}$; in optical spectra, transitions are forbidden for $\mathbf{f} \neq 0$. Thus when neutron scattering cross section is plotted against frequency, we see broad peaks which are projections of the dispersion curves onto the $\mathbf{f} = 0$ axis. If, however, momentum discrimination for coherent scatterers is used, as in the three-axis spectrometer, more information can be obtained than in the infrared. Second, there is some truth in the statement, "There are no selection rules in neutron spectroscopy." This is not entirely true, since scattering can only be observed when the quantity $(\mathbf{C}_{ij} \cdot \mathbf{S})$ is nonzero. This is, however, a far less restrictive condition than the selection rules involving dipole moments and polarizabilities in infrared and Raman spectroscopy. If an atom is in motion, the energy levels of this motion can in principle be studied in some directions in reciprocal space. Any normal mode to which hydrogen contributes should give rise to a substantial amount of incoherent inelastic scattering. Although most of the work to date on hydrogen-containing materials has been confined to polycrystalline samples, the dependence of the scattering on $(\mathbf{S} \cdot \mathbf{C}_{ij})$ could give information on the directions of motion of the hydrogen atoms if the scattering were examined as a function of the orientation of a single crystal; such an application would be analogous to the study of single-crystal polarized infrared spectra.

AMMONIUM SULFATE. As an example of incoherent neutron spectroscopy, we might consider the work of Rush and Taylor (1965) on ammonium sulfate, $(NH_4)_2SO_4$. This compound undergoes a ferroelectric transition at $224°K$, changing from a structure in the centrosymmetric space group *Pnam* to a polar structure in space group *Pna2₁*. The spectrum of inelastically scattered neutrons for each phase is shown in Figure 4-7. There are two independent ammonium ions in the structure; these differ in their environments and in their hydrogen-bonding schemes. Rush and Taylor tentatively assigned the two peaks at 335 and 200 cm^{-1} in the spectrum of the low temperature phase to modes which can be identified with the torsional oscillations of the two ammonium ions, although it is possible that the latter might be identified with a translational mode.[7] The peak at 85 cm^{-1} may be assigned

[7] Neutron diffraction studies (Schlemper and Hamilton, 1966) indicate that the two frequencies observed may be due to different rotational modes of a single ammonium group, the two groups being rather similar in this respect. (See Section 7-3 for a fuller discussion of the neutron diffraction work.)

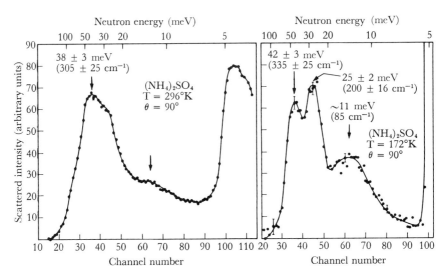

Figure 4-7 *Energy gain curves for ammonium sulfate in the paraelectric and ferroelectric phases. Aside from the increased resolution and the effect of the Boltzmann factor in determining the level population, the two curves are very similar, indicating that the rotational freedom of the ammonium ions must be the same in both phases. (From Rush and Taylor, 1965.)*

to acoustic modes. The important point is that the spectrum at room temperature is similar to that of the low temperature phase. There is less resolution of the observed peaks, and the relative intensities have changed because of the changes in the Boltzmann factors.[8] Aside from these changes, the peak positions are reasonably close above and below the ferroelectric transition. The peak centered at 305 cm^{-1} in the high temperature form is clearly an unresolved doublet which corresponds to the two peaks observed at low temperature; there is no abrupt change in the spectrum at the transition temperature. Thus the motions of the ammonium groups are probably not very different in the two phases, and the differences in the structures must be due to shifts in the positions of the atoms—not to profound differences in the rotational freedom of the ammonium groups as has been suggested (Burns, 1962).

AMMONIUM PERCHLORATE. Two other examples might be cited here to show the value of neutron inelastic scattering in detecting a difference between the rotational motions of groups in solids. The spectrum for ammonium perchlorate (Janik *et al.*, 1964) is shown in Figure 4-8. A very broad band,

[8] Since this type of experiment corresponds to deexcitation of the crystal, the peak intensities are proportional to the populations of the various states; hence the low energy peaks will increase in intensity relative to the high energy peaks as the temperature is lowered.

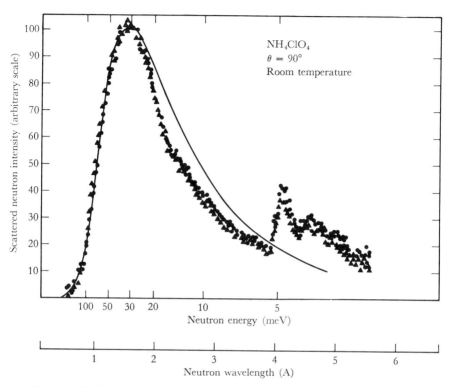

Figure 4-8 *The energy gain spectrum of ammonium perchlorate. The broad maximum is characteristic of a free rotor with many closely spaced energy levels. The solid line is the theoretical curve for a free rotor with effective mass 2.1. (From Janik et al., 1964.)*

which has much the shape of a Maxwell distribution curve, is seen. Total neutron cross-sectional measurements (discussed below) and neutron diffraction studies (Smith and Levy, 1962) have shown that the ammonium group in ammonium perchlorate is probably almost freely rotating. The neutron spectrum may be interpreted as being due to transitions occurring between many closely spaced levels of an almost free rotor.

PHOSPHONIUM IODIDE. In great contrast to the spectrum of ammonium perchlorate is that of phosphonium iodide, PH_4I (Rush, 1966), shown in Figure 4-9. The single very sharp band centered at 335 ± 11 cm^{-1} is interpreted as being the 1-0 transition of a hindered rotor. The peak at 614 ± 40 cm^{-1} may be the 2-0 transition, while the peak at 110 ± 6 cm^{-1} is assigned to a translation of the phosphonium ion. Phosphonium iodide has a distorted CsCl structure, in which each phosphonium ion is surrounded by eight iodide ions. If the structure were undistorted, the potential barrier

hindering the rotation around an axis parallel to the cube edge would have
fourfold symmetry.   In an interpretation of the NMR data on ammonium
bromide, which has the same structure (*vide infra*), Gutowsky, Pake, and
Bersohn (1954) assumed that a fourfold cosine potential

$$V = \frac{V_0}{2}(1 - \cos 4\theta) \qquad (4\text{-}44)$$

is hindering the rotation.   In this case, the barrier height V_0 is given approximately in terms of the frequency of transition ν_t and the moment of inertia
I around the rotation axis by the formula

$$V_0 = \frac{1}{16}\left[\frac{[h\nu_t + (5\hbar^2/2I)]^2}{\hbar^2/2I}\right] \qquad (4\text{-}45)$$

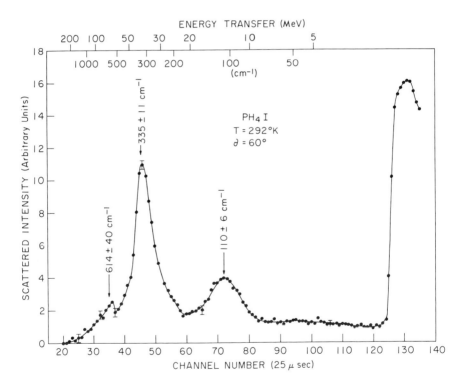

Figure 4-9 *The energy gain spectrum of phosphonium iodide.   The sharp peak is characteristic
of the librational mode of a very tightly bound ion.   The peak at 614 cm⁻¹ is perhaps associated with a
two-quantum transition and that at 110 cm⁻¹ with a translational degree of freedom.   (From Rush,
1966.)*

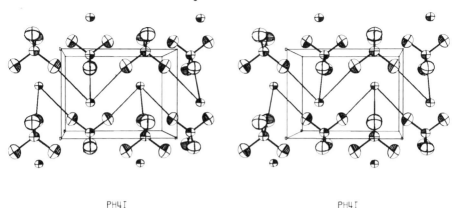

Figure 4-10 *The structure of phosphonium iodide viewed along the a axis.   The outlines of one unit cell are drawn in.   Each iodine atom is surrounded by eight hydrogen atoms at the corners of a tetragonal prism.   Four of these hydrogen atoms are close enough to be considered as forming hydrogen bonds.   (Only three bonds are shown in the figure.)   The other four are at normal van der Waals distances.   The structure consists of hydrogen-bonded sheets which form only van der Waals contacts with neighboring sheets.*

In the absence of a complete diffraction study, Rush assumed that this was a valid model for PH_4I and calculated a barrier of 7.1 kcal mole^{-1}. It is interesting to note that the estimated barrier height in ammonium iodide in its analogous phase is only 2.9 kcal mole^{-1}. Since one would expect hydrogen bonding to be stronger in ammonium iodide than in phosphonium iodide, it would seem at first sight that the height of the barrier is probably not due to strong hydrogen bonding but may best be explained on the basis of ionic sizes and electrostatics. A detailed interpretation in this case, as well as in most other spectroscopic studies of the solid state, can only be given once the hydrogen positions are known from a diffraction study. Such a study has been carried out by Sequeira and Hamilton (1967). The structure of PH_4I is illustrated in Figure 4-10. Each hydrogen atom has an iodide neighbor at 2.85 A, a distance some 0.50 A shorter than the sum of the van der Waals radii. The P—H $\cdots$ I configuration is nearly linear; thus from a geometrical point of view a hydrogen bond exists. Each iodide ion is apparently involved in four hydrogen bonds and also has four hydrogen neighbors at the van der Waals contact distance of 3.35 A. The structure consists of hydrogen-bonded pleated sheets which are held together only by van der Waals forces.

An examination of the details of the intermolecular packing makes plausible the high barrier to rotation. Calculations of the electrostatic and Lennard-Jones energies of the crystal as a function of the rotation of the

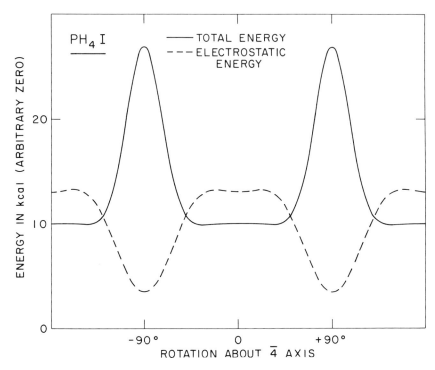

Figure 4-11 *Crystal energy curves for phosphonium iodide as a function of angle of rotation φ of phosphonium ion around 4̄ axis. The dotted curve is the electrostatic contribution. The full curve is the total energy which includes the electrostatic terms and a term using a Lennard-Jones 12-6 potential.*

PH_4^+ ion about the 4̄ axis show that the potential function, which must have twofold symmetry, consists of broad minima at the experimental configuration, separated by narrow and high barriers (Figure 4-11). The derivation of barriers from single spectroscopic measurements is thus seen to be a rather uncertain procedure, even in this simple case. We must always bear in mind that the notion of a rotational barrier implies the assumption of a particular model for the shape of the potential, and the height of the maximum peak in the potential—the barrier—as derived from any physical measurement is strongly dependent on the shape assumed. As will again be illustrated in Chapter 6 in a discussion of ammonium fluorosilicate, the assumption of a cosine barrier in highly symmetric crystals is rarely a good approximation.

AMMONIUM CHLORIDE. Cold neutron measurements have also been performed on many ammonium salts in which the ammonium ions possess rotational freedom intermediate between that in ammonium perchlorate and phosphonium iodide.

One such case is ammonium chloride, which has been studied by the energy gain technique with fairly good resolution (Venkataraman *et al.* 1964). The spectra at three different temperatures are shown in Figure 4-12.   The split peak at the higher temperatures is thought to be associated with the 0-1 and 1-2 transitions of the hindered rotor.   If the motion were harmonic, these transitions would have the same frequency.   The splitting can be used to obtain a measure of the anharmonicity.   The first excited level is not well populated at the lowest temperature of measurement; hence the 1-2 transition is not seen.   A phase change (see Section 6-7) occurs at 242°K. There seems to be no appreciable effect on the spectrum.

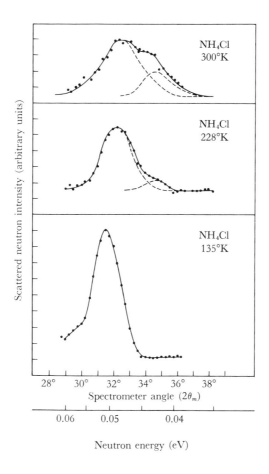

Figure 4-12 *Energy gain spectra of ammonium chloride.   The peaks are associated with the torsional oscillations of the ammonium ion.   (From Venkataraman et al., 1964.)*

Table 4-2 *Frequencies (in cm⁻¹) in Inelastic Scattering Spectra of Some H,F Compounds*

Frequency	Solid HF	NaH$_2$F$_3$	KHF$_2$
A	535	896	1176
B	260	364, 390	600
C	—	117	104
D	53	65	—
$R(\text{F} \cdot \cdot \cdot \text{F})$ (A)	2.49	2.33	2.26

HYDROGEN FLUORIDE SYSTEM   In another application, Boutin, Safford, and Brajovic (1963) have used the technique to investigate the relationship between the dynamic structures of the F—H—F⁻ ion, the (F—H—F—H—F)⁻ ion, and solid and liquid HF.   As we have seen in Section 3-7, the F—H—F ion is symmetric and linear.   The H$_2$F$_3$⁻ ion has a zigzag structure with an F—F distance that probably is too long for a centered hydrogen bond.[9]   The HF structure in the solid is composed of zigzag strings of HF with an F—F distance of 2.49 A.   Liquid HF is also extensively hydrogen bonded.   One might expect that the H$_2$F$_3$⁻ ion would exhibit some characteristics intermediate between FHF⁻ and HF.   The energy gain experiments show well-resolved spectra with peaks approximately as indicated in Table 4-2.   The frequencies A have been assigned to the F—H—F bend.   The assignment for KHF$_2$ agrees well with the observed infrared absorption at 1225 cm⁻¹.   The bending frequency is greatly reduced as the strength of the hydrogen bond goes down.   Frequency B has been assigned to a stretching mode involving F; this is the symmetric stretch in FHF⁻.   Frequencies C and D may be assigned to librational motions, the first of the whole ion, the second to the libration of a single FH bond about an axis.   Since the lower frequency does not appear in FHF⁻, it is tempting to suggest that these frequencies may be associated with transitions between two levels in a double-minimum potential in the other compounds.   This ambiguity in assignment is characteristic of any kind of spectroscopy and remains to be resolved in this particular case.

[9] A NMR experiment has shown that the bonds are not symmetric.   The best agreement with the line width and line shape data was obtained with a model which places the hydrogen atoms on the F $\cdot \cdot \cdot$ F lines, displaced from the bond centers by 0.10 A toward the outer two fluorine atoms.   The structure might be represented as F—H $\cdot \cdot \cdot$ F $\cdot \cdot \cdot$ H—F (Blinc, Trontelj, and Volavšek, 1966).

Total Cross Section Measurements

Another application of neutron scattering which has been of some use in understanding the motions in hydrogen-bonded systems is that which makes use of total cross section measurements. In this technique the diminution in intensity of a neutron beam passing directly through a hydrogenous material is measured. The ratio of the transmitted intensity to the incident intensity is given by

$$\frac{I}{I_0} = \exp(-\mu t) \tag{4-46}$$

(Section 2-7) where μ is the linear absorption coefficient and t is the thickness of the sample. The linear absorption coefficient μ is related to the total cross section σ_a per atom of type a by

$$\mu = \sum_a \sigma_a N_a \tag{4-47}$$

where N_a is the number of atoms per cubic centimeter. At very low neutron energies ($E \ll 200$ cm^{-1}), when the neutron is capable only of gaining energy from the crystal lattice, the incoherent scattering cross section becomes a linear function of the incident neutron wavelength, as seen from the expression for the scattering cross section which includes the term $1/k_0 = \lambda_0/2\pi$. If the neutron cross section is plotted against the wavelength of the incident neutron beam, a straight line will result. The slope of this line will be characteristic of the energy level structure of the material in the sample. If the energy E_0 of the incident neutron is much less than the energy $\hbar\omega$ of the excited vibrational mode and if harmonic motion is assumed, the energy gain incoherent cross section is given very approximately by

$$\sigma = \left(\frac{\hbar\omega}{E_0}\right)^{1/2}\left[\frac{f(\omega, T)}{A}\right] \tag{4-48}$$

where A is the reduced mass for the vibration and

$$f(\omega, T) = \frac{e^{-\hbar\omega/2kT}}{2\sinh(\hbar\omega/2kT)} \tag{4-49}$$

Thus

$$\sigma = k\lambda \tag{4-50}$$

where k depends only on the mass, the frequency, and the temperature. The dependence of slope on frequency using the approximate equation is

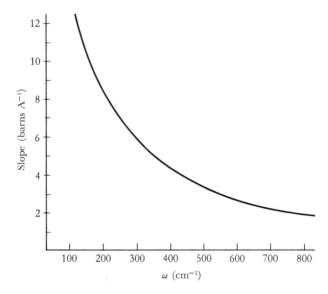

Figure 4-13 *Total cross section slope as a function of librational frequency for an ammonium ion.*

shown in Figure 4-13.   The more closely spaced the energy levels, the higher the slope.

Rush, Taylor, and Havens (1960) have studied a number of hydrogenous substances by this technique.   As an example, some cross section versus wavelength curves are shown for various ammonium salts in Figure 4-14. The curve for NH_4I has a very large slope—approaching that for gaseous ammonia.   In this crystal, the rotation of the ammonium group must be only very slightly hindered; there is little hydrogen bonding.   On the other hand, a low-slope curve is indicative of highly constrained hydrogen motion and perhaps of strong hydrogen bonds.   Such is the case for NH_4F.   Rush, Taylor, and Havens (1962) have shown (Figure 4-15) that a good correlation exists between the slopes of the total cross section curves and the barriers hindering rotation as derived from NMR second moments and from infrared spectra.   Leung, Rush, and Taylor (1966) have measured the differential scattering cross sections as well as the total cross sections for a number of ammonium salts.   Using the frequencies of hindered rotation so obtained, they have calculated the expected slopes by a more accurate and complex version of equation (4-49).   The agreement between observed and calculated slopes is remarkable (Table 4-3) and leads to the conclusion that for compounds with groups of a similar nature a simple quick measurement of the cross section slope can lead to a frequency for the internal rotational modes. The derivation of a barrier height from the observed frequency depends

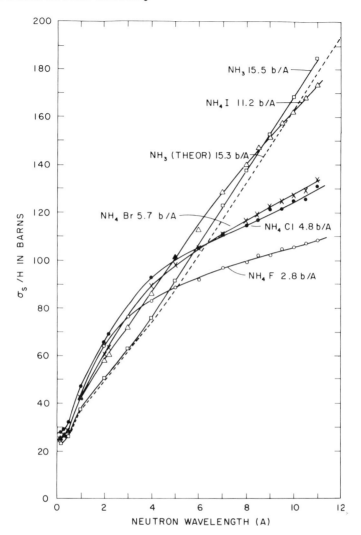

Figure 4-14 *Total cross section per hydrogen atom in the ammonium halides as a function of wavelength. The slope of the linear portion is related to the librational frequency. A high slope corresponds to nearly free rotation.* (*From Rush, Taylor, and Havens, 1960.*)

sensitively on the shape of the barrier, and barrier heights obtained in this way should not be taken seriously.

Single-Crystal Studies

In dealing with a crystal containing hydrogen, it would appear that there is little point in using a single crystal for most neutron scattering experiments.

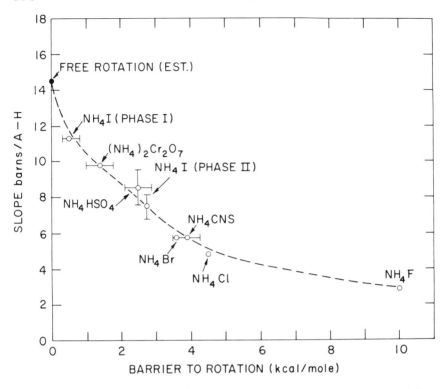

Figure 4-15 *Total cross section slopes as functions of barriers to rotation as estimated from spectroscopic and resonance experiments. The latter estimates generally assume a potential of the form* $V = \frac{1}{2}\nu_0(1 - \cos n\phi)$. *This assumption may not always be valid.*

Table 4-3 *Experimental and Theoretical Cross-Sectional Slopes[a]*

Compound	Experimental slope[b]	Theoretical slope[c,d]	Frequency (cm^{-1})
NH$_4$F	2.8 ± 0.3	2.8	555
NH$_4$Cl	4.8 ± 0.3	5.0	350
NH$_4$Br	5.7 ± 0.3	5.6	315
NH$_4$CNS	5.8 ± 0.3	5.2	330 ± 20
(NH$_4$)$_2$CrO$_4$	5.5 ± 0.3	4.9	340 ± 20
(NH$_4$)$_2$S$_2$O$_8$	10.0 ± 0.4	9.6	160 ± 10

[a] After Leung, Rush, and Taylor (1966). The theoretical slopes are calculated from the observed frequencies in the last column.

[b] Barns per angstrom per hydrogen atom. All values at room temperature (23°C).

[c] Calculated using a rotational mass of 4.0 atomic mass units (amu) and a translational mass of 18 amu.

[d] Uncertainties in these calculated slopes due to the possible errors in torsional and translational frequencies are not shown. The addition of the contribution of acoustic modes to the cross section slope would increase the results slightly.

Since the scattering is incoherent and is governed by equation (4-39), there are no interference effects due to the spatial relationships of one atom *vis-a-vis* another, that is, the crystal structure. On the other hand, if the crystal has a fairly simple structure, the fact that the intensity depends on the relationship between the reciprocal lattice vector and the coefficient vector C_i of the normal mode indicates that single-crystal studies could aid in the assignment of the observed bands to various normal modes and help determine directional relationships of hydrogen bonds.

For coherent scattering, the structure enters in a very specific way, and it seems clear that single-crystal studies and examination of the dispersion curves for the optical modes may be extremely important in looking at the detailed nature of interatomic forces. For application to hydrogen-bonded systems, such techniques would involve the use of deuterated crystals in order to increase greatly the ratio of the coherent to the incoherent scattering.

Although the greatest attention has been given by physicists to the determination of dispersion curves in simple solids by the method of neutron inelastic scattering, it is in the study of the complex motions in molecular crystals that the greatest impact will be felt in chemistry.

REFERENCES

Abragam, A. (1961), *The Principles of Nuclear Magnetism.* Clarendon Press, Oxford. In particular, see Chapter 10.

Andrew, E. R., and Eades, R. G. (1953a), Separation of the Intramolecular and Intermolecular Contributions to the Second Moment of the Nuclear Magnetic Resonance Spectrum, *Proc. Phys. Soc.* **A66**, 415.

Andrew, E. R., and Eades, R. G. (1953b), A Nuclear Magnetic Resonance Investigation of Three Solid Benzenes, *Proc. Roy. Soc. London* **A218**, 537.

Andrew, E. R., and Newing, R. A. (1958), The Narrowing of Nuclear Magnetic Resonance Spectra by Molecular Rotation in Solids, *Proc. Phys. Soc.* **72**, 959.

Blinc, R., Trontelj, Z., and Volavšek, B. (1966), NMR Spectrum of a Nearly Linear 5-Spin System: Hydrogen Bonding in KH_2F_3, *J. Chem. Phys.* **44**, 1028.

Bloembergen, N., Purcell, E. M., and Pound, R. V. (1948), Relaxation Effects in Nuclear Magnetic Resonance Absorption, *Phys. Rev.* **73**, 679.

Boutin, H., Safford, G. J., and Brajovic, V. (1963), Study of Low-Frequency Molecular Motions in HF, KHF_2, KH_2F_3 and NaH_2F_3, *J. Chem. Phys.* **39**, 3135.

Burns, G. (1962), Nuclear Magnetic Resonance in $(NH_4)_2(BeF_4)_x(SO_4)_{1-x}$ and Other Ferroelectric Systems, *Phys. Rev.* **123**, 64.

Cooke, A. H., and Drain, L. E. (1952), Proton Magnetic Resonance and Molecular Motion in Solids, *Proc. Phys. Soc.* **A65**, 894.

Egelstaff, P. A. (ed.) (1965), *Thermal Neutron Scattering.* Academic Press, New York.

Gutowsky, H. S., and Pake, G. E. (1950), Structural Investigations by Means of Nuclear Magnetism. II. Hindered Rotation in Solids, *J. Chem. Phys.* **18**, 162.

Gutowsky, H. S., Pake, G. E., and Bersohn, R. (1954), Structural Investigations by Means of Nuclear Magnetism. III. Ammonium Halides, *J. Chem. Phys.* **22**, 643.

Janik, J. A., Janik, J. M., Mellor, J., and Palevsky, H. (1964), Study of Molecular Rotations in Solids and Liquids by the Inelastic Scattering of Cold Neutrons, *J. Phys. Chem. Solids* **25**, 1091.

Kubo, R., and Tomita, K. (1954), A General Theory of Magnetic Resonance Absorption, *J. Phys. Soc. Japan* **9**, 888.

Leung, P. S., Rush, J. J., and Taylor, T. I. (1966), unpublished work.

Muetterties, E. L. (1965), Stereochemically Nonrigid Structures, *Inorg. Chem.* **4**, 769.

Richards, R. E., and Schaefer, T. (1961), Motional Narrowing and Line Shapes in Some Ammonium Salts, *Trans. Faraday Soc.* **57**, 210.

Rush, J. J. (1966), Low-Frequency Motions and Barrier to Rotation in Phosphonium Iodide, *J. Chem. Phys.* **44**, 1722.

Rush, J. J., and Taylor, T. I. (1965), Study of Low-Frequency Motions in Several Ferroelectric Salts by the Inelastic Scattering of Cold Neutrons, in *Inelastic Scattering of Neutrons*, Vol. II, p. 333. International Atomic Energy Agency, Vienna. (Proc. Symp. 3rd, Bombay, India, 1964.)

Rush, J. J., Taylor, T. I., and Havens, W. W., Jr. (1960), Proton Motions in Ammonium Halides by Slow Neutron Cross-Section Measurements, *Phys. Rev. Letters* **5**, 507.

Rush, J. J., Taylor, T. I., and Havens, W. W., Jr. (1962), Rotational Freedom of Ammonium Ions and Methyl Groups by Cross-Section Measurements with Slow Neutrons, *J. Chem. Phys.* **37**, 234.

Schlemper, E. O., and Hamilton, W. C. (1966), A Neutron Diffraction Study of the Structures of Ferroelectric and Paraelectric Ammonium Sulfate, *J. Chem. Phys.* **44**, 4498.

Sequeira, A., and Hamilton, W. C. (1967), Hydrogen Bonding in Phosphonium Iodide, A Neutron Diffraction Study, *J. Chem. Phys.* **47**, 1818.

Smith, H. G., and Levy, H. A. (1962), Neutron Diffraction Study of Ammonium Perchlorate, *Acta Cryst.* **15**, 1201.

Venkataraman, G., Deniz, K. U., Iyengar, P. K., Vijayaraghavan, P. R., and Roy, A. P. (1964), Anharmonicity of the Torsional Oscillations of the Ammonium Ion in NH_4Cl, *Solid State Communications* **2**, 17.

Wert, C., and Marx, J. (1953), A New Method for Determining the Heat of Activation for Relaxation Processes, *Acta Met.* **1**, 113.

Hydrogen-Bonded Organic and Biological Molecules

chapter five

Although it is perhaps in crystals of simple inorganic compounds that we are best able to study in detail the nature of the hydrogen bond and the potential function governing the motion of the hydrogen atom, some of the more interesting hydrogen bonds occur in organic crystals. Furthermore, the hydrogen bonds in biological systems may be of extreme importance, inasmuch as they determine in large part the gross structure and shape of protein molecules and also affect the structures of the genetically important deoxyribonucleic acid (DNA) and ribonucleic acid (RNA). It was in fact the known approximate geometries of N—H · · · O hydrogen bonds that led to the first successful predictions of structure for proteins (Pauling, Corey, and Branson, 1951) and for DNA (Crick and Watson, 1954).

We shall discuss a few examples of hydrogen bonding in organic and biochemical systems in this chapter.

5-1 STRUCTURES OF THE AMINO ACIDS AND PROTEINS

The crystal structures of almost all the naturally occurring amino acids have been studied by x-ray diffraction. These molecules usually exist in the crystal in the zwitterion form:

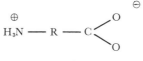

The rather acidic hydrogens on the amino group are hydrogen bonded to oxygen atoms of other molecules. Although most of the x-ray studies have not been of sufficient accuracy to place the hydrogen atoms unambiguously, the usual equivalence of the two C—O bond distances at an average value of about 1.28 A is strong evidence that neither oxygen is covalently bonded to hydrogen. In some more recent x-ray studies, the hydrogen atoms have been located in difference electron density maps, and there is no doubt that the zwitterion conformation is correct. In crystalline amino acids, the molecules are linked together, usually in infinite networks, by strong N—H · · · O hydrogen bonds.

L-*Alanine*

The crystal structure of L-alanine has been determined by Simpson and Marsh (1966) using x-ray diffraction techniques. This was one of the few really accurate determinations of a free amino acid structure. The hydrogen atoms were located, and the ion clearly has the zwitterion structure

The two C—O bond lengths are equal (1.247 and 1.256 A) to within the accuracy of the investigation. One of the oxygen atoms is the acceptor in one N—H · · · O hydrogen bond; the other is the acceptor in two hydrogen bonds. There is no evidence that this difference in environments has any effect on the C—O bond lengths, and the two bonds may be considered to be chemically equivalent. An earlier study of the racemic crystal DL-alanine, which surprisingly has an almost identical structure as far as

Table 5-1 *Hydrogen Bond Parameters in L-Alanine from the x-Ray Diffraction Study*[a]

N—H (A)	N—H · · · O (A)	H · · · O (A)	∠N—H · · · O (deg)
0.95	2.88	1.92	166
0.88	2.84	2.00	157
0.90	2.78	1.91	173

[a] The estimated standard errors in the bond lengths are 0.04 A for bonds involving hydrogen and 0.004 for distances involving only nitrogen and oxygen.

molecular packing goes, indicated a possible difference between the two C—O bond lengths which was attributed to differences in the hydrogen-bonding environments.   In Table 5-1 we present some of the interesting parameters concerning the N—H · · · O hydrogen bonds.   The N—H bond lengths are clearly shorter than standard internuclear values, as is usual with x-ray diffraction determinations of hydrogen atom position.   (See Section 2-7.)

A Comparison of L-Alanine with Potassium Bicarbonate

Although the results on L-alanine would seem to indicate that the hydrogen bonding has little effect on the covalent bond length of the acceptor oxygen atom, it is not at all clear that this is a general result.   The carbonate ion CO_3^{--} has a planar structure (Figure 5-1a) with three equal bond lengths.   One would expect that the bicarbonate ion HCO_3^- would have

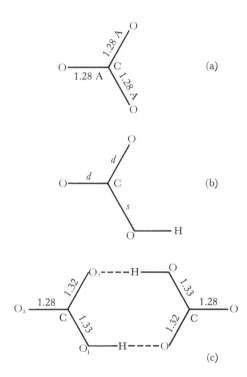

Figure 5-1 (a) *The carbonate ion has three equal bond lengths.   A value of 1.28 A is found in calcite, CaCO₃.   (b) One would expect that the bicarbonate ion would have two equal bonds of length d and one longer bond of length s.   (c) An x-ray study of the bicarbonate ion dimer suggests that the hydrogen bonding affects one of the shorter C—O bond lengths in a dramatic way.   An accurate neutron diffraction study of this species would be desirable.   Disorder seems likely.*

Table 5-2 *Force Constants in Millidynes per Angstrom in Potassium Bicarbonate*[a]

$K(\text{O—H})$	3.20
$K(\text{C—O}_1)$	4.00
$K(\text{C—O}_2)$	5.50
$K(\text{C—O}_3)$	7.50
$K(\text{H} \cdots \text{O}_2)$	0.76
$H(\text{O}_1\text{—C—O}_2)$	0.66
$H(\text{O}_1\text{—C—O}_3)$	0.30
$H(\text{O}_2\text{—C—O}_3)$	0.40
$H(\text{C—O}_1\text{—H})$	0.092
$H(\text{C—O}_2 \cdots \text{H})$	0.042
$H(\text{O}_1\text{—H} \cdots \text{O}_2')$	0.22

[a] The oxygen atoms are numbered as in Figure 5-1c. O_1 is covalently bound to hydrogen. O_2 is hydrogen bonded to hydrogen. O_3 is the nominally double-bonded oxygen with no hydrogen interactions. K is a stretching force constant, and H is a bending force constant.

one long C—O bond distance and two equivalent and shorter ones (Figure 5-1b). In actual fact an x-ray structural study of potassium bicarbonate indicates that the anions form hydrogen-bonded dimers with the bond lengths indicated in Figure 5-1c (Nitta, Tomiie, and Koo, 1952). Although this study of the structure is not of high accuracy, there is some indication that the hydrogen bonding has caused enough redistribution of charge in the anion to result in a longer bond length for the hydrogen-bonded oxygen atom than for the one which is a more conventional double bond.[1] Naka-moto, Sarma, and Ogoshi (1965) have made assignments of all the infrared vibrational frequencies in this compound. Using a modified Urey-Bradley force field in their normal coordinate treatment (see Section 3-1), they obtained the force constants of Table 5-2. There are obvious differences among the three carbon-oxygen stretching force constants. It is also interesting to note that the bending force constant C—O $\cdots$ H is comparable in magnitude to that for the C—O—H bend. The hydrogen bonding clearly has an effect on the structure of the bicarbonate ion. This structure is an example of a rather strong hydrogen bond; the O—H $\cdots$ O distance is 2.61 A.

ε-*Aminocaproic Acid*

The crystal structure of this nonbiological amino acid exhibits a rather pretty network of hydrogen bonds (Figure 5-2). Each of the hydrogens of the —NH$_3^+$ function is hydrogen bonded to a carboxyl oxygen at the end of

[1] It is probable that there is some disorder in the hydrogen position which may lead to apparent equality between C—O$_1$ and C—O$_2$.

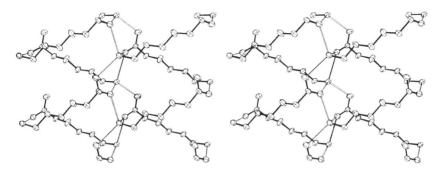

EPSILON-AMINOCAPROIC ACID   EPSILON-AMINOCAPROIC ACID

Figure 5-2 ε-*Aminocaproic acid* (*From Bednowitz, 1967*).

another molecule.   One of the carboxyl oxygens is thus the acceptor in two
hydrogen bonds.   A chain of hydrogen-bonded rings extending in a vertical
direction may be seen in the figure.   Each of these rings contains six covalent
and four hydrogen bonds.

Taurine

Very interesting hydrogen bonding occurs in the noncarboxylic amino
acid taurine, $^{\ominus}O_3S$—CH_2—CH_2—$NH_3^{\oplus}$, which, as the notation implies,
has the zwitterion structure (Okaya, 1966).   The structure is held together
by N—H · · · O hydrogen bonds.   Two of these are normal.   The third
is equidistant from an oxygen atom in another molecule and one of the

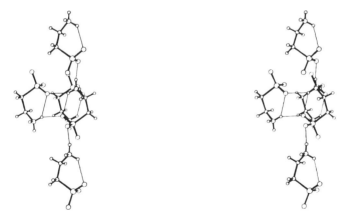

Figure 5-3 *The structure of the amino acid taurine.   One hydrogen atom is involved in both
an intramolecular hydrogen bond and an intermolecular hydrogen bond.*

oxygen atoms of the sulfonate group of the same molecule. This is a good example not only of an *intramolecular* hydrogen bond, but also of a *bifurcated* bond.[2] The configuration of the molecule and the hydrogen bonds is illustrated in Figure 5-3.

Cystine and Hydrogen Bonds Involving Sulfur

Another amino acid for which a high quality x-ray diffraction study is available is cystine (Figure 5-4a) (Peterson, Steinrauf, and Jensen, 1960). The structures of the hydrobromide and hydrochloride salts have been determined. These results are pertinent to the question of whether sulfur is an important participant in hydrogen bonding. In this case it appears not to be. Although the determination of the hydrogen atom positions from these x-ray data is probably not beyond question because of the presence of the heavy anions, the authors of the paper assigned hydrogen bonds only of the types O—H · · · Cl, O—H · · · Br, N—H · · · O, N—H · · · Cl, and N—H · · · Br. The closest nonbonded neighbor of sulfur is the oxygen atom of a carboxyl group at 3.30 A, which is about the expected van der Waals contact distance. From the bond lengths it can be inferred that the oxygen is double-bonded to C, so that the possibility of hydrogen bonding to sulfur is remote.

It is interesting that the O—H · · · Br⁻ hydrogen bond is 0.175 A

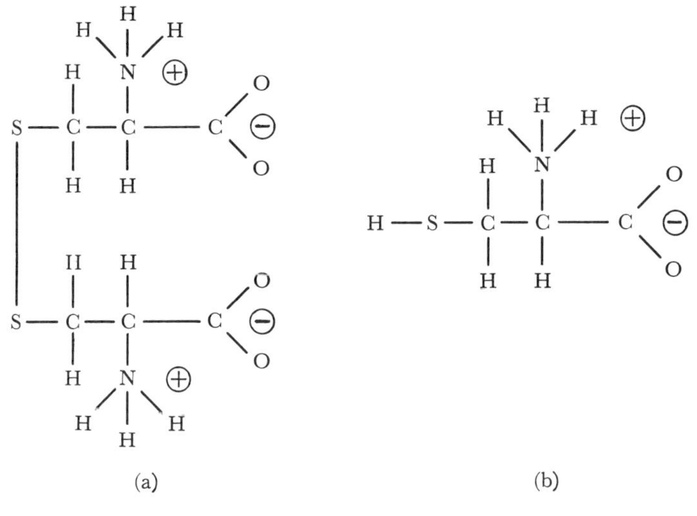

Figure 5-4 *The amino acids cystine (a) and cysteine (b).*

---

[2] A bifurcated hydrogen bond is a hydrogen bond in which the hydrogen atom is more or less equidistant from two acceptor atoms.

longer than the O—H $\cdots$ Cl⁻ hydrogen bond in this pair of crystals. This is about the difference in the ionic radii of Br⁻ and Cl⁻.

These results on cystine suggest that S may not be a satisfactory hydrogen bond acceptor atom in biological systems, for they indicate that the sulfur in the bisulfide link does not compete favorably with other hydrogen bond acceptors. The crystal structure of cysteine, the reduced form of cystine (Figure 5-4b), has not been determined. With the other possibilities for hydrogen bonding present, it would seem unlikely that there are S—H $\cdots$ S hydrogen bonds in this system.[3]

Sulfur as an Acceptor in N—H $\cdots$ S Hydrogen Bonds

The existence of many possible N—H $\cdots$ S hydrogen bonds has been pointed out by Hossain and Carlisle (1966). Their results are tabulated in Table 5-3. A typical example is xanthane hydride (Stanford, 1963) (Figure 5-5). The N—S distance of 3.35 A is equal to the sum of the van der Waals radii for S and N. The hydrogen atoms were located approximately and the geometry of the molecule makes it apparent that there is indeed an N—H $\cdots$ S hydrogen bond, almost linear, with an H $\cdots$ S distance of approximately 2.4 A, as compared with the van der Waals distance of 3.05 A. This and other examples suggest that it would not be wise to discount the possible importance of N—H $\cdots$ S hydrogen bonds in biological systems.

Neutron Diffraction Studies of Amino Acids

It is somewhat surprising that very little neutron diffraction work has been done on amino acid structures. Some preliminary results on glycine have been reported (Burns and Levy, 1958). A more complete descrip-

---

[3] That S—H $\cdots$ S hydrogen bonds do exist is suggested by the crystallography of H_2S (Harada and Kitamura, 1964). First of all, the existence of several solid phases in the H_2S system—a cubic phase at high temperature and two low temperature tetragonal phases—is suggestive of subtle but specific intermolecular attractions. As we shall illustrate in Chapter 6, the possibility of hydrogen bonding in simple inorganic compounds is often accompanied by the existence of several crystalline polymorphs—ranging from a highly disordered structure at the highest temperatures to a completely ordered structure at low temperatures. The structure of H_2S in the tetragonal phase stable below $-168°C$ is probably ordered. The S $\cdots$ S distance is 3.86 A, and the S $\cdots$ S $\cdots$ S angle is 75°. This suggests that the H_2S molecule (with a bond angle of 90°) is oriented so as to form two slightly bent hydrogen bonds to other sulfur atoms. Although the S $\cdots$ S van der Waals distance is 3.7 A, the sum of the S $\cdots$ H van der Waals distance of 3.05 A and the S—H distance of 1.35 A in gaseous H_2S is 4.40 A. This is 0.54 A longer than the S $\cdots$ S distance in the crystal. We conclude that weak S—H $\cdots$ S hydrogen bonding does exist in this case. The lower boiling point and lower entropy of vaporization (Trouton constant) for H_2S as compared with H_2O indicate that the intermolecular forces are not nearly so strong in the former.

Table 5-3 *Intermolecular S—N Distances*[a]

N—H · · · S distance (A)	Molecule	Reference[b]
3.24	3-Hydro-5-thiol-1,2,4-triazole	4
3.26	α-Thiopyridone	3
3.35	Xanthane hydride	5
3.396 3.420 3.469 3.504	Thioacetamide	6
3.40	1-Thiocarbamyl-imidazolidine-2-thione	7
3.40	2:5-Diamino-4-mercapto-6-methyl pyrimidine	2
3.44 3.48	Ethylenethiourea	8
3.366	Pyridaz-3-thione	1

[a] We are indebted to Dr. M. B. Hossain for supplying this table.

[b] (1) Hossain and Carlisle (1966); (2) Maslen *et al.* (1958); (3) Penfold (1953); (4) Senko and Templeton (1958); (5) Stanford (1963); (6) Truter (1960); (7) Valle *et al.* (1963); (8) Wheatley (1953).

tion is available for N-acetylglycine (Peterson, Levy, and Schomaker, 1957), which is a substituted amino acid containing a peptide link.

The bond lengths and hydrogen bonds in this molecule are shown in Figure 5-6. The acetyl group on the nitrogen atom apparently destabilizes the possible zwitterion structure, and the acid is found in the normal carboxylic acid configuration with the hydrogen on the oxygen of the

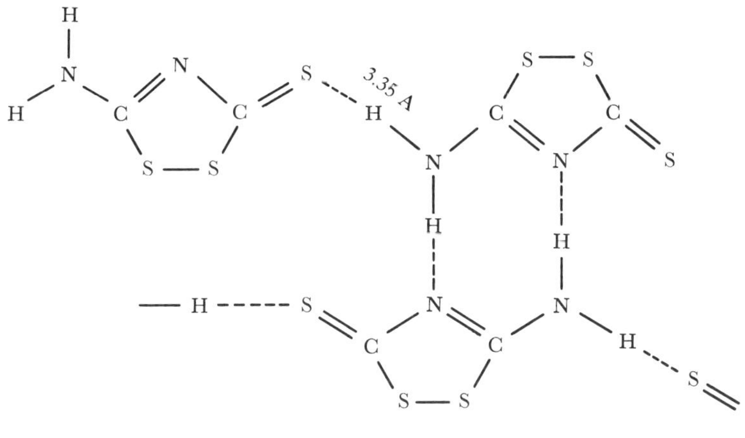

Figure 5-5 *N—H · · · S hydrogen bonding in xanthane hydride.*

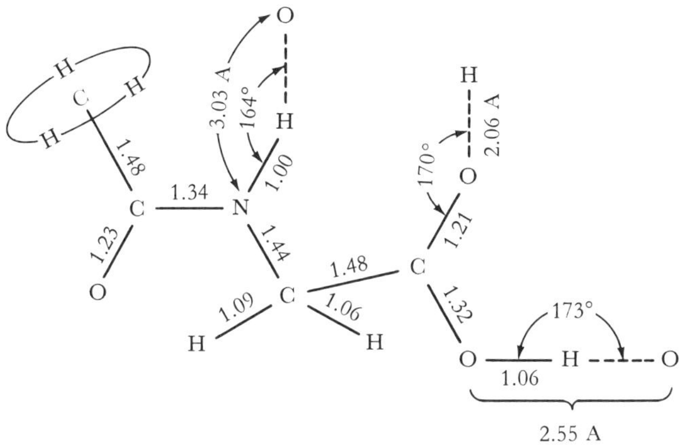

Figure 5-6 *Hydrogen bond parameters and bond lengths in N-acetylglycine as determined by neutron diffraction.   The methyl group is in almost free rotation, or is rotationally disordered.*

carboxyl group.   The O—H $\cdots$ O hydrogen bond is rather short, and the long O—H distance is compatible with this.   Note that the environment of the nitrogen atom is almost perfectly trigonal.   The neutron diffraction study, which was not based on three-dimensional data, suggests that the methyl group is in almost free rotation.

Proteins

Proteins are composed for the most part of long polypeptide chains; these result from the condensation of alpha amino acids with the loss of one molecule of water for each peptide link formed:

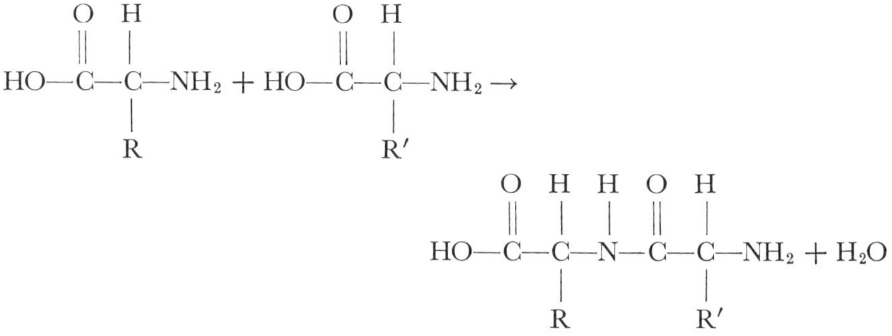

$$
\text{HO—C—C—NH}_2 + \text{HO—C—C—NH}_2 \rightarrow
$$

$$
\text{HO—C—C—N—C—C—NH}_2 + \text{H}_2\text{O}
$$

Pauling, Corey, and co-workers, with the knowledge of the structures of some amino acids and bipeptides, assumed that hydrogen bonds must play an important role in the configuration of the polypeptide chain.   It was known from x-ray diffraction patterns that some proteins contain helical polypeptide chains.   Under the assumptions that N—H $\cdots$ O hydrogen

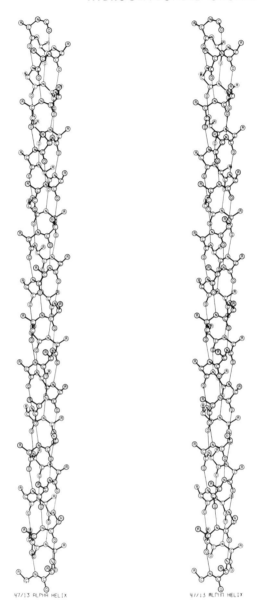

47/13 ALPHA HELIX   47/13 ALPHA HELIX

Figure 5-7 *Hydrogen bonding in the α helix.*

bonds of length 2.72 A are formed between amino acid residues several links apart along the chain and that these hydrogen bonds are within 30° of being linear, only two helical models are reasonable sterically.   In one of these, the γ helix, there are 5.1 amino acid residues per turn of the helix; the hydrogen bond departs from linearity by 25°.   The other possible structure, the α helix (Figure 5-7), has 3.7 amino acid residues in one turn of the helix; the depar- ture of the hydrogen bond from linearity is only 10°.   The hydrogen bond is formed from one amide group to the amide group which is three residues down the chain; the hydrogen bonds are thus approximately parallel to the axis of the helix.

    That the α helix is common· in protein structures attests to the usual linearity of the hydrogen bond.   Departures from linearity, however, are not sufficient to destroy the stability of the structure, and this suggests that the flexibility in the acceptable geometry of the hydrogen bond may be an impor- tant reason for its ubiquitous appearance in biological systems.

    Further evidence that small variations in hydrogen bond geometry are allowed without destroying the integrity of the α helix is provided by the experiments on the effects of deuteration, carried out by Tomita and co- workers (1962).   x-Ray diffraction fiber patterns of normal and deuterated synthetic polypeptides suggest that there is an increase of about 0.025 A in the N—H · · · O hydrogen bond length on deuteration.[4]   This change in hydrogen bond length appears to affect only the repeat distance along the helix but not the pitch of the helix; thus angular relationships in the hydrogen bonds do not change significantly.   There are some changes in van der Waals contact distances between heavy atoms, and there are necessarily some small changes in bond angles in the helix.

5-2   HYDROGEN BONDING BETWEEN PURINE AND PYRIMIDINE BASES

    The nucleic acids DNA and RNA are high molecular weight polymers composed of monomer units of ribose phosphate derivatives of purine and pyrimidine bases (Figures 5-8 and 5-9).   The basic structural unit in the nucleic acids is thought to be a helical chain composed of the phosphate ester moities, with the bases extending with their planes perpendicular to the axis of this spiral backbone.   Two such chains can wind about each other, and the factor of importance in allowing this relationship is the geometry of possible hydrogen bonds which may be formed between a purine base on one

---

[4] As we have seen from the results on oxalic acid dihydrate (Section 3-6) the changes in bond length as derived from changes in lattice constants on deuteration are not always reliable.

chain and a pyrimidine base on the other. The two purine bases adenine and guanine, and the two pyrimidine bases cytosine and thymine, are the only ones found to any large extent in DNA. In RNA, the pyrimidine base uracil replaces thymine. The pairing of the bases between chains is always of the type guanine-cytosine and adenine-thymine or adenine-uracil.

Because the hydrogen bonding between the bases is probably a determining factor in the structure of nucleic acids, it has seemed profitable to study in some detail the crystal structures of 1:1 adducts of purine and pyrimidine bases. x-Ray diffraction studies have been carried out on several such systems. The 1:1 adducts do indeed contain hydrogen-bonded base pairs. An examination of Figures 5-8 and 5-9 suggests that there are a number of different ways in which hydrogen-bonded dimers can be formed. Guanine-cytosine pairs have been found to hydrogen-bond together in the way proposed by Crick and Watson (1954). Of several adenine-thymine or adenine-uracil pairs which have been studied, none has the Crick-Watson configuration. The meager x-ray data on DNA itself is interpreted as being compatible only with the Crick-Watson pairing scheme (Marvin, Wilkins, and Hamilton, 1966).

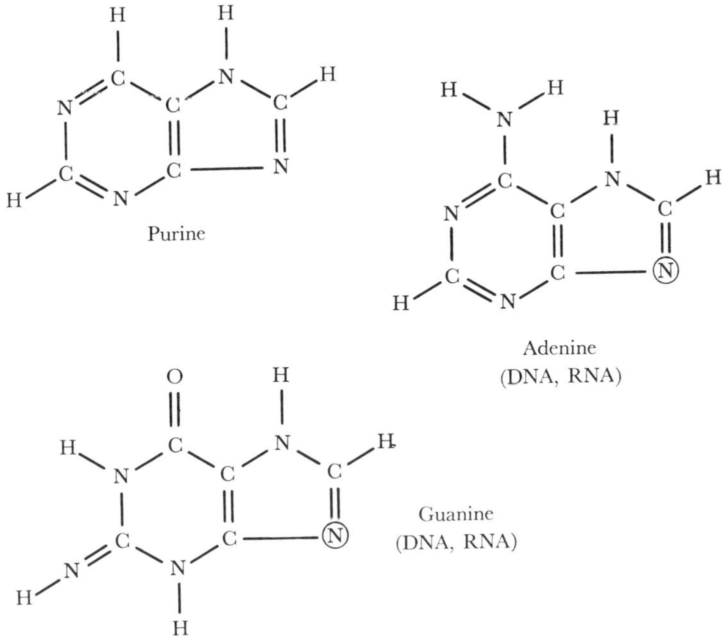

Figure 5-8 *Purine and the purine bases adenine and guanine, both of which are present in DNA and RNA. The circled N is the point of attachment of the ribose molecule in the polynucleotides.*

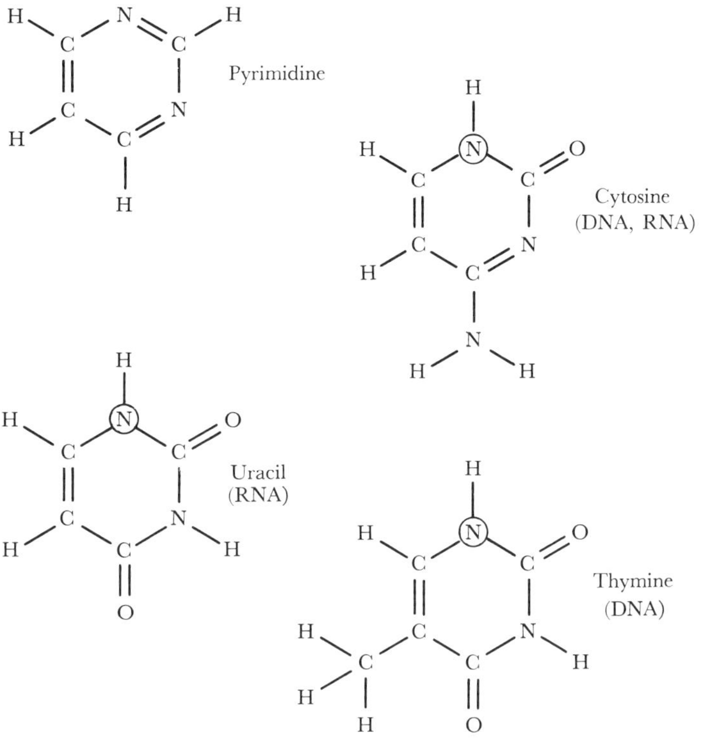

Figure 5-9 *Pyrimidine and the pyrimidine bases cytosine, uracil, and thymine.   Cytosine is a major component of both DNA and RNA, while uracil appears mainly in RNA and thymine in DNA. The circled N is the point of attachment of the ribose ring.*

The Structures of Two Guanine-Cytosine Complexes

The structures, as determined by x-ray diffraction, of 9-ethylguanine: 1-methylcytosine and 9-ethylguanine:1-methyl 5-bromocytosine have been reported (O'Brien, 1963; Sobell, Tomita, and Rich, 1963).   Both structures are hydrogen bonded according to the Crick-Watson scheme as shown in Figure 5-10.   The corresponding hydrogen bond lengths vary between the two compounds by up to 0.1 A, which indicates some degree of flexibility in the geometrical requirements for hydrogen bonding.   The hydrogen atoms were clearly seen in the difference synthesis for the unbrominated compound. The assignment is that which would be expected.   The methyl and ethyl groups are bonded to the rings at the points where the ribose moieties are attached in the nucleic acids.   The ring systems of the individual bases are planar.   The dihedral angle between the planes of the two rings is 6.5° in the bromo derivative.

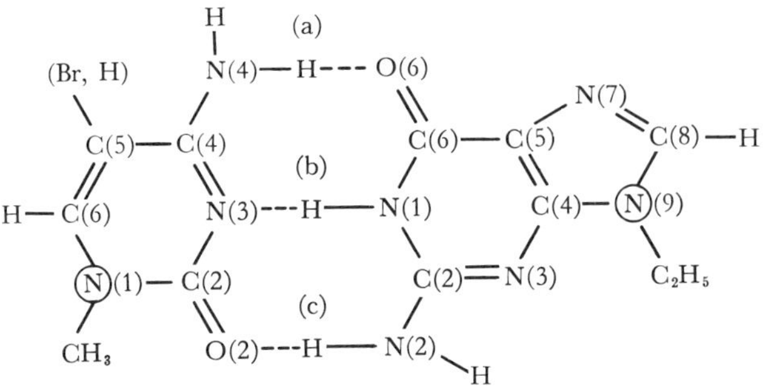

H bond lengths

	Br	H
(a)	2.86	2.93
(b)	2.95	2.91
(c)	2.91	2.82

Figure 5-10 *Hydrogen bonding in the guanine-cytosine base pair as determined by x-ray studies of 9-ethylguanine-1-methylcytosine, and the bromo derivative indicated. The pairing is identical to that predicted by Crick and Watson.*

The Structures of Two Complexes Involving Adenine

One of the more recent structures reported is that of a complex of adenosine and bromouridine (Haschemeyer and Sobell, 1965). The bromine atom was added in order that the structure could be solved by the heavy atom method; it may possibly have had enough influence on the electron distribution in the rings to make the hydrogen-bonding scheme different from what it otherwise would have been. This did not seem to be so in the guanine-cytosine pairs. In this structure the purine and pyrimidine rings are again approximately coplanar. The planes of the ribose rings make dihedral angles of approximately 70° with the planes of the bases.

The hydrogen bond system is different from that postulated by Crick and Watson. A comparison of the Haschemeyer-Sobell structure, the Crick-Watson model, and the structure of a complex studied by Hoogsteen (1963) is given in Figure 5-11. No common hydrogen-bonding scheme is found, although the structures found both involve hydrogen bonds to the five-membered ring in adenine, while the six-membered ring is involved in the Crick-Watson model. There is, of course, no reason to believe that the bonding in the nucleic acids is always the same as it is in isolated base pairs. Rather subtle energy relationships must determine the stability of one configuration over the other, and the additional terms involved in the helical structures of the nucleic acids themselves might well be enough to favor one structure over another.

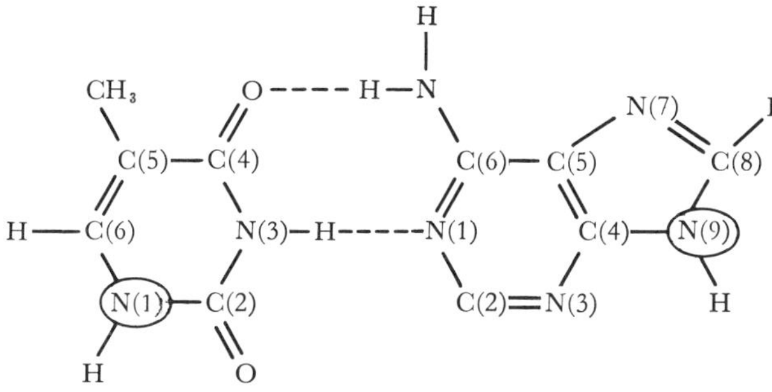

Crick-Watson

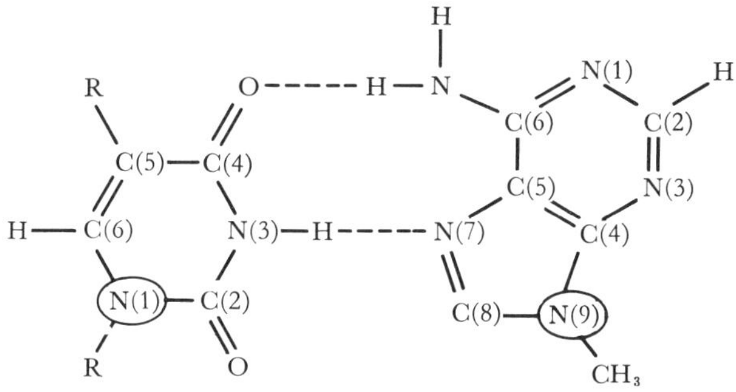

Hoogsteen

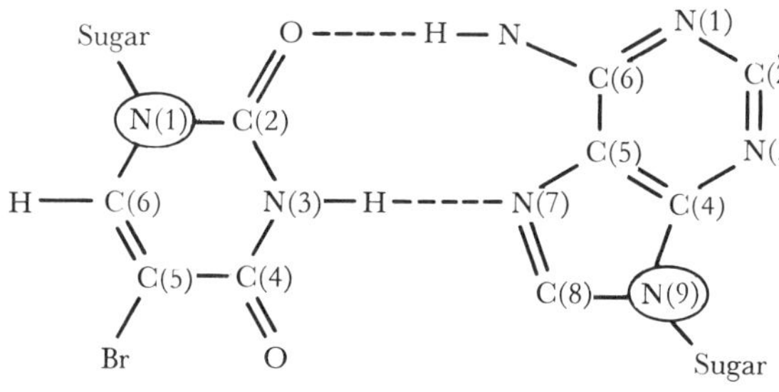

Haschemeyer-Sobell

Figure 5-11 *Hydrogen bonding in adenine-thymine and adenine-uracil base pairs. The structure predicted by Crick and Watson, although probably occurring in DNA and RNA, has not been demonstrated in the isolated base pairs. The two schemes found by Hoogsteen and by Haschemeyer and Sobell are different.*

Pullman, Claverie, and Caillet (1966) have made some estimates of the relative energies of various base pairs. Dipole-dipole, dipole-induced dipole, and dispersion forces were considered; the charge densities were obtained from simple molecular orbital treatments. The Crick-Watson guanine-cytosine configuration was found to be energetically far more favorable than any other pairing of guanine-cytosine or any other combination of base pairs. This result is consistent with the fact that the Crick-Watson scheme is indeed found in the crystal structures determined by O'Brien and by Sobell, Tomita, and Rich. The energies for the Crick-Watson, Hoogsteen, and Haschemeyer-Sobell structures for adenine-thymine and adenine-uridine are nearly equal, so that the more subtle forces must come into play.

In the Haschemeyer-Sobell structure, the two hydrogen bonds in the dimer are N—H $\cdots$ N at 2.80 A and N—H $\cdots$ O at 3.10 A, which is rather long. In addition to these hydrogen bonds between the two members of the base pair, there are additional hydrogen bonds in the crystal involving all the hydroxyl hydrogens on the sugar residues as well as the other hydrogen bond acceptor atoms in the two bases, namely, the other two nitrogen atoms of adenine and the other carbonyl group of uracil.

Proton Tunneling and Mutations

Since the base pairing in DNA is thought to be the basis of genetic reproduction, and since this base pairing is determined in large part by the possibility of favorable hydrogen bond geometries, Löwdin (1963) has made the interesting suggestion that proton tunneling during the replication process may be responsible for errors in the genetic code (i.e., mutations). Consider, for example, the adenosine-thymine pair (A-T as indicated in Figure 5-12). During the separation process involved in replication, if the two protons have been cooperatively exchanged between bases, there results a base pair which may be denoted as A*-T*. If the strands now separate, and if the synthesis of a new strand is governed by the bases appearing in a given strand, A* is no longer able to pair with T, since the protons do not match. Similarly, T* will not pair with A, G* will not pair with C, and C* will not pair with G. Rather, better hydrogen bonding will result if the pairs A*-C, T*-G, G*-T, and C*-A are formed. The newly replicated strand will thus have an error. A possible sequence of events is as follows:

(a) original sequence, A G T C A T;
(b) result of H transfer, A G T* C A T;
(c) replicated strand, T C G G T A;
(d) complement of (c), A G C C A T.

The normal replication process would have resulted at (d) in a sequence identical to that in (a). Instead, the cooperative proton transfer has resulted in the substitution of C for T at one step in the strand. Thus the existence of a double-minimum potential, particularly where a two-proton exchange is involved, may be of great biological significance. This story seems to be a bit spoiled by the fact that the crystallographic work on base pairs indicates that a variety of different hydrogen-bonding schemes are

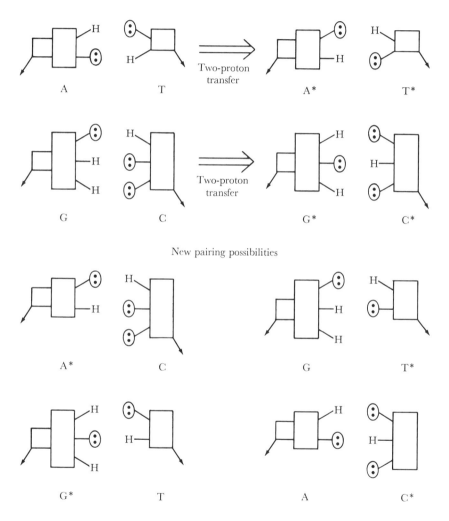

Figure 5-12 *Elements of the mutation theory proposed by Löwdin. By double proton tunneling, a base pair AT becomes a pair A*T*. If the chain is uncoiled while in this relationship, A* will no longer be able to pair with T but will perhaps prefer C.   Thus in the replication process, it is possible for T to be transformed to C and for G to be transformed to A.*

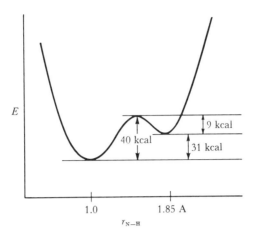

Figure 5-13 *Potential energy E as a function of N—H bond length for a single proton transfer in the guanine-cytosine base pair as calculated by Rein and Harris (1964) in a very simple molecular orbital calculation.*

possible; it is not at all certain that the geometrical requirements of hydrogen bonding are the sole requirements for the remarkable specificity shown in base pairing in the nucleic acids.

In an attempt to show the reasonableness of Löwdin's suggestion, Rein and Harris (1964) have considered the guanine-cytosine base pair, which makes use of three hydrogen bonds, in a quantum mechanical treatment of the hydrogen bond potential. Using the π electrons for the rings and only the σ electrons involved in the hydrogen bonds, they have used the LCAO-SCF molecular orbital method to obtain potential energy curves for the motion of the hydrogen in the central bond. For certain values of the parameters used in the approximations of some of the integrals, it was possible to obtain a reasonable double-minimum potential function. Because of the approximations involved, however, the exact values of the energy differences in Figure 5-13 are probably meaningless.

5-3 INTRAMOLECULAR HYDROGEN BONDS

Sucrose

One of the most complex hydrogen-bonded crystals to have been studied by neutron diffraction is sucrose (Brown and Levy, 1963) (Figure 5-14). The structure consists of intricately hydrogen-bonded planar networks with but one hydrogen bond per molecule connecting the planes perpendicular to them. There are two strong *intra*molecular hydrogen bonds; such bonds are relatively rare. In sucrose these bonds are between oxygen atoms which are rather remote from each other in the carbon framework. In fact, in both cases, one of the oxygen atoms is in the glucose half of the molecule and the other in the fructose. The molecule can easily twist around to satisfy the geometrical requirements of hydrogen bond formation.

1,3,5-Triamino-2,4,6-trinitrobenzene

It is more unusual to find internal hydrogen bonds between atoms rigidly constrained only a few bonds distant from one another. An interesting example is 1,3,5-triamino-2,4,6-trinitrobenzene (Figure 5-15). The nitrogen atom of the amino group is about 2.5 A away from the oxygen of the ortho nitro group in the same molecule. There are also nitro groups of neighboring molecules about 3.0 A away. The hydrogen atoms, which were seen in difference electron density syntheses of the x-ray diffraction data (Cady and Larson, 1965), lie approximately half-way between the lines joining the amino nitrogen to the two nearest nitro oxygens—one intramolecular and one intermolecular. Thus the hydrogen bonds are bifurcated and both intra- and intermolecular. The density of 1.94 g cm^{-3} is indicative of the very tight structure which is formed by the extensive hydrogen bonding.

o-Nitrobenzaldehyde

An internal C—H $\cdots$ O hydrogen bond has been suggested in o-nitrobenzaldehyde (Pinchas, 1957), but the geometry is far from favorable for hydrogen bonding; the neutron diffraction work by Coppens (1964) (Figure 5-16) reveals a C—H $\cdots$ O angle of 94° with an H $\cdots$ O distance of 2.38 A. In o-nitrobenzaldehyde, the C—H stretching frequency is 2753

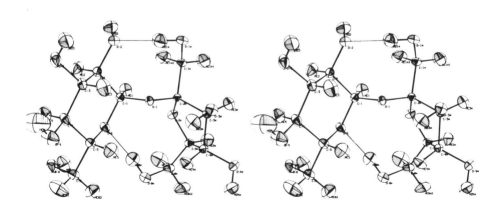

Figure 5-14 *The structure of a single molecule of sucrose showing the intramolecular hydrogen bonds.*

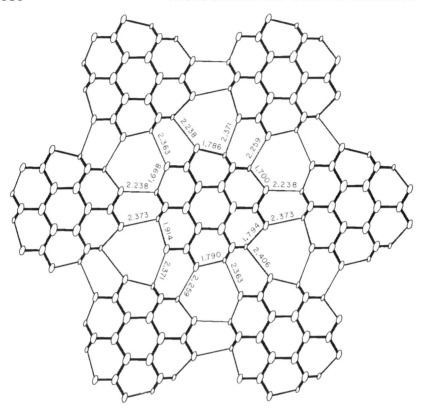

Figure 5-15 *The hydrogen bonding in triaminotrinitrobenzene. This is an example of a bifurcated hydrogen bond, one branch of which is intermolecular and the other branch of which is intramolecular.*

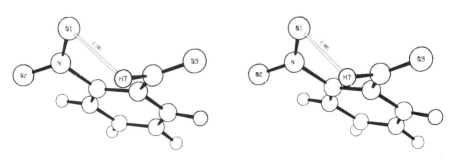

Figure 5-16 *The configuration around the aldehyde and nitro groups in o-nitrobenzaldehyde. Whether or not there is a C—H · · · O hydrogen bond is questionable.*

cm^{-1} as opposed to 2729 cm^{-1} in the unsubstituted benzaldehyde.   Thus, there is an unusual frequency shift up rather than down.   Pinchas postulated that this increase in the stretching frequency is because the C—H $\cdots$ O angle is 90° and an interaction between H and O tends to tie the hydrogen down more in one place.   Coppens found that both the nitro and the aldehyde group are twisted out of the plane of the benzene ring by 30° and concluded that the interaction between H and O is repulsive.   Coppens has shown that the van der Waals repulsion energy at the rather short O $\cdots$ H distance is approximately balanced by the loss in resonance energy due to the nonplanarity.

5-4   SHORT BONDS IN ACID SALTS

An important type of intramolecular hydrogen bond is that found in potassium hydrogen chloromaleate (Section 3-4, Figure 3-19).   Short symmetric bonds seem to be the rule in other acid salts of carboxylic acids. The structures of many such salts of the formula MHA$_2$ have been determined by Speakman and co-workers.   The structure of one of these is shown in Figure 5-17.   Six of these salts have been the subject of accurate three-dimensional x-ray structural analyses.   The data are summarized in Table 5-4.   It seems probable that the hydrogen atom is truly centered in all of these.

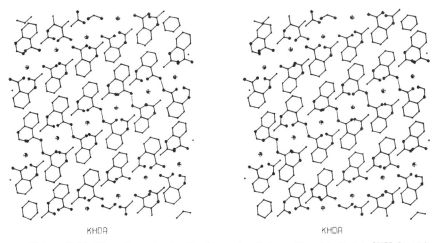

KHDA   KHDA

Figure 5-17 *View of several unit cells of potassium hydrogen bisacetylsalicylate (KH diaspiri-nate).   This crystal contains one of the shortest O—H—O hydrogen bonds known.   A few of the short hydrogen bonds connecting the carboxyl groups are shown.*

Table 5-4 *Short O—H—O Bonds in the Compounds MHA$_2$[a]*

Acid	M	O—H—O (A)[b]	Symmetry[c]	Reference[d]
Acetic	Na	2.443 (10)	2	1
p-Chlorobenzoic	K	2.457 (13)	$\bar{1}$	2
Trifluoroacetic	K	2.437 (7)	$\bar{1}$	3
Aspirin	K	2.455 (5)	$\bar{1}$	4
Anisic	K	2.450 (10)	2	5
Phenylacetic	K	2.443 (5)	$\bar{1}$	6
p-Hydroxybenzoic	K	2.458 (7)	$\bar{1}$	7

[a] This table was kindly supplied by Dr. J. C. Speakman (1967).

[b] Estimated standard deviation in the least significant figures is in the parentheses.

[c] Point symmetry at the hydrogen site. 2 indicates a twofold axis; $\bar{1}$, a center of symmetry.

[d] (1) Speakman and Mills (1961); (2) Mills and Speakman (1963); (3) Golic and Speakman (1965); (4) Manojlović and Speakman (1967a); (5) McGregor and Speakman (1967); (6) Manojlović and Speakman (1967b); (7) Manojlović (1967).

5-5 CARBON AS A HYDROGEN BOND DONOR

The possibility of a C—H · · · O hydrogen bond in *o*-nitrobenzaldehyde leads one to inquire whether C—H might occasionally act as a donor in a hydrogen bond. It seems certain that there are compounds which can best be understood by postulating such bonds. A survey of such possibilities has been given by Sutor (1962). Some examples are given in Table 5-5. In each the proposed hydrogen bonding is from a C—H to a highly electronegative oxygen.

All the hydrogen bonds in the table are to keto oxygen atoms. A structure determined by Palenik (1965) indicates a probable hydrogen bond from a methylene group to a nitroso oxygen, as illustrated in Figure 5-18. The geometry seems favorable, with H · · · O equal to 2.27 A and the C—H · · · O angle 164°.

Table 5-5 *Some Possible C—H · · · O Hydrogen Bonds*

	C · · · O (A)	H · · · O (A)	∠C—H · · · O (deg)
Theophylline	3.22	2.25	173
Caffeine	3.18	2.07	167
1,3,7,9-Tetramethyluric acid	3.00	2.26	121

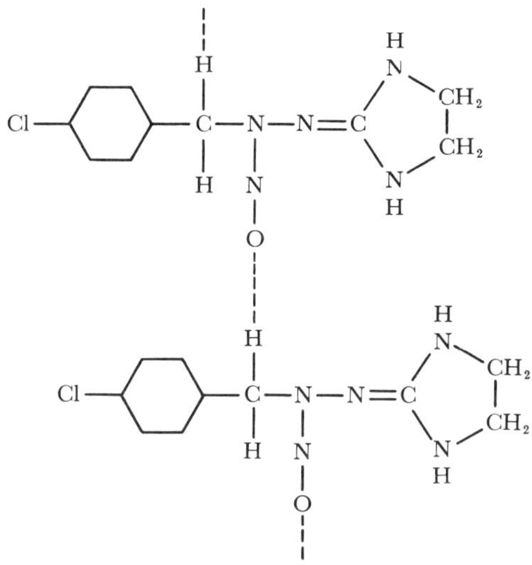

Figure 5-18 *A well-established C—H · · · O hydrogen bond.*

Although the evidence for C—H · · · O hydrogen bonds seems clear, they are certainly fairly weak bonds and they do not play a very important role in crystal chemistry.

One of the most obvious examples of a C—H hydrogen bond donor is provided by the structure of HCN (Dulmage and Lipscomb, 1951). The structure consists of infinite linear chains:

$$H—C—N \cdot \cdot \cdot H—C—N \cdot \cdot \cdot H—C—N \cdot \cdot \cdot H—C—N$$

The C—H · · · N distance is 3.2 A; the H · · · N distance is 2.2 A and the bond is linear.

The C—H stretching frequency (Hoffman and Hornig, 1949) drops from 3312 cm^{-1} in the vapor to 3132 cm^{-1} in the crystal. At the same time, the bending frequency increases from 712 to 830 cm^{-1}, indicating a rigidity of the whole chain as a result of the hydrogen bonding.

5-6 HYDROGEN BONDING IN METHYLGLYOXAL BISGUANYLHYDRAZONE

The compound methylglyoxal bisguanylhydrazone·2HCl·H$_2$O has been used in Section 2-5 to provide a comparison between x-ray and neutron diffraction methods. It is interesting that in this structure the predominant factor in the intermolecular packing seems to be a specific interaction between the π-bonding systems of the planar molecules, the interplanar spacing of

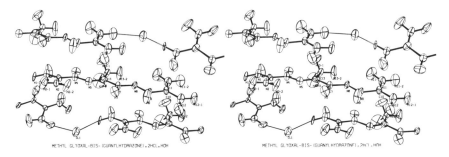

METHYL GLYOXAL-BIS-(GUANYLHYDRAZONE).2HCL.HOH   METHYL GLYOXAL-BIS-(GUANYLHYDRAZONE).2HCl.HOH

Figure 5-19 *Planar molecules of methylglyoxal bisguanylhydrazone in the hydrated hydro-chloride salt. The interplanar spacing is unusually short. Hydrogen bonding occurs only through water molecules and chloride ions in the crystal lattice. (See also Figure 2-4 in Section 2-5.)*

3.10 A being one of the shortest observed in any organic compound (see Figure 5-19). The molecules are not hydrogen bonded together. All of the hydrogen bonds are between the molecule and either Cl^- ions or water molecules. The parameters of the N—H $\cdots$ Cl hydrogen bonds are given in Table 5-6. The distances in the table are uncorrected for thermal motion. There seems to be no good correlation, however, between N—H and N $\cdots$ Cl distances, as occurs for O—H $\cdots$ O hydrogen bonds (Section 2-5). The geometry is also remarkably flexible.

We are not surprised that the N—H, N $\cdots$ Cl correlation is not obvious, for these are weak hydrogen bonds As shown earlier, the differences in O—H bond length for the weaker hydrogen bonds tend to be obscured by other factors. The range of hydrogen bond angles found here is greater than that typical for the class of O—H $\cdots$ O hydrogen bonds.

Table 5-6 *N—H $\cdots$ Cl⁻ Hydrogen Bonds in Methylglyoxal Bisguanylhydrazone Dihydrochloride Monohydrate[a]*

N—H (A)	H $\cdots$ Cl⁻ (A)	N $\cdots$ Cl⁻ (A)	∠N—H $\cdots$ Cl⁻ (deg)
1.03	2.51	3.39	144
1.01	2.20	3.21	171
1.01	2.34	3.27	152
0.97	2.32	3.16	146
1.02	2.17	3.15	160
1.04	2.82	3.48	122
1.03	2.58	3.45	143
0.97	2.63	3.51	151

[a] From Hamilton and La Placa (1967).

REFERENCES

Bednowitz, A. L. (1967), The Crystal Structure of ϵ-Aminocaproic acid, *Acta Cryst.* in press.

Brown, G. M., and Levy, H. A. (1963), Sucrose: Precise Determination of Crystal and Molecular Structure by Neutron Diffraction, *Science* **141,** 921.

Burns, J. H., and Levy, H. A. (1958), The Hydrogen Positions in Glycine by Neutron Diffraction, *Abstracts American Crystallographic Association*, p. 38. Marquette University, Milwaukee, Wisconsin.

Cady, H. H., and Larson, A. C. (1965), The Crystal Structure of 1,3,5-Triamino-2,4,6-trinitrobenzene, *Acta Cryst.* **18,** 485.

Coppens, P. (1964), A Neutron Diffraction Study of 2-Nitrobenzaldehyde and the C—H $\cdots$ O Interaction, *Acta Cryst.* **17,** 573.

Crick, F., and Watson, J. (1954), The Complementary Structure of Deoxyribonucleic Acid, *Proc. Roy. Soc. London* **A223,** 80.

Dulmage, W. J., and Lipscomb, W. N. (1951), The Crystal Structures of Hydrogen Cyanide, HCN, *Acta Cryst.* **4,** 330.

Golic, L., and Speakman, J. C. (1965), The Crystal Structures of the Acid Salts of Some Monobasic Acids. Part X. Potassium, Rubidium, and Cesium Hydrogen Di-trifluoroacetates. *J. Chem. Soc.* **1965,** 2530.

Hamilton, W. C., and La Placa, S. J., (1967) Neutron and x-Ray Diffraction Studies of the Anti-Leukemia Agent, Methylglyoxal-bisguanylhydrazone Dihydrochloride Monohydrate, *Acta Cryst.* in press.

Harada, J., and Kitamura, N. (1964), Structure and Phase Transition of Solid Hydrogen Sulphide, *J. Phys. Soc. Japan* **19,** 328.

Haschemeyer, A. E. V., and Sobell, H. M. (1965), The Crystal Structure of a Hydrogen Bonded Complex of Adenosine and 5-Bromouridine, *Acta Cryst.* **18,** 525.

Hoffman, R. E., and Hornig, D. F. (1949), The Infrared Spectrum of Solid HCN, *J. Chem. Phys.* **17,** 1163 (1949).

Hoogsteen, K. (1963), The Crystal and Molecular Structure of a Hydrogen-Bonded Complex between 1-Methylthymine and 9-Methyladenine, *Acta Cryst.* **19,** 907.

Hossain, M. B., and Carlisle, C. H. (1966), The Crystal Structure of Pyridaz-3-thione, $C_4H_4N_2S$, *Abstracts American Crystallographic Association*, p. 49. Austin, Texas.

Levy, H. A., Peterson, S. W., and Schomaker, V. (1957), Crystal Structure of *N*-Acetylglycine, in Chemistry Division Progress Report Ending June 20, 1957, *U.S. Atomic Energy Commission* **ORNL 2386,** 132.

Löwdin, P. O. (1963), Proton Tunneling in DNA and Its Biological Implications, *Rev. Mod. Phys.* **35,** 724.

Manojlović, L. (1967), A Reinvestigation of the Crystal Structure of Potassium Hydrogen Di-*p*-hydroxybenzoate Hydrate, *Acta Cryst.*, in press.

Manojlović, L., and Speakman, J. C. (1967a), The Crystal Structures of the Acid Salts of Some Monobasic Acids. Part XII. Potassium Hydrogen Diaspirinate [Bisacetylsalicylate]. *J. Chem. Soc.* (*A*) **1967,** 971.

Manojlović, L., and Speakman, J. C. (1967b), The Crystal Structure of, and Hydrogen Bond in, Potassium Hydrogen Bisphenylacetate: a Redetermination, *Acta Cryst.*, in press.

Marvin, D. A., Wilkins, M. H. F., and Hamilton, L. D. (1966), Application of Fourier Synthesis Techniques to Low Resolution Fibre Diffraction Data: Preliminary Study of Deoxyribonucleic Acid, *Acta Cryst.* **20**, 663.

Maslen, E. N., Jukes, D. E., Clews, C. J. B., (1958), The Crystal and Molecular Structure of 2:5-Diamino-4-Mercapto-6-Methyl-Pyrimidine, *Acta Cryst.* **11**, 115.

McGregor, D. R., and Speakman, J. C. (1967), The Crystal Structures of the Acid Salts of Some Monobasic Acids, Potassium Hydrogen di-anisate, unpublished.

Mills, H. H., and Speakman, J. C., (1963), The Crystal Structures of the Acid Salts of Some Monobasic Acids. Part VIII. Potassium (or Ammonium, or Rubidium) Hydrogen Di-p-chlorobenzoate. *J. Chem. Soc.* **1963**, 4355.

Nakamoto, K., Sarma, Y. A., and Ogoshi, H. (1965), Normal Coordinate Analysis of Hydrogen-Bonded Compounds. IV. The Acid Carbonate Ion, *J. Chem. Phys.* **43**, 1177.

Nitta, I., Tomiie, Y., and Koo, C. H. (1952), The Crystal Structure of Potassium Bicarbonate, $KHCO_3$, *Acta Cryst.* **5**, 292.

O'Brien, E. J. (1963), The Crystal Structure of a Complex of 9-Ethylguanine with 1-Methylcytosine, *J. Mol. Biol.* **7**, 107.

Okaya, Y. (1966), Refinement of the Crystal Structure of Taurine, 2-Aminoethylsulfonic acid; an Example of Computer-Controlled Experimentation, *Acta Cryst.* **21**, 726.

Palenik, G. (1965), The Structure of 1-(4-Chlorobenzyl)-1-nitroso-2-(4,5-dihydro-2-imidazolyl)hydrazine Monohydrate, *Acta Cryst.* **19**, 47.

Pauling, L., Corey, R. B., and Branson, H. R. (1951), The Structure of Proteins: Two Hydrogen-Bonded Helical Configurations of the Polypeptide Chains, *Proc. Nat. Acad. Sci. US* **37**, 205.

Penfold, B. R., (1953), The Crystal Structure of α-Thiopyridone, *Acta Cryst.* **6**, 707.

Peterson, J., Steinrauf, L. K., and Jensen, L. H. (1960), Direct Determination of the Structure of L-Cystine Dihydrobromide, *Acta Cryst.* **13**, 104.

Pinchas, S. (1957), Infrared Absorption of Aldehydic C—H Group. Ortho-Substituted Benzaldehydes, *Anal. Chem.* **29**, 334.

Pullman, B., Claverie, P., and Caillet, J. (1966), Van der Waals-London Interactions and the Configuration of Hydrogen-Bonded Purine and Pyrimidine Pairs, *Proc. Nat. Acad. Sci. US* **55**, 904.

Rein, R., and Harris, F. E. (1964), Studies of Hydrogen-Bonded Systems. I. The Electronic Structure and the Double Well Potential of the N—H · · · N Hydrogen Bond of the Guanine-Cytosine Base Pair, *J. Chem. Phys.* **41**, 3393.

Senko, M. E., and Templeton, D. H. (1958), Crystal Structure of 3-Hydrazino-5-thiol-1,2,4-triazole, *Acta Cryst.* **11**, 808.

Simpson, H. J., Jr., and Marsh, R. E. (1966), The Crystal Structure of L-Alanine, *Acta Cryst.* **20**, 550.

Sobell, H. M., Tomita, K., and Rich, A. (1963), The Crystal Structure of an Intermolecular Complex Containing a Guanine and a Cytosine Derivative, *Proc. Nat. Acad. Sci. US* **49**, 885.

Speakman, J. C. (1967), Some "Very Short" Hydrogen Bonds, *Chem. Comm.* **1967,** 32.

Speakman, J. C., and Mills, H. H., (1961), The Crystal Structures of the Acid Salts of Some Monobasic Acids, Part VI. Sodium Hydrogen Diacetate., *J. Chem. Soc.* **1961,** 1164.

Stanford, R. H., Jr. (1963), The Crystal Structure of Xanthane Hydride, *Acta Cryst.* **16,** 1157.

Sutor, D. J. (1962), The C—H · · · O Hydrogen Bond in Crystals, *Nature* **195,** 68.

Tomita, K., Rich, A., de Lozé, C., and Blout, E. R. (1962), The Effect of Deuteration on the Geometry of the Alpha-Helix, *J. Mol. Biol.* **4,** 83.

Truter, M. R., (1960), An Accurate Determination of the Crystal Structure of Thioacetamide, *J. Chem. Soc.* **1960,** 997.

Valle, G., Cojazzi, G., and Busetti, V. (1963), Crystal Structure Analysis of 1-thio-carbamyl-imidazolidine-2-thione, *Acta Cryst.* **16,** A53.

Wheatley, P. J. (1953), The Structure of Ethylenethiourea, *Acta Cryst.* **6,** 369.

Hydrogen Bonds in Hydrates and Other Inorganic Crystals

chapter six

In this chapter we shall discuss a number of examples of hydrogen bonding in inorganic solids, but the major emphasis will be on water and the hydrates. Most of the interesting properties of water are due to its versatility in forming hydrogen bonds. "Water of crystallization" is often found in the crystals of inorganic salts, and in these salts the water is almost invariably involved in hydrogen bonding. This hydrogen bonding is often between the anions of oxy-acids and water molecules, but it also occurs between different water molecules in the structure.

The first sections of this chapter will be concerned with the structure of water itself in the crystalline state, namely, ice in its various forms. Because of the possible quasi-crystalline nature of liquid water, it seems also appropriate at this point to discuss its structure.

The discussions of water itself will be followed by a discussion of hydrogen bonding in hydrates, starting with the clathrate hydrates, which are almost pure water, and going down to substances where it may be argued whether a single water molecule which is present is involved in hydrogen bonding at all. Although this chapter is primarily concerned with inorganic substances, organic hydrates will also be discussed briefly at this point.

Next to water, probably the most ubiquitous of hydrogen-bonding inorganic species is the ammonium ion, and the structures of a number of ammonium salts will be discussed.

We shall close the chapter with descriptions of a few interesting but miscellaneous inorganic structures. The discussion of a number of hydrogen-bonded ferroelectric substances will be deferred to Chapter 7.

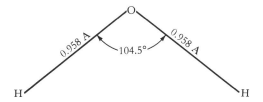

Figure 6-1 *The geometry of an isolated water molecule. The values given are equilibrium values. The mean values in the ground state are 0.957 for the distance and 105.1° for the angle.*

6-1 THE WATER MOLECULE

In our discussions of crystals containing hydrogen-bonded water molecules, it will be of interest to compare the geometry of water in these crystals with that of an isolated water molecule. The geometry of an isolated water molecule in the gas phase is well known from spectroscopic measurements and is illustrated in Figure 6-1. The important spectroscopic constants are given in Table 6-1.

The equilibrium H—O—H angle is near enough to the tetrahedral angle of 109° 28′ so that the structures of ice and hydrates often involve ordering of water molecules to give the oxygen atoms characteristic tetrahedral groupings of atoms. The oxygen atoms are then connected by hydrogen atoms which lie approximately along the interoxygen vectors.

Table 6-1 *Spectroscopic Data for the Gaseous Water Molecule*

Force Constants (mdynes A^{-1}) in the Quadratic Approximation[a]

k_1	8.425
k_θ/r^2	0.768
k_{11}	−0.201
$k_{1\theta}/r$	0.505

Observed Vibrational Frequencies (cm^{-1})[b]		
	H_2O	D_2O
Symmetric stretch[c]	3652	2666
Bend	1595	1179
Antisymmetric stretch[c]	3756	2789

[a] $2V = k_1(\Delta r_1{}^2 + \Delta r_2{}^2) + k_\theta \Delta \theta^2 + k_{11} \Delta r_1 \Delta r_2 + k_{1\theta}(\Delta r_1 + \Delta r_2) \Delta \theta$ (Heath and Linnett, 1948).

[b] Herzberg (1945).

[c] The average stretching frequencies of 3704 and 2727 cm^{-1} are sometimes quoted.

6-2 THE STRUCTURE OF ORDINARY ICE

There are nine known crystalline forms of ice (see Figure 6-2 for the phase diagram). Most of these are stable only at high pressures. As we shall see below, the structures of ice II, III, V, and VI have been determined about as well as is possible with x-ray diffraction. Ice Ic (c for cubic) has also been thoroughly examined by electron diffraction. Our most complete structural information is for ordinary ice Ih (h for hexagonal), both because it has been extensively studied and because it has been the subject of a precision neutron diffraction investigation. Ice Ih has a rather open hexagonal crystal structure (Figure 6-3) in which every oxygen atom is surrounded by a tetrahedron of oxygen atoms at a distance of 2.75 A. In most ice crystals[1] the two hydrogen atoms are directed at random along two of the four possible $O \cdot \cdot \cdot O$ vectors from a given oxygen position. This structure, suggested by Pauling (1935) to explain the discrepancy between the third law entropy

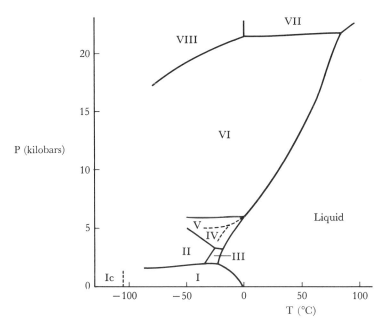

Figure 6-2 *Part of the phase diagram of H_2O (adapted from Kamb, 1965). The polymorphs of ice are indicated by roman numerals. Ice IV is a metastable phase, unstable everywhere with respect to ice V. Ice Ic (cubic ice) is also metastable with respect to ice I.*

---

[1] There are experiments in the literature which suggest that some crystals of ordinary ice are polar.

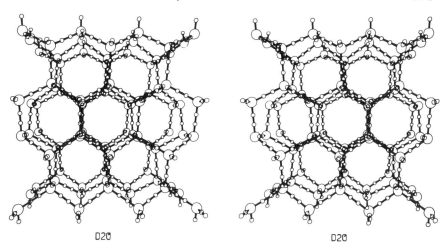

Figure 6-3 *The structure of ice Ih viewed down the hexagonal axis.   The possible hydrogen atom positions are indicated by the small spheres.   Only half of these are occupied at any one time. The parameters are those determined for the deuterated crystal.*

and the experimental entropy of ice of R log $\frac{3}{2}$, has been confirmed by a careful neutron diffraction study of heavy ice, D_2O (Peterson and Levy, 1957). The structure is described in terms of two *half-hydrogen* atoms along each O $\cdots$ O bond.   There are two independent O—D bond lengths in the structure; each of these is 0.997 A before correction for thermal motion.   This correction (see Section 2-4) gives the best estimate of the bond length as 1.009 A.   The difference between this value and the value of 0.96 A for the isolated water molecule is presumably due to the hydrogen bonding.

Although the oxygen array is tetrahedral in nature, and although the model described above does give a good fit to the single-crystal neutron diffraction data, it seems entirely possible that the equilibrium positions of the hydrogen atoms are not on the O—O lines.   The bond angle may be 105° as it is in the isolated molecule, and there may be some further disorder around the O—O lines.   Chidambaram (1961) has reported some calculations which indicate that a model with a smaller bond angle is consistent with the neutron diffraction data.

The amplitudes of thermal motion derived from the neutron diffraction experiment may provide additional information on the hydrogen positions. If we look at the components of thermal motion of the various atoms at −150°C, the principal root mean square amplitudes for the oxygen atom are 0.139, 0.139, and 0.137 A.   Those for the two crystallographically independent deuterium atoms are 0.174, 0.174, 0.152, and 0.175, 0.178, 0.149. The first of the two deuterium atoms lies on the threefold axis of the crystal;

one of the principal axes of the thermal motion ellipsoid is constrained by symmetry to lie along the threefold axis. The other two principal axes must be equal in length and perpendicular to the threefold axis, which is the O—D bond direction for this D atom. The second atom is unconstrained by symmetry. The high quality of the study is indicated by the fact that the amplitudes for the two independent atoms agree well, and the short axis of the ellipsoid lies along the bond in each case. It seems reasonable that we may subtract the motions of the oxygen atoms from the motions of the deuterium atoms to obtain amplitudes of vibration which are, for the motions perpendicular to the bond, associated mainly with the librations of the water molecules in the lattice. From the numbers above, we may estimate frequencies for the librational modes. The mean square amplitude $\langle x^2 \rangle$ of a harmonic oscillator in the ground state with reduced mass μ is related to the frequency ω (cm^{-1}) by

$$\langle x^2 \rangle = \frac{h}{8\pi^2 c\omega\mu} \tag{6-1}$$

If the mass is expressed in atomic mass units and the mean square displacement in A^2, we find that

$$\langle x^2 \rangle = \frac{16.8}{\omega\mu} \tag{6-2}$$

In the present problem we find that for the librational motion

$$\langle x^2 \rangle = 0.175^2 - 0.139^2 = 0.0113 \text{ A}^2 \tag{6-3}$$

The reduced mass for the motion around the H—O—H bisectrix is 2. The expected librational frequency is then

$$\omega = \frac{16.8}{(2 \times 0.0113)} = 745 \text{ cm}^{-1} \tag{6-4}$$

This number agrees well with that deduced from the infrared spectrum. If there were substantial disorder perpendicular to the bonds, this would show up as increased thermal motion in this direction, and the agreement with the spectroscopic values of the librational frequencies would not be as satisfactory.

The approach described in the preceding paragraph leads, for the component *along* the bond, to stretching frequencies of 2200 and 2660 cm^{-1}, in comparison with the experimental value of approximately 2300 cm^{-1}. The error in the quantities derived from the diffraction experiment is about 500 cm^{-1}; diffraction methods are obviously not the way to measure accurate vibrational frequencies. There is no evidence, however, that the two types of measurements lead to different results.

The spectra of ice have been extensively studied. Disorder along the bonds and accidental overlaps of bands have made the assignment of the observed bands to particular normal modes the subject of a great deal of controversy.   One of the problems is the splitting and broadening of the bands by intermolecular coupling.   This difficulty can be eliminated by looking at the spectrum of molecules of HDO in dilute solution in either H_2O or D_2O (Haas and Hornig, 1960; Hornig, White, and Reding, 1958). The spectrum of HDO under these circumstances is in a sense the spectrum of an independent but hydrogen-bonded molecule of ice.   The stretching vibrations for O—D and O—H occur at 2416 cm^{-1} and 3275 cm^{-1}.   These shifts from the values of 2727 cm^{-1} and 3704 cm^{-1} in the vapor phase are characteristic of intermediate strength hydrogen bonds (see Chapter 3). The constant $\omega_e x_e$, which is a measure of the anharmonicity of the potential function for the O—H stretch, increases from -80 cm^{-1} in the gas to -125 cm^{-1} in the crystal.   This is not a very significant increase, indicating that the shape of the potential function for the O—H stretch has not changed much on hydrogen bonding.

The O—D stretch of HDO is well resolved and is observed as a relatively narrow band—only 20 cm^{-1} in half-width.   This is in contrast to the bands, sometimes hundreds of wave numbers in width, which are often associated with the O—H stretch in hydrogen-bnoded systems (see Chapter 3).   Haas and Hornig concluded that a hydrogen bond is not necessarily accompanied by broad absorption, but that the observed width must usually be ascribed to coupling to other modes of motion.   Nevertheless, even 20 cm^{-1} is broad for a stretching band, and it is the consensus of those working in this field that the breadth in ice can best be explained by the fact that a variety of O $\cdots$ O distances exist in the crystal.   The O $\cdots$ O distance for any particular bond will depend on the local environment.   Associated with each of these different O $\cdots$ O distances will be a different force constant and hence a different frequency.   Bertie and Whalley (1964a) have estimated that a half-width of a few hundredths of an angstrom in the distribution of O $\cdots$ O distances would be sufficient to account for the observed width of the band. This is less than the amplitude of vibration due to the lattice vibrations and would not have a significant effect on the neutron diffraction data.

The librational frequencies are apparently in the neighborhood of 800 cm^{-1} for H_2O, 600 cm^{-1} for D_2O, and at intermediate values for HDO. These values are characteristic also of hydrogen-bonded water in crystalline hydrates.

Another quantity related to the potential surrounding the water molecule in ice is given by the deuteron resonance study of Waldstein, Rabideau, and Jackson (1964).   Several lines are seen which would be averaged to a smaller number of lines if there were pronounced rotational motion.   If a potential barrier of the type $\frac{1}{2}V_0(1 - \cos 2\theta)$ is assumed, a barrier height of 7 kcal mole^{-1} is obtained from these experiments.   As we shall show in Section 6-8, such barrier heights deduced from cosine potentials are likely to be low, so that a lower limit of $\frac{7}{2} = 3.5$ kcal mole^{-1} is found for the energy of a single hydrogen bond in ice.

In the same experiment the quadrupole coupling constant is found to be 30% less than in the gas phase. This implies that the electric field gradient is less at the deuteron nucleus; the amount of the shift, however, does not seem to be explainable merely on the basis of a lengthened bond but must imply a significant change in the general shape of the electron density distribution when the hydrogen bond is formed. A more quantitative interpretation of these results is difficult.

6-3 THE STRUCTURES OF OTHER FORMS OF ICE

Aside from the seven stable phases shown in Figure 6-2, there are two metastable crystalline forms which have been identified. One of these, cubic ice (Ic), is obtained at ordinary pressures when water vapor is condensed at temperatures between $-80°$ and $-140°$C. The positions of the oxygen atoms have been determined by x-ray and electron diffraction by Honjo and co-workers (1956), among others. The structure, in which the oxygen atoms are arranged as are the carbon atoms in the diamond structure,

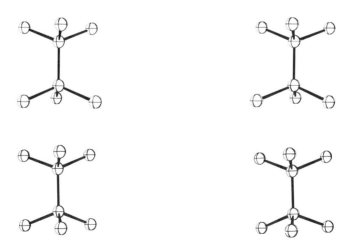

Figure 6-4 *Comparison of the oxygen atom environments in hexagonal ice Ih (above) and cubic ice Ic (below). The nearest-neighbor configurations are the same, but there are differences in the second-nearest neighbors.*

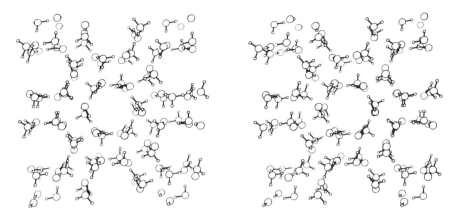

Figure 6-5 *The structure of ice II, viewed from a direction similar to that in ice I as illustrated in Figure 6-3. Notice the large distortions and the ordering of the hydrogen atoms.*

is closely related to that of ice Ih, as illustrated in Figure 6-4.   The nearest-neighbor environment of a given oxygen atom is the same in both phases, and it seems unlikely that there is much difference in the hydrogen bonding. The infrared spectra are indistinguishable.   A disorder of the hydrogen positions similar to that in Ice Ih is also likely in Ice Ic.   This appears to have been confirmed by later electron diffraction work (Honjo and Shimaoka, 1957; Shimaoka, 1960).

The structure of ice II (Figure 6-5) has been the subject of a careful x-ray examination by Kamb (1964).   The density of this rhombohedral structure is 1.17.   It is probably characteristic of all the high pressure ices that a greater packing density is obtained at the expense of distorting hydrogen bonds from their most ideal geometry.   Kamb has assigned hydrogen positions on the basis of energy and geometrical considerations, as well as consistency with the x-ray data.   Distortion of the oxygen arrangement is such that there are no longer equally favored sites for hydrogen, and Kamb has concluded that the structure must be ordered.   This is in agreement with infrared work (Bertie and Whalley, 1964b), which shows that the O—H and O—D bands in dilute solutions of HDO in ice II are very sharp; the band width is about 5 cm^{-1}.

Kamb has defined the ideal hydrogen bond geometry for water as being that which has an H—O—H bond angle of 104.6° and linear hydrogen bonds.   Furthermore, the hydrogen atom being donated to the hydrogen bond should lie in the bisecting plane of the water molecule.   Finally, the angle between the plane of the water molecule and the O · · · H vector should be half the tetrahedral angle.   These considerations are illustrated in Figure 6-6.

The distortions from the ideal angles are defined as follows:

(1) $\Omega = \frac{1}{2}(\alpha - 104.6°)$, where α is the donor angle, that is, the angle $O_1 \cdots O_2 \cdots O_3$, where O_1 and O_3 are accepting hydrogen atoms from O_2;

(2) ϕ is the angle which the $O \cdots H$ vector makes with the plane of the molecule, projected onto the bisecting plane;

(3) ω is the angle which the projection of the $O \cdots H$ vector onto the plane of the molecule makes with the twofold axis of the molecule.

Thus ϕ and ω are angles which have to do with the properties of the water molecule as a hydrogen bond acceptor. In cases where the H positions were unknown, Kamb used the $O \cdots O$ rather than the $O \cdots H$ directions. Kamb concluded that ϕ is unimportant and that the strain energy of a hydrogen bond is given by

$$E = K(\Omega^2 + a\omega^2)$$

where a is a constant which may be about 1. For the most favorable assign-

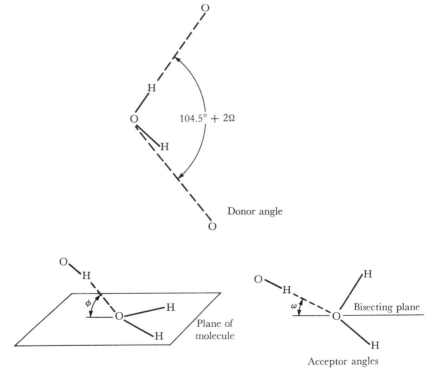

Figure 6-6 *Some geometrical parameters which may determine the energies of the ice structures. According to Kamb the ideal values for ω, ϕ, and Ω are $0°$, $55°$, and $0°$.*

ment of hydrogen positions in ice II, the values (in degrees) of Ω are 8.0, 8.0, 2.5, 2.5; of ω, 0.5, 11.5, 3.5 and 2; and of ϕ, 53.5, 45, 35, and 32. The corresponding quantities for ice I are 2.5, 0, and 54.7. The difference between the hydrogen bond energies of ice I and ice II is calculated on this basis to be 0.81 kcal mole^{-1}, with ice II being less favorable energetically. Most of this is, however, made up by a more favorable van der Waals energy, for the measured energy difference is only 0.01 kcal mole^{-1}.

Although the quantitative validity of such a procedure might be open to some question, the simplicity of the model is useful in considering the hydrogen bonding of water in other situations. The oxygen atom does indeed tend to act as a hydrogen-bond acceptor in the plane bisecting the water molecule. Furthermore, if two hydrogen bonds are formed, the angle between them tends to be tetrahedral. There is, however, little evidence that the H—O—H angle is ever much distorted from its ideal value—even though the O $\cdot\cdot\cdot$ O $\cdot\cdot\cdot$ O angle may vary over a wide range. Hydrogen bonds are rarely linear.

Ices III, V, and VI have also been studied by single-crystal x-ray diffraction techniques (Kamb and Datta, 1960; Kamb, Prakash, and Knobler, 1967; Kamb, 1965). These are all tetrahedrally coordinated structures, as was suggested by earlier x-ray powder patterns (Bertie, Calvert, and Whalley, 1963, 1964) [2] and extensive infrared and Raman spectroscopic work (Bertie and Whalley, 1964a,b; Marckmann and Whalley, 1964; Taylor and Whalley, 1964). The structure of ice VII, the densest form of ice, has been shown by an x-ray powder study (Kamb and Davis, 1964) to contain oxygens with eightfold rather than fourfold coordination. The arrangement of oxygen atoms is essentially body-centered cubic. This phase probably also has disordered hydrogen atoms, although the recently discovered phase VIII, which seems to be closely related to phase VII, is probably ordered (Whalley, Davidson, and Heath, 1966; Brown and Whalley, 1966). Thus it seems that the only proton-ordered forms are II, VIII, and a possible phase at low temperatures which is related to phase III.

The spectroscopic work shows frequency shifts which indicate less favorable hydrogen bonding in the higher pressure polymorphs, but there is less difference between these phases than between any one of them and the vapor. The assignment of the fundamental stretching band is difficult, but Whalley and co-authors have suggested the following frequencies: Ice I, 3085 cm^{-1}; ices II, III, V, VI, 3159–3204 cm^{-1}; ice VII, 3348 cm^{-1}.

It is interesting that ice is one of those rare substances where the most favorable hydrogen bonding leads to a decrease in the density of the structure. For most organic molecules, the more extensive the hydrogen bonding, the denser is the material for a given molecular weight.

[2] The work of these authors suggests that there are more phases, particularly at low temperatures, than are indicated in the phase diagram of Figure 6-2.

6-4 CLATHRATE HYDRATES

A wide variety of simple nonpolar molecules form crystalline hydrates in which the ratio of the number of water molecules to the number of other molecules is very high.   The important feature of all these structures is that

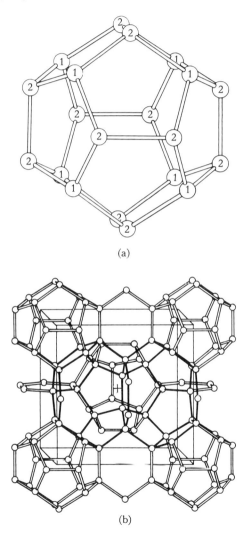

(a)

(b)

Figure 6-7 (a) *The pentagonal dodecahedron of oxygen atoms which forms the basic building block in the structures of the clathrate hydrates (from McMullan and Jeffrey, 1965).* (b) *A framework of dodecahedra linked by larger polyhedral voids.   This is the basic structure of the type I gas*

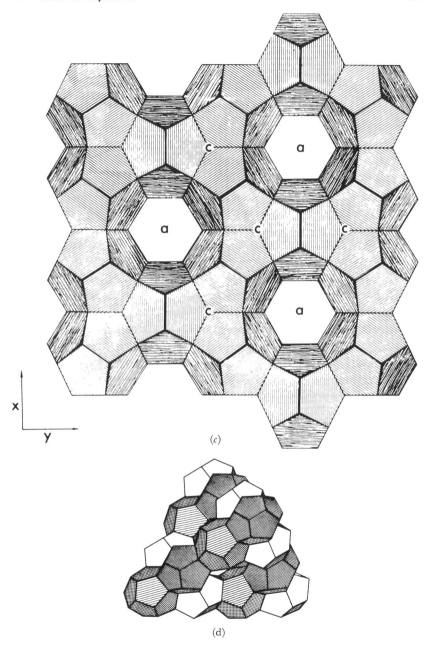

(c)

(d)

hydrates.   (From McMullan and Jeffrey, 1965.)   (c) A layer of pentagonal dodecahedra linked by larger polyhedra as found in the tetraalkylammonium fluoride hydrate structures (from Feil and Jeffrey, 1961).   (d) Another type of gas hydrate structure formed by the linking of dodecahedra (from Feil and Jeffrey, 1961).   The labels in (a) and (c) refer to sites discussed in the original papers.

they can best be thought of as structures of solid water which have been stabilized by the presence of other molecules or ions in the voids of a water lattice. Some of the simplest structures are cubic structures with the formula $6X·46H_2O$; in these compounds X is typically a monatomic gas such as argon, krypton, or xenon, or a simple molecule such as CH_4, H_2S, Cl_2, CO_2, or C_2H_6. Larger molecules form crystals with the formulas $8X·136H_2O$ and $8X·16H_2S·136H_2O$. There are also many examples of hydrates of tetraalkylammonium salts with up to 40 water molecules per cation.

The structural principle involved in many of these hydrates was first suggested by Claussen (1951a,b) and confirmed by x-ray diffraction (von Stackelberg and Mueller, 1951; Pauling and Marsh, 1952). Since then, many such structures have been elegantly established and described by Jeffrey and co-workers (McMullan and Jeffrey, 1965, for example). The basic building block is the pentagonal dodecahedron composed of 20 water molecules (Figure 6-7a). There are 20 oxygen atoms at the vertices of the dodecahedron; 30 hydrogen atoms may lie along the edges of the dodeca-hedron to form a tightly hydrogen-bonded entity. The remaining 10 hydrogen atoms may be used for hydrogen bonding to adjacent polyhedra, and 10 of the oxygen atoms can thus act as acceptors for hydrogen bonds from other polyhedra. The internal angle of the pentagon is 108°, not an unreasonable value for a pair of hydrogen bonds. This configuration would thus seem to be a very stable one for water itself, and it has in fact been proposed that this configuration may be the dominant one in liquid water (Pauling, 1960, p. 472).[3] Unfortunately, however, pentagonal solids cannot pack in a space-filling way, so that it is necessary that any regular lattice including these pentagonal dodecahedra also include other, larger coordina-tion polyhedra (Figure 6-7b,c,d). These larger coordination polyhedra now have voids at their centers which are large enough to accommodate the gas molecules mentioned above. The presence of these molecules in the voids or "cages" is sufficient to stabilize the structure. Without them the structure collapses into liquid water.

6-5 THE STRUCTURE OF LIQUID WATER

Although we have purposely restricted the discussions in this book to hydrogen bonding in solids, it is impossible to discuss the structure of ice and hydrates without making some remarks concerning the structure of liquid water.

---

[3] This does not seem to be supported by the experimental evidence page 203.

Water (liquid) is denser than ice; it appears to be possible to form energetically more favorable hydrogen bonds if disorder is allowed. This suggests that water should also form glasses easily, and indeed vitreous water is well characterized as one of the possible forms of solid water. The extent of icelike crystalline order in liquid water and the dynamics of liquid water have been the subjects of intense speculation.

Various models have been proposed for the structure of water; these are essentially of two types [4]:

(1) Water may have a structure which has several different types of distinct molecular complexes, ranging from free nonhydrogen-bonded water molecules to quasi-crystalline regions with order extending over many molecules. One such model involves only two species: free molecules and large crystalline chunks; in this view, water is a mixture of vapor and ice. More elaborate models have been proposed in which water is composed of single molecules and complexes with two, four, or eight molecules.

(2) An alternative view postulates that water is essentially homogeneous in that there are no large perfectly crystalline regions separated by free molecules. Rather, the entire liquid is quasi-crystalline in the sense that an individual molecule has an environment and behaves much as if it were a molecule in the solid, but the regularity of the structure has broken down, with consequent variations in the lengths of the hydrogen bonds. The irregular structure may be thought to be continually changing on a time scale which is, however, slow compared with the internal motions of the water molecule.

The first type of model can be used to predict successfully some of the thermodynamic properties of water. In the extreme, one can consider that liquid water is composed of two types of molecules: one as firmly bound as in the solid state, another completely free. This model has been called the *significant structure* model (Eyring, Ree, and Hirai, 1958); liquid water is described as a mixture of ice and water vapor. This can be further refined to include more than two significant structures. An excellent review of this type of model has been given by Nemethy and Scheraga (1962), who have made an extensive analysis of a model in which there exist water molecules involved in 4, 3, 2, 1, or 0 hydrogen bonds. Best agreement with the thermodynamic properties is obtained if the number of free, nonhydrogen-bonded molecules accounts for 25 to 40% of the total. This conclusion is untenable in view of the structural evidence cited below. Furthermore, the model

---

[4] The idea that water may best be described as being quasi-crystalline was first discussed in detail by Bernal and Fowler (1933), who postulated that ice, has an irregular four-coordinated structure, which below 4°C is a distortion of the structure of ice, but at higher temperatures is closely related to the structure of quartz (SiO_2). Tridymite, another form of SiO_2, has a structure related to that of ice.

loses a great deal of its utility when the number of different structures, and hence the number of adjustable parameters, becomes large.

Models of type (2) have more intuitive appeal and have been given a great deal of support by the work of Wall and Hornig (1965), who have examined the Raman spectrum of HDO in liquid water. The vibrations of the HDO molecule are uncoupled because of the dilution. No distinct bands at different frequencies are observed for the O—H or O—D stretching vibrations. The authors have concluded that this is strong evidence against the existence of two or at most a few distinct types of water molecules in water. Rather, there is a continuous distribution of frequencies with maxima at 2516 cm^{-1} for O—D and 3439 cm^{-1} for O—H. These may be compared with values of 2421 and 3277 cm^{-1} in ice I and 2727 and 3704 cm^{-1} in the vapor. The most probable hydrogen bond strength is less in the liquid than in ice, but it is still quite strong. Using the bond length frequency relationship (Section 3-2), we may obtain a bond length distribution from the frequency distribution. The distribution of bonds lengths so obtained is shown in Figure 6-8. A similar study by Falk and Ford (1966), using infrared rather than Raman spectra, leads to identical results.

The distance distribution derived by Wall and Hornig is similar to that obtained by Danford and Levy (1962) from a radial distribution curve obtained from an x-ray diffraction pattern from liquid water. This radial distribution curve (Figure 6-9) is not compatible with a model containing but a few distinct types of water molecules. There is a peak in the radial distribution curve at 2.9 A, which is 6% greater than the distance in ice I. The area under the curve is consistent with a model in which each oxygen has four nearest neighbors. The number of next-nearest neighbors is, however, greater than that in ice. Danford and Levy have refined a model of water in which an icelike structure, slightly expanded, accommodates

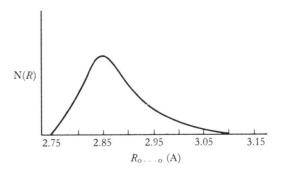

Figure 6-8 *O · · · O distance distribution in liquid water as determined by analysis of the infrared spectrum of isotopic mixtures by Wall and Hornig (1965).*

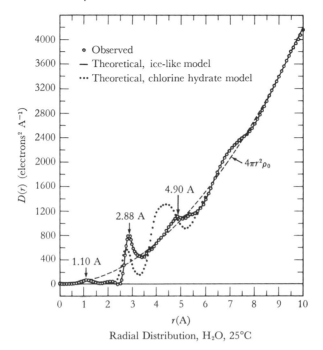

Radial Distribution, H_2O, 25°C

Figure 6-9 *Interatomic radial distribution curve in water from the x-ray scattering experiment of Danford and Levy (1962).*

"interstitial" water molecules in some of the open polyhedra of the ice structure. The first neighbor and next-nearest neighbor distances were refined, together with thermal vibration parameters and an occupancy factor for the interstitial water. In the refined model, each framework water molecule has one neighbor at 2.77 A and three at 2.94 A. The interstitial water has three neighbors at each of the distances 2.94 A, 3.30 A, 3.40 A, and 3.92 A. Fifty percent of the possible cavities are filled with interstitial water. The data are obviously too limited to allow one to say that this is the only possible model; the general features are probably correct since the essential parameters are the numbers and distances of the neighbors. A number of models can be rejected by their failure to predict the proper radial distribution curve; in particular Danford and Levy assert that the pentagonal dodecahedral model of water similar to that of the clathrate hydrates does not give a reasonable fit to the data. Rather than superimpose too much geometrical detail on the structure, it would seem more reasonable to refine a model which is described in terms of various short-range order parameters.

The torsional frequencies of the water molecule in ice and in liquid water, as obtained from both infrared spectra and neutron inelastic scattering, are in reasonable agreement.   This indicates that most of the water molecules in water probably have an icelike environment (see, for example, Larsson, 1965).

6-6 HYDROGEN BONDING IN CRYSTALLINE HYDRATES

Perhaps the most widely studied of hydrogen-bonded substances are the hydrates of inorganic salts.   One might even guess that these are the most widespread of hydrogen-bonded substances in nature, for although the hydrogen bonding of amino acids and nitrogen-containing bases is of the greatest significance as far as life as we know it goes, the crust of the earth is abundant with minerals which contain water of crystallization.   The studies of the structures of these hydrates can lead to answers to questions such as the following:

(1) Is the geometry of the water molecule distorted in the formation of hydrates from the geometry which it has in the vapor phase or in crystalline water?

(2) How important is the role of water in stabilizing the crystal structures of salts containing possible hydrogen bond acceptors?   Are ionic crystal structures predictable on the basis of the minimization of electrostatic potentials?

(3) Does the water molecule ever appear in a crystal without being hydrogen bonded or without being a ligand of a metal ion?   That is, does it sometimes simply fill a hole without forming any specific directional bonds?

(4) Are there any well-defined classifications of types of water molecules in solids which may be useful in discussing them?

Classification of Hydrates

Let us attempt to answer the final question first.   How may we describe water molecules as they exist in inorganic crystals?

In many crystalline hydrates, the water molecule performs a dual role. First, it is a very satisfactory ligand for many cations.   Typically one finds the negative end of the water dipole directed toward the metal ion.   This can be described in terms of overlap of the lone pair orbitals on the water molecule with various empty hybrid orbitals on the metal ion.   Second, the interposition of water molecules hydrogen bonded to anions in the crystal may be of importance in minimizing electrostatic repulsions between these anions.

As an especially simple example of this dual function, we illustrate the structure of $FeSiF_6 \cdot 6H_2O$ (Figure 6-10) (Hamilton, 1962a).   An anhydrous salt $FeSiF_6$ is not known.   The large SiF_6^{--} ions probably cannot pack to

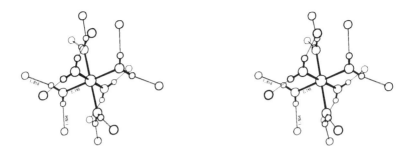

Figure 6-10 *Hydrogen bonding in ferrous fluorosilicate hexahydrate.   Each fluorine atom is the acceptor for two hydrogen bonds, only one of which is shown.*

form a stable structure with Fe^{++} atoms in the interstices, because of large electrostatic interactions between the F atoms.   Thus the water molecules, entering into hydrogen bonding with the F atoms, allow the SiF_6^{--} ions to be further apart.   Examination of Figure 6-10 will also readily indicate that the molecular formula might better be written as $Fe(H_2O)_6 \cdot SiF_6$, for the six water molecules are bound to the Fe to form a large octahedral complex ion.   The twofold axis of the water molecule is directed toward the metal atom to contribute its electrons to the d^2sp^3 octahedral orbitals of the iron. Each of the hydrogen atoms is bonded to a single F atom, while each of the F atoms serves as an acceptor in two hydrogen bonds.

In most crystals the lone pair orbitals of water either are directed toward metal atoms or are acting as acceptors in other hydrogen bonds.   Because of the common occurrence of the lone pair coordination of the water molecule in inorganic crystalline solids, Chidambaram, Sequeira, and Sikka (1964) have proposed a classification of hydrates based on the type of coordination of the lone pair orbitals.   These are of essentially two types, those where each of the lone pair orbitals is involved in a specific bond [5] (we call these class 1) and those where the twofold axis of the water molecule or the bisectrix of the lone pair orbitals is directed toward a single bonding entity (we call these class 2) (see Figure 6-11).   Chidambaram *et al.* have further subdivided these broad classifications by considering the nature of the bonding entities X and Y, which they allow to take four possible values: M^+, a univalent cation; M^{++}, a divalent cation; $\cdot \cdot \cdot$ H, a hydrogen bond; and —, no specific interaction discernible.   These types are listed in Table 6-2, which is adapted from that given by Chidambaram *et al.*   Type I does not appear to have

---

[5] In this context and elsewhere in this chapter, we take *bond* to mean both hydrogen bond and the attraction between a metal atom and its ligands, as well as the more restrictive covalent bond.

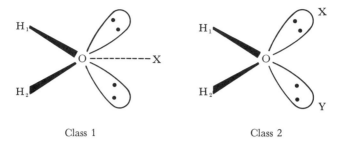

Class 1   Class 2

Figure 6-11 *Two types of coordination of water molecules as related to the configuration of the lone-pair orbitals. Class 1 has one ligand along the twofold axis of the molecule. Class 2 has two ligands such that X, Y, H_1, and H_2 are directed toward the corners of a tetrahedron.*

been observed, and the only occurrence of type L which has been definitely established is that of potassium oxalate monohydrate. The hydrogen bonds in the latter compound, of course, are between water and the organic anion, so it is perhaps not fair to include this example. Furthermore, the alkali metal ions do not generally form complexes of regular geometry.

In Figure 6-12 are shown two types which are not included in the classification of Chidambaram *et al.* but which have been observed in the structure of sodium perxenate octahydrate (Ibers, Hamilton, and MacKenzie, 1964). In each of these types the oxygen atom of the water molecule forms five bonds: the two covalent O—H bonds, a metal coordinated to the lone pair bisectrix,

Table 6-2 *Classification of Hydrogen-Bonded Water Molecules by Nature of Water Molecule Coordination*

Type	X	Y
Class 1		
C	M^+	
D	M^{++}	
F	$\cdots$ H	
Class 2		
A	M^+	M^+
B	M^{++}	M^{++}
E	$\cdots$ H	$\cdots$ H
G	M^+	$\cdots$ H
H	M^{++}	$\cdots$ H
I	M^+	—
J	M^{++}	—
K	$\cdots$ H	—
L	—	—

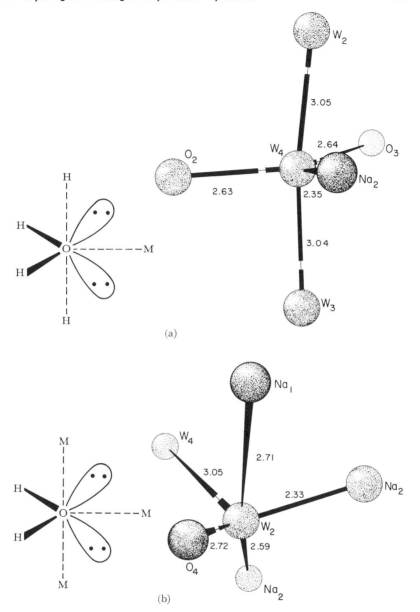

Figure 6-12 (a) *Trigonal bipyramidal coordination of oxygen in a water molecule in sodium perxenate octahydrate.   The water molecule acts as the acceptor in two hydrogen bonds perpendicular to the molecular plane.   It is coordinated to a single metal ion in the plane.   (b) Another type of trigonal bipyramidal coordination found in sodium perxenate octahydrate.   In this case the water molecule does not act as a hydrogen bond acceptor.*

and either two hydrogen bonds or two other coordinated metals perpendicular to the plane of the molecule. The coordination is essentially that of a trigonal bipyramid.[6]

Whether or not these detailed classifications are useful is a moot point, but they do illustrate the flexibility of the water molecule for forming hydrogen bonds and taking part in a crystalline complex under many different circumstances. The principal features are that the hydrogen atoms of the water molecule are almost always involved in hydrogen bonds, and that in the opposite direction, that of the negative end of the water dipole, there are almost always one or more coordinated cations, or the water molecule is also acting as a hydrogen bond acceptor.

Baur's Semiquantitative Electrostatic Theory

Although it was often assumed in early discussions of hydrogen bonding that the $O-H \cdots O$ is always linear or nearly so, it has been pointed out by several authors (Hamilton, 1962b; Chidambaram, 1962; and Fuller, 1959) that this is not a necessary criterion for the formation of a hydrogen bond and that, indeed, linearity appears to be more an exception than the rule. Of far more importance in hydrates is the more or less constant geometry of the water molecule itself. (We shall have more to say about this below.) The hydrogen bonding adapts itself to the fixed geometry of the water molecule, the sizes of the ions, and other packing considerations.

These considerations have been placed on a semiquantitative basis by Baur (1965), who has attempted through energy calculations to understand several unusual hydrogen bonds in hydrates. Among the several structures discussed by Baur are two with bifurcated hydrogen bonds. In $MgSO_4 \cdot 4H_2O$ (Baur, 1964; Figure 6-13) one of the two crystallographically distinct water molecules contributes one of its hydrogen atoms to a hydrogen bond involving another oxygen, but the other hydrogen atom participates in two hydrogen bonds at a somewhat longer than normal $O-H \cdots O$ hydrogen bond distance. A similar situation occurs in violuric acid monohydrate (Figure 6-14) (Craven and Takei, 1964).

Baur's model is purely electrostatic and thus cannot be expected to be strictly quantitative. In most hydrogen-bonded crystals, van der Waals attractive forces and repulsive forces must also be important in determining the molecular packing. Baur assumed that in crystalline hydrates the water molecule has a fixed geometry with $O-H$ bond length of 0.97 A and a bond angle of 109.5°. The molecule was described as consisting of three point charges, ϵ at each of the hydrogen positions and -2ϵ at the oxygen position.

---

[6] This type of configuration may possibly be found only in the presence of alkali metal ions, where the coordination geometry does not seem to be governed by strong directional considerations.

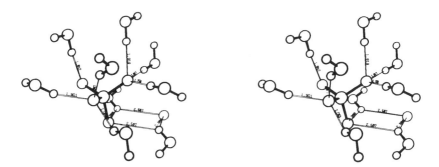

Figure 6-13 *Hydrogen bonding in MgSO$_4$·4H$_2$O.*

Monatomic ions were assigned appropriate charges, and electric charges of $-0.5e$ were assigned to each oxygen of sulfate groups. Charges in the organic part of violuric acid were estimated from simple molecular orbital calculations and ranged from $-0.4e$ for oxygen to $0.6e$ for nonwater hydrogen atoms. The positions of the heavy atoms, including the oxygens of the water molecules, were taken as known, and the electrostatic energies based on this point-charge distribution were calculated as a function of the hydrogen atom positions. Those hydrogen atom positions which led to the least electrostatic energy were then determined by the use of a computer program. The computed hydrogen positions and those determined in neutron diffraction studies were compared and found to agree very well indeed. The best agreement was found for a charge of $+0.5e$ on each hydrogen and $-e$ on the oxygen of each water molecule. The model was successful in predicting the bifurcated bonds in the compounds mentioned above as well as predicting the orientation of the water molecules in some more conventional systems. In this study Baur predicted the positions of 28 hydrogen atoms and found that the average deviation of the calculated position from the observed position was 0.1 A. Some representative results are shown in Table 6-3.

The small angles for O—H · · · Cl in BaCl$_2$·2H$_2$O are perhaps indicative of weak hydrogen bonds and are not unusual when Cl$^-$ is the acceptor in a hydrogen bond. A similar situation is found in methylglyoxal bisguanylhydrazone (Section 5-6). The structure of hydronium chloride (Section 3-7), however, has nearly linear hydrogen bonds.

In MgSO$_4$·4H$_2$O there is available an alternative orientation of the second water molecule which would allow it to form a second hydrogen bond with an O · · · O distance of 3.02 A, an O · · · H distance of 2.2 A, and an O—H · · · O angle of 147°. One might expect at first glance that this would be a more favorable hydrogen bonding situation than that found experimentally, which involves two rather long hydrogen bonds.

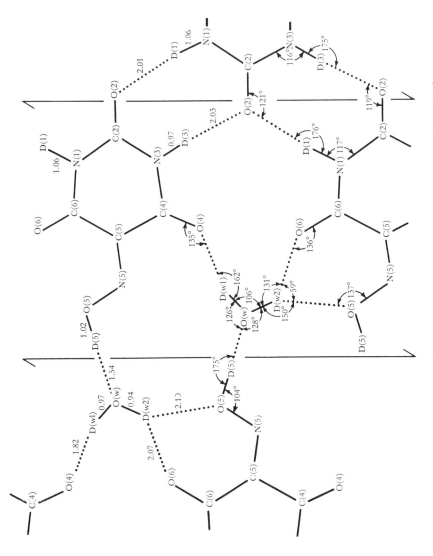

Figure 6-14 Hydrogen bonding in violuric acid monohydrate (from Craven and Takei, 1964).

Table 6-3 *Observed Hydrogen Bond Parameters in Three Compounds Compared with Those Predicted by Electrostatic Considerations (Baur, 1965)*

Compound	H $\cdots$ X (A)		$\angle$O—H $\cdots$ X (deg)	
	Obs.	Calc.	Obs.	Calc.
MgSO$_4\cdot$4H$_2$O	2.06	1.98	149	140
	1.85	1.88	174	166
	1.95	1.91	151	158
Bifurcated	$\begin{cases}2.39\end{cases}$	2.48	127	117
O—H $\cdots$ O	$\begin{cases}2.59\end{cases}$	2.50	132	137
Violuric acid$\cdot$H$_2$O	1.82	1.83	162	159
Bifurcated	$\begin{cases}2.11\end{cases}$	2.05	150	157
O—H $\cdots$ O	$\begin{cases}2.07\end{cases}$	2.13	131	124
BaCl$_2\cdot$2H$_2$O	2.22	2.23	171	167
Bifurcated	$\begin{cases}2.66\end{cases}$	2.66	125	124
O—H $\cdots$ Cl	$\begin{cases}2.49\end{cases}$	2.50	135	132

Although Baur's model depends on a number of assumptions and demands knowledge of the heavy atom positions, it should be useful in predicting approximate orientations of water molecules when the heavy atom positions are known.   It could thus be a useful model in helping to design further experiments to locate the hydrogen atoms more precisely.

Structure of the Water Molecule in Hydrates

We may now ask the question whether the water molecule in crystalline hydrates has a geometry that deviates significantly from that in the vapor phase.   For a definitive answer to this question, we must look at neutron diffraction studies and at the determinations of interproton distance by NMR methods, although these are somewhat less reliable (Section 3-3). (An excellent review of the NMR results is given by El Saffar, 1966.) Chidambaram (1962) has given an excellent summary of the experimental data up to 1961, as well as a description of some energy calculations which will be discussed below.   Most of the reliable neutron diffraction data on water molecule geometry are summarized in Table 6-4.

Although the angle O $\cdots$ O $\cdots$ O varies from 80 to 130° [7] (Figure 6-15) the H—O—H angles deviate less than a few degrees from the value in

---

[7] Fuller (1959) has given a very excellent summary of determinations of hydrogen bond angles up to the date of his paper.

Table 6-4 *Water Molecule Geometry in Crystalline Hydrates*[a]

Compound	O—H₁ (A)	O—H₂ (A)	∠H₁—O—H₂ (deg)	Acceptor angle	Reference[b]
CuSO₄·5H₂O	0.97	0.97	114	119	1
	0.94	0.96	111	121	
	0.96	1.00	109	130	
	0.96	0.94	109	105	
	0.97	0.96	106	122	
UO₂(NO₃)₂·6H₂O	0.97	0.97	107	113	2
	0.98	0.93	107	110	
	0.95	0.87	115	81	
Th(NO₃)₄·5H₂O	0.95	0.95	110	100	3
	0.97	0.96	111	109	
	0.95	0.98	107	122	
D₂O	1.01[c]	1.01[c]	109	109	4
CaSO₄·2H₂O	1.00	0.98	106	106	5
Oxalic Acid·2H₂O	0.97	0.95	106	84	6
Na₂CO₃·NaHCO₃·2H₂O	0.99	1.03	107	114	7
CuF₂·2H₂O (298°K)	0.98[c]	0.98[c]	116	97	8
CuF₂·2H₂O (4.2°K)	0.96[c]	0.96[c]	110	95	9
FeSiF₆·6H₂O	0.92[c]	0.92[c]	112		10
CuCl₂·2H₂O	0.95	0.95	108	85	11
MgSO₄·4H₂O	0.97	0.95	110	105	12
	0.97	0.93	111	92, 147, bifurcated	
	0.95	0.99	109	138	
	0.96	0.98	109	114	
CrK(SO₄)₂·12H₂O	1.02	1.03	107	102	13
	1.03	0.95	103	94	
Violuric acid·H₂O	0.97	0.94	106	61, 115, bifurcated	14
(NH₄)₂C₂O₄·H₂O	0.97	0.97	106	125	15
K₂C₂O₄·H₂O	0.96	0.96	108	120	16

[a] With a few exceptions this table includes results only from three-dimensional neutron diffraction studies which have been published in the regular scientific literature, excluding meeting abstracts and technical reports of government agencies. The standard deviations are rarely worse than 3° in the angles and 0.04 in the bond lengths. Some of the values are of course much better than this; reference should be made to the original papers if these numbers are to be used elsewhere.

[b] (1) Bacon and Curry (1962); (2) Taylor and Mueller (1965); (3) Taylor, Mueller, and Hitterman (1966); (4) Peterson and Levy (1957); (5) Atoji and Rundle (1958); (6) Garrett (1954); (7) Bacon and Curry (1956); (8) Abrahams and Prince (1962); (9) Abrahams (1962); (10) Hamilton (1962a); (11) Levy and Peterson (1957); (12) Baur (1964); (13) Bacon and Gardner (1958); (14) Craven and Takei (1964); (15) Padmanabhan, Srikantha and Ali (1965); (16) Chidambaram, Sequeira and Sikka (1964).

[c] O—H bond lengths corrected for thermal motion.

water vapor. The mean value obtained in several neutron diffraction investigations is 109°. The energy of bending the H—O—H molecule is, in the harmonic approximation, $0.016(\Delta\theta)^2$, where the energy is in kilocalories per mole and $\Delta\theta$ is the change in the bond angle in degrees. (See, for example, Heath and Linnet, 1948.) To change the O—H $\cdots$ O hydrogen bond angle by $\Delta°$ from the presumably ideal value of 180° requires, according to the Lippincott-Schroeder potential (Section 3-5) for an O—O distance of 2.76 A, $0.003\Delta^2$ kcal mole^{-1}. The hydrogen bonds will thus tend to accommodate themselves to keep the covalent bond angles close to the equilibrium values for the free molecule. A meaningful quantitative treatment would demand knowledge of the anharmonic terms in the potential functions. This knowledge is available for the covalent bond, but not for the hydrogen bond. In any event it is not clear that the energetically most favorable configuration for the hydrogen bond is the linear one. It is entirely possible that it is better for the covalent O—H bond to be directed toward the center of gravity of a lone pair orbital rather than toward the nucleus with which the orbital is associated. Whatever the reasons, hydrogen bonds in crystals often show large deviations from linearity (see Figure 6-16).

In general, then, one expects that the H—O—H angle will differ little from what it is in water vapor. This should be especially true when the water molecule is only weakly coordinated to metal ions. If there is a strong interaction between water and a metal ion, one might expect some rehybridization of the oxygen orbitals which could lead to changes in bond angle. In fact the few angles determined by neutron diffraction which seem to be unusually high are all in hydrates of transition metals: $CuCl_2 \cdot 2H_2O$ (108°), $CuF_2 \cdot 2H_2O$ (115° at 298°K, and 110° at 4.2°K), and $CuSO_2 \cdot 5H_2O$

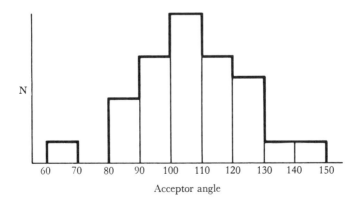

Figure 6-15 *Distribution of* O $\cdots$ O $\cdots$ O *angles in a number of hydrogen-bonded hydrates. Although the mean value is near the H—O—H bond angle in water, considerable leeway is allowed in this acceptor angle. Angles are in degrees.*

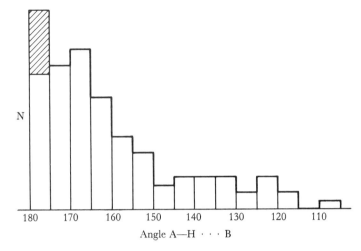

N

180   170   160   150   140   130   120   110

Angle A—H · · · B

Figure 6-16 *Histogram of A—H · · · B angles in all hydrogen-bonded systems studied by neutron diffraction prior to September 1966.   The shaded area represents those angles required to be 180° by the symmetry of the crystal.   Angle is in degrees.*

(mean of several, 109°).   These values may all be inadequately corrected for thermal motion.   In fact the results on $CuF_2 \cdot 2H_2O$ at the two temperatures suggest that there are large motional effects on the apparent angle; there is no phase transition involved here, and one would not expect that the equilibrium value of the H—O—H angle would change if there is no change in the crystal structure.   If this is indeed a thermal motion effect, there is a very anharmonic motion in the bending mode which renders an accurate determination of the bond angle by diffraction methods hopeless.

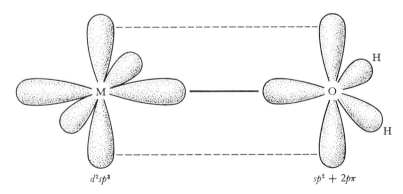

d^2sp^3 $sp^2 + 2p\pi$

Figure 6-17 *If the $2p\pi$ orbital on water interacts with the octahedral orbitals on a metal atom to which it is coordinated, the hybridization in the plane may approach sp^2, and one can therefore expect angles nearer 120°.*

Chidambaram (1962) has quoted two examples in which a crystal with two water molecules, one bound to a transition metal and one not, shows two different angles, the smaller angle being in the water molecule not coordinated to the transition metal. If more s character is needed in the plane of the molecule for good overlap with the metal orbital, then there might be some tendency for sp^2 hybridization in the plane, leading to a larger bond angle; the remaining π orbital could also be involved in bonding to the metal (see Figure 6-17).

Some Typical Hydrate Structures

URANYL NITRATE HEXAHYDRATE. The structure has been determined by neutron diffraction, and the configuration around the uranium atom and the hydrogen bonding are shown in Figure 6-18 (Taylor and Mueller, 1965). One water molecule has its twofold axis directed toward uranium. It forms hydrogen bonds to other water molecules. The other two water molecules each are surrounded approximately tetrahedrally by four oxygen atoms and four hydrogen bonds. Each molecule donates one hydrogen bond to a nitrate group and one to a water molecule and accepts two hydrogen bonds from other water molecules. The thermal motion is slightly less for the water molecule bound to the uranium than for the other water molecules. The hydrogen-bonded water molecules form infinite sheets perpendicular to the a axis of the crystal. Two of the water molecules extend their hydrogen atoms up or down to permit hydrogen bonding to the nitrate groups in alternate layers. It is interesting to note (see Table 6-4) that the most severe distortion of the water valence angle is associated with an O $\cdots$ O $\cdots$ O angle which is somewhat less than ideal for hydrogen bonding. The standard deviations in this structure were estimated to be 0.01 A. The range of the O—H distances suggests that this estimate may be overly optimistic.

COPPER SULFATE PENTAHYDRATE. This structure (Figure 6-19) has been accurately determined by neutron diffraction (Bacon and Curry, 1962). There are five crystallographically distinct water molecules. Four of these are in the coordination sphere of the copper ion, while one is not. Each of the coordinated water molecules forms two hydrogen bonds; the free molecule forms four: two accepted and two donated. The O $\cdots$ O $\cdots$ O angles and the corresponding H—O—H angles are shown in Table 6-4. Note that the smallest H—O—H angle is associated with the free water molecule, and that the mean of the H—O—H angles for the four molecules coordinated to copper is somewhat larger than that for water vapor. This is consistent with the arguments given in the paragraphs above. On the other hand, the spread of values for these four angles is so great as to render such comparisons rather speculative.

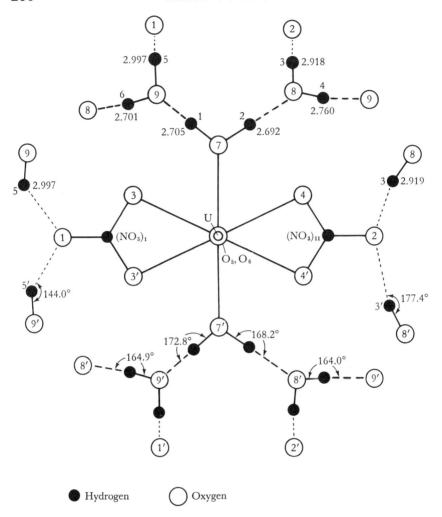

Figure 6-18 *The equatorial plane in uranyl nitrate hexahydrate, which has the structure of a hexagonal bipyramid. The water-water hydrogen bonds are shorter, and presumably stronger, than the water-nitrate hydrogen bonds. (From Taylor and Mueller, 1965.)*

POTASSIUM FLUORIDE TETRAHYDRATE, $KF \cdot 4H_2O$. The crystal structure (Figure 6-20) has been determined by x-ray diffraction (Beurskens and Jeffrey, 1964). This interesting structure consists of K^+ ions and F^- ions separated by water molecules in such a way that both the positive and negative ions are surrounded by octahedra of oxygen atoms. One edge of each octahedron is shared with an adjacent octahedron. The hydrogen

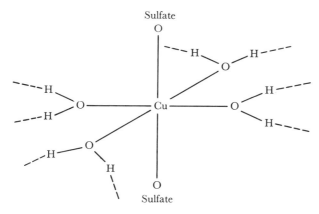

Figure 6-19 *The coordination of Cu in CuSO$_4$·5H$_2$O. Hydrogen bonds are formed from water to water and from water to sulfate oxygen. There seems to be no significant difference between the two types.*

atoms were not precisely located, but peaks in the electron density difference synthesis did occur near expected hydrogen positions. The fluorine atom is an acceptor for six hydrogen bonds at the corners of a somewhat irregular octahedron (the angles vary from 82 to 101 degrees). Each oxygen atom has an approximately tetrahedral coordination, so that the water molecules may be described as Chidambaram's type A and type G (Table 6-2).

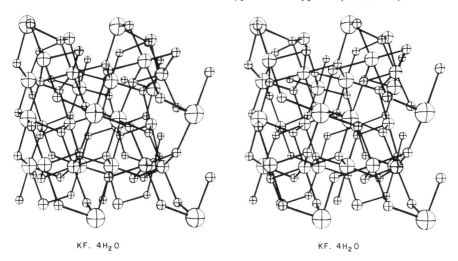

KF. 4H$_2$O   KF. 4H$_2$O

Figure 6-20 *The structure of KF·4H$_2$O. The large balls represent potassium ions; and the smallest, water molecules. Notice that each fluoride is surrounded octahedrally by six water molecules, as is each potassium ion. Each water molecule is approximately tetrahedrally coordinated, but all four contacts are not shown.*

SODIUM PERXENATE OCTAHYDRATE AND HEXAHYDRATE. The perxenate (XeO_6^{4-}) ion is a well-established species in solution. An anhydrous salt may exist, but if so it is poorly crystalline. There are, however, a variety of hydrates of the sodium and potassium salts. We again have an example of a large, highly charged anion which crystallizes as a hydrate because of the minimization of electrostatic forces. The water molecules serve to keep the anions apart; at the same time they form coordination spheres around the alkali metal ions, although this would seem to be of secondary importance. The two structures which have been done of sodium salts are very different. The octahydrate (Ibers, Hamilton, and MacKenzie, 1964) (Figure 6-21) is a very complex network of hydrogen-bonded water molecules and perxenate ions and sodium ions which cannot be simply described. The perxenate oxygen atoms act as acceptors in a varied number of hydrogen bonds (Table 6-5). Several of these are short O—H · · · O bonds and are shorter than the interwater molecule hydrogen bonds in the same structure; this suggests that the oxygen atom in perxenate is a more electron-rich hydrogen bond acceptor than is another water molecule, and adds further weight to the evidence that there is a good deal of ionic character in bonds to the noble gas atoms. Although two of the water molecules in this structure have an approximate tetrahedral configuration, two others have trigonal bipyramidal configuration as was illustrated in Figure 6-12.

Sodium perxenate hexahydrate (Zalkin, Forrester, and Templeton, 1964)

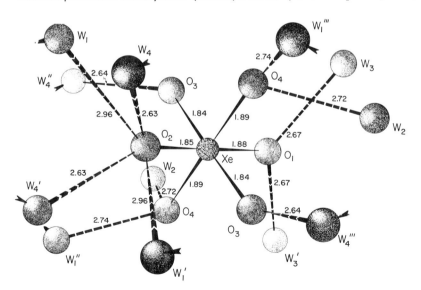

Figure 6-21 *Hydrogen bonding in part of the structure of sodium perxenate octahydrate, showing the surroundings of a single perxenate ion.*

Table 6-5 *Hydrogen Bonding in the Perxenate Hydrates*

X_1	X_2	X_3	$X_1 - X_2$ (A)	$X_2 - X_3$ (A)	$\angle X_1 - X_2 - X_3$ (deg)
			Octahydrate		
O_1	W_3	W_4	2.67	3.04	112
O_2	W_4	O_3	2.63	2.64	127
O_2	W_1	O_4	2.96	2.74	116
O_4	W_2	W_4	2.72	3.05	85
			Hexahydrate		
O_1	W_1	O_2	2.81	2.77	88
O_1	W_2	O_3	2.69	2.76	88
O_2	W_3	W_2	2.79	2.97	107

has a much simpler structure, which can be described in terms of alternating layers of $(XeO_6^{4-}, 2Na^+)$ and $(6H_2O, 2Na^+)$ (Figure 6-22). In the first layer, each sodium atom is surrounded by six water molecules. The layers ⁀re held together by hydrogen bonds between the water molecules and the perxenate oxygens. There are also water-water hydrogen bonds in the water-sodium layers. As in the octahydrate, the water-perxenate hydrogen bonds are shorter (see Table 6-5) than the water-water hydrogen bonds. The average hydrogen bond distances in the two types are 2.76 and 2.97 A. In the octahydrate, they are 2.72 and 3.05 A for the averages with two of the former type being as short as 2.64 A.

SODIUM NITROPRUSSIDE, $Na_2Fe(CN)_5(NO) \cdot 2H_2O$. This structure (Manoharan and Hamilton, 1963) has one independent water molecule, which is coordinated to the Na^+ ion at one corner of a distorted octahedron. It appears to be an example of a water molecule which is not forming a definite pair of hydrogen bonds. Only the oxygen atom of the water molecule was located in the x-ray diffraction study. Its closest neighbors are the nitrogens of two CN groups at distances of 3.27 A and 3.36 A. These two nitrogen atoms

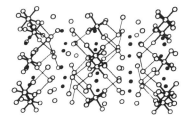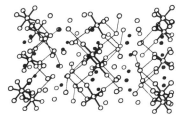

Figure 6-22 *Hydrogen bonding in sodium perxenate hexahydrate, which forms a beautiful layer structure, perxenate and sodium layers alternating with sodium and water layers.*

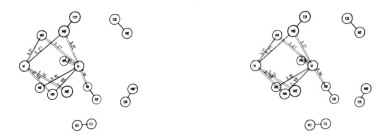

Figure 6-23 *Environment of the water molecule in sodium nitroprusside.   The possibility of strong hydrogen bonding is remote.   All atoms within 4 A are shown, with distances less than 3.5 A being specifically labeled.*

(Figure 6-23), however, subtend an angle of 63° and are part of the same sodium coordination octahedron.   There are no known cases where hydrogen bonds exist between water molecules of the same metal coordination polyhedron, so it appears unlikely that these are hydrogen bonds.   There are, however, several O · · · N distances between 3 A and 4 A.   It would be very interesting to determine the hydrogen atom positions by neutron diffraction to see whether the configuration can be reasonably interpreted in terms of hydrogen bonding and whether Baur's electrostatic model would explain the configuration found.   There are undoubtedly many similar examples in monohydrates, and perhaps the function of the water is to serve only to complete the coordination around the cation.   It seems reasonable, though, that the acidic character of the water protons can always help stabilize the structure if there are atoms with unshared electron pairs in the structure.

Organic Hydrates

The subject of organic hydrates seems best treated at this point, since it is again the behavior of the "inorganic" water molecule which is of interest. We shall not discuss the subject in great detail but shall only summarize the results of an excellent review of a few years ago (Clark, 1963).   This review describes the structures of many organic hydrates in some detail.

The most common type of hydrogen bond in these compounds is the O—H · · · O hydrogen bond, of which there are 180 cases tabulated (mean bond length, 2.84 A).   When two such bonds are formed by a single water molecule, the spread in O · · · O · · · O angles is from 57° to 144° with a mean value of 110°.

There were 32 hydrogen bonds observed between water and an organic N atom, and water was in almost all cases the acceptor in the hydrogen bond from an NH_x group; this is presumably because of the frequent positive nature of nitrogen in many of the compounds included in the list. Hydrogen bonding to Cl^-, Br^-, and I^- is more common than to nitrogen, and a recurrent feature in a large class of organic compounds is the existence of spiral chains of water and halogen ions. The mean lengths for $O—H \cdots X$ bonds were 3.20, 3.34, and 3.53 A for Cl^-, Br^-, and I^-. Many of the compounds in the compilation were in fact hydrated salts of organic compounds; whenever possible, the water molecule in these compounds is coordinated to a metal ion as well as being involved in hydrogen bonding.

6-7 AMMONIA AND AMMONIUM SALTS

Next to water, the ammonium ion is perhaps the most ubiquitous hydrogen-bonding entity in inorganic compounds. Ammonia itself is one of the simplest of hydrogen-bonded substances, and the structures of many ammonium salts have been determined. Many ammonium salts exhibit a number of phase transitions. The ammonium ion is capable of forming four hydrogen bonds by contributing hydrogen atoms. It does not act as a hydrogen bond acceptor. Because the four hydrogen atoms are directed toward the corners of a surrounding tetrahedron, the most favorable hydrogen bonding can take place when the environment of the ammonium ion consists of a tetrahedral array of hydrogen bonding acceptors. This is a rather stringent condition, and often there will be more than four hydrogen bond acceptors at nearly equal distances from the nitrogen atom. It then becomes possible to have several ammonium ions of equivalent or nearly equivalent energy. If the energies are equivalent, there arises the possibility of a disordered structure, with the ammonium ion spending its time half in one place and half in the other for twofold disorder; if the energies are only slightly different for many possible orientations, one expects to see evidence of large anharmonic thermal motion, such as hindered rotation with a low barrier (Chapter 4).

Because of these possibilities and the rather delicate energy considerations that determine stability in hydrogen-bonded systems, it is not surprising that one frequently finds several stable phases for the same material. We shall discuss in this section the structures of several ammonium salts; ammonium sulfate, which exhibits ferroelectric behavior, will be discussed in Chapter 7.

Ammonia

The structure of solid ammonia has been studied both by single-crystal x-ray (Olovsson and Templeton, 1959) and by powder neutron diffraction

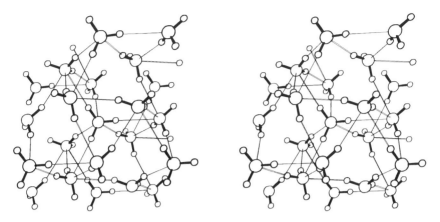

Figure 6-24 *The ordered, hydrogen-bonded structure of solid ammonia.*

methods (Reed and Harris, 1961). The latter study was of ND_3 and placed the deuterium atoms far more accurately than the x-ray study could do for hydrogen. In contrast to the structures of a number of other simple molecules, the ammonia structure is ordered. Each nitrogen atom is surrounded by six other nearest-neighbor nitrogen atoms at the corners of a polyhedron which is half-way between a trigonal prism and an octahedron. The ammonia molecule contributes hydrogen to hydrogen bonds to nitrogen in the layer above and accepts three hydrogen bonds from ammonia molecules in the layer below.

A meaningful anisotropic refinement could not be obtained on the powder data, so no corrections for thermal motion could be made to the bond length of 1.005 ($\sigma = 0.023$). The bond length in gaseous ammonia is 1.015. The D—N—D angle here is 110.4° as compared with 106.6° in the free molecule. The N—D $\cdots$ N angle is 164°, and the D $\cdots$ N distance is 2.374 A. Short D $\cdots$ D distances between molecules are 2.34, 2.55, and 2.77 A. A view of the structure is presented in Figure 6-24.

Olovsson and Templeton (1959) looked at both NH_3 (at $-102°C$) and ND_3 (at $-160°C$) and found that the N $\cdots$ N distance in ND_3 is 0.031 A shorter than in NH_3, a rather substantial isotope effect (see Section 3-6). This difference is much greater than would be accounted for by the expansion with temperature, although it is a pity that the experiments were not done at the same temperature.

Ammonium Halides

The ammonium halides NH_4X crystallize in a number of different structures, some of which show disorder. Ammonium fluoride, where one would expect the strongest hydrogen bonds, has a completely ordered hexagonal structure at room temperature; this structure, illustrated in Figure 6-25, is not shared by the other salts of this class.   The arrangement of both the fluoride ions and the ammonium ions is the same as that found in hexagonal close packing of spheres.   Each ammonium ion is surrounded tetrahedrally by four ammonium ions.   Thus it is possible to form four linear N—H · · · F hydrogen bonds, while retaining the regular tetrahedral geometry of the ammonium ion.   Each fluoride ion acts as a hydrogen bond acceptor for four hydrogen bonds at the corners of a tetrahedron.   A neutron diffraction study has not been carried out to determine the hydrogen atom positions. The reported cell constants and single positional parameter for F^- would lead to one hydrogen bond of length 2.56 A and three hydrogen bonds of length 2.71 A.   The parameter is probably in error.   From a study of the infrared spectrum, Plumb and Hornig (1955) concluded that the NH_4^+ ion is strictly tetrahedral.   The N—H symmetric stretching frequency is 2870 cm^{-1}, a shift of about 450 cm^{-1} from the frequency observed in crystals where the ammonium ion is only weakly hydrogen bonded, if at all.   An N—H distance of 1.041 ± 0.017 at $-75°C$ had been derived from the NMR line width data on the assumptions of tetrahedral symmetry and four linear N—H · · · F bonds of equal length (Ibers and Stevenson, 1958).

   NH_4Cl, NH_4Br, and NH_4I are similar in their structures.   Each of these salts has a high temperature phase with the sodium chloride structure.   As the temperature is lowered, a first order transition leads to a CsCl-like structure, which at lower temperatures undergoes an order-disorder transition to what is in some cases a tetragonal structure closely related to the CsCl structure. ND_4Br, which has been carefully studied by neutron diffraction,

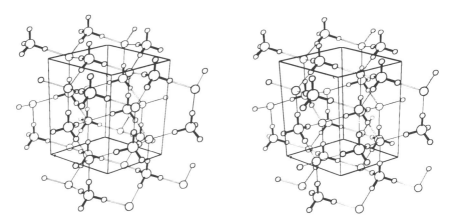

Figure 6-25 *The ammonium fluoride structure, which is completely ordered with strong hydrogen bonds.*

Table 6-6 *Phase Transformations and Structure Types in the Ammonium Halides*

Salt	Phase I	T	Phase II	T	Phase III	T	Phase IV
NH_4Cl	NaCl	184°C	CsCl	−31°C	CsCl		
NH_4Br	NaCl	138°C	CsCl	−38°C	Tetragonal CsCl		
ND_4Br	NaCl	125°C	CsCl	−58°C	Tetragonal CsCl	−104°C	CsCl
NH_4I	NaCl	−14°C	CsCl	−42°C	Tetragonal CsCl		

transforms to a fourth phase with the CsCl structure at −104°C. The temperatures at which these phase transitions take place are given in Table 6-6. The temperatures of the transitions increase as the stability of the hydrogen bonds goes up in the sequence N—H · · · I, N—H · · · Br, N—H · · · Cl. There is also a pronounced isotope effect. The neutron diffraction study (Levy and Peterson, 1953) of the phases of NH_4Br has shown that the phase IV structure (Figure 6-26) is an ordered cubic CsCl structure. Each ammonium ion is surrounded by a cube of Br ions at a distance of 3.47 A. Hydrogen bonds are formed to four of these ions at the corners of a tetrahedron. Each Br⁻ ion is the acceptor for four hydrogen bonds in a tetrahedral geometry. The phase II structure (Figure 6-27) is similar to the phase IV structure, but the ammonium ion exhibits a twofold disorder, in some cells directing its hydrogen bonds toward one tetrahedral set of surrounding anions, in other cells toward the other such tetrahedral set. At any time a given Br⁻ ion may be the acceptor in from zero to eight hydrogen bonds. Because each Br⁻ is in a slightly different environment, the Br⁻

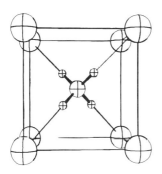 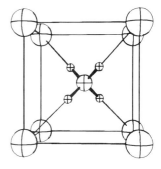

NH4BR-PHASE4   NH4BR-PHASE4

Figure 6-26 *The phase IV NH_4Br structure, an ordered low-symmetry cubic structure of the CsCl type.*

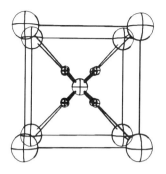

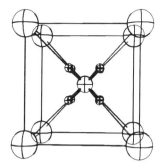

NH4BR-PHASE2

NH4BR-PHASE2

Figure 6-27 *The phase II NH_4Br structure, a twofold disordered cubic structure of the CsCl type. Eight half-hydrogen atoms are shown. Similar structures are exhibited by NH_4Cl and NH_4I.*

ion position is somewhat disordered. This disorder is evidenced in the fact that the apparent thermal motion of Br^- is greater in this phase than in phase IV.

The phase III structure (Figure 6-28) is an ordered structure with a CsCl arrangement of ions. The cell is, however, twice as large as the primitive CsCl cell, and the two ammonium ions in the cell differ in their orientations. The hydrogen bonds are formed in such a way that each Br^- ion is the acceptor in four hydrogen bonds at the corners of a *square*. Each ammonium ion has four Br^- neighbors which are closer than the other four. The hydrogen bonds are directed toward the nearest neighbors. (This is different from the PH_4I structure, Section 4-2.) The phase I structure in

NH4BR-PHASE3

NH4BR-PHASE3

Figure 6-28 *The phase III NH_4X structure typified by NH_4Br. This is an ordered tetragonal distortion of the CsCl structure. The unit cell contains two formula units.*

all the compounds is highly disordered. Neither the neutron diffraction data nor the infrared spectra (Wagner and Hornig, 1950) are compatible with a model involving completely free rotation of the ammonium ion, as was originally suggested by Pauling (1930). The neutron diffraction data as well as the infrared spectra (Plumb and Hornig, 1953) are compatible with a model in which the ion forms one strong hydrogen bond at a time but is freely rotating about this bond (Figure 6-29). In this model, the axis of rotation must be disordered among eight possible positions. The data are also compatible with more than one static disordered model which involves either two or three close hydrogen bond contacts at one time. Each of these models is probably but a poor approximation to the actual structure, and the need is apparent for a treatment of single-crystal neutron diffraction data which refines parameters in a more general potential function than has previously been used. The N—D bond lengths are quoted as being 1.03 ± 0.02 A in all phases. This value is in good agreement with the NMR data (Ibers and Stevenson, 1958) for the ammonium halides and may be taken as a normal value for a hydrogen-bonded ammonium ion.

Wagner and Hornig (1950) observed bands in the infrared spectra of all the phases which they interpreted as being combination bands involving torsional oscillation modes with frequencies in the range 200–300 cm^{-1}. The presence of these modes rules out the possibility of free rotation.

These compounds have also been studied by Rush, Taylor, and Havens (1960) by the method of total neutron cross section measurement discussed in Section 4-2. The experimental curves are presented in Figure 4-14. These data are in agreement with a very tightly bound ammonium group in ammonium fluoride, for almost free rotation in ammonium iodide (phase I) at room temperature, and for intermediate barriers to rotation in the chloride and bromide (phase II).

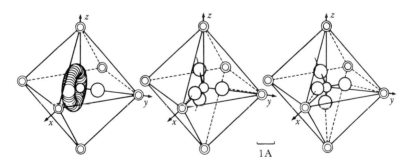

Figure 6-29 *Possible models for the phase I structure of the ammonium halides, a highly disordered structure of the cubic NaCl type. The ammonium groups may be in almost free rotation around single threefold axes, or they may exhibit a multiple disorder.* (*From Levy and Peterson, 1953.*)

Ammonium Fluorosilicate

Ammonium fluorosilicate, $(NH_4)_2SiF_6$, provides a good example of dimorphism and disorder. This compound has a cubic phase and a trigonal phase, both stable over a wide range of temperatures. When crystallization from solution occurs below 5°C, the trigonal phase is obtained; for crystallization above this temperature, the cubic phase is obtained. Apparently because the structures are very different, the transition between them is very sluggish, so that both phases seem indefinitely stable at room temperature, and the cubic phase may be held at 77°K for long periods with no change. The trigonal phase exhibits a second-order phase transition at 38.6°K.

A neutron diffraction study of the cubic phase at room temperature (Schlemper, Hamilton, and Rush, 1966) shows that the structure exhibits a threefold disorder of a rather unusual type. The structure is shown in Figure 6-30; each ammonium ion is surrounded by 12 fluorine atoms at the corners of a cube which has been truncated at four tetrahedral corners. These fluorine atoms are crystallographically equivalent, so that with four hydrogen atoms available, one expects the possibility of threefold disorder. Although the scattering density of the hydrogen atoms in a plane perpendicular to the threefold axis of the cube is indicative of three equiprobable hydrogen positions (each of the bumps in the Figure 6-31 corresponds to one third of a hydrogen atom), it seems better to describe the structure in terms of a single configuration with a very anharmonic type of thermal motion. One can think of a single hydrogen atom of the ammonium group as moving in a potential well much the shape of that indicated by the scattering density contours in Figure 6-31. The peaks of the scattering density are only 0.75 A apart, and it seems unrealistic to talk about these positions in terms of static disorder. If the hydrogen atom is at its mean position, it may be thought of as forming a trifurcated (three-forked) hydrogen bond to each of three fluorine atoms. The four mean hydrogen atom positions do lie at the corners of a tetrahedron. Examination of the positions of the 12 small one-third hydrogen atom peaks indicates that no two of these differ by the tetrahedral angle. This is an interesting fact, and one that can probably best be explained by superimposing the bending vibrations on the hindered rotations which the group is undergoing. The work on ammonium sulfate to be discussed in Chapter 7 indicates that large apparent distortions of the ammonium group from tetrahedral symmetry in these salts are not unusual. The N—H bond length uncorrected for thermal motion is 0.985 in this compound. The thermal motion correction for the riding model, which may be inadequate, brings the distance to 1.064.

The structure of the trigonal phase is very different (Schlemper and

Hamilton, 1966). At room temperature there is a twofold disorder of the ammonium group—obtained by reflection of the group in a plane perpendicular to its threefold axis. The $SiF_6{}^{--}$ environment is not exactly the same on both sides of the N atom, so that the disorder does not necessarily involve 50% of each configuration. There is, at room temperature, a large thermal motion superimposed on the disordered structure, so that it becomes difficult to obtain good parameter values for the atomic positions with use of the usual harnonic model for thermal motion.

The transition at 38.6°K in the trigonal phase is probably a transition from the twofold disordered model to an ordered model. It does not seem

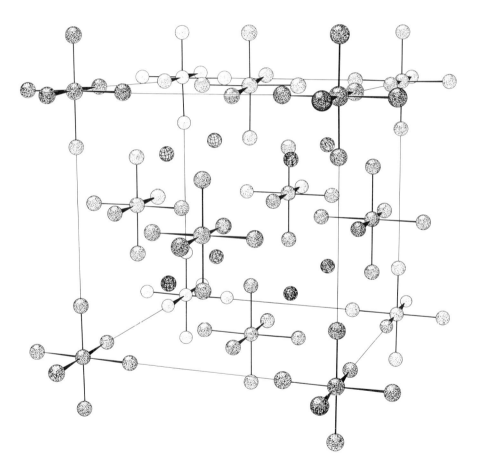

Figure 6-30 *One unit cell of cubic ammonium fluorosilicate. The SiF_6 groups are at the corners and face centers, while the ammonium ions are in the sites of tetrahedral symmetry: $(\pm\frac{1}{4}, \pm\frac{1}{4}, \pm\frac{1}{4})$. Only the central nitrogen atom is shown for each ammonium ion.*

Figure 6-31 *Scattering density through the plane of the hydrogen atom in ammonium fluorosilicate. It is probably better to look upon this as dynamic disorder rather than static disorder. The scattering density map may also represent the general shape of the potential well in which the hydrogen atom moves.*

likely that it is a transition from a freely rotating model to a hindered rotation model.

The energy gain, neutron inelastic scattering spectra have been obtained for the cubic phase of this compound; these data show a peak at a frequency of 168 cm^{-1}, which can probably be identified with a transition in a librational mode. Yet as Schlemper, Hamilton, and Rush have pointed out, a barrier height has meaning only if the shape of the hindering potential is known. On the assumption of a threefold cosine potential—which seems to be unrealistic in this case—we obtain a barrier height of 2.1 kcal mole^{-1}. On the other hand, an infinite barrier height is possible if the potential is one which is very flat in the neighborhood of the mean hydrogen position (see Figure 6-32).

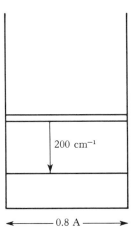

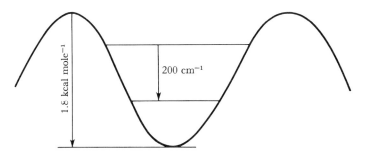

Figure 6-32 *A two-dimensional square well with the indicated parameters has the same transition energy between the first two levels as does the indicated threefold cosine potential. It is thus extremely hazardous to guess "barrier heights" from spectral data.*

Ammonium Perchlorate

In ammonium perchlorate the ammonium group is apparently in almost free rotation. The neutron diffraction data (Smith and Levy, 1962) show no evidence of fixed hydrogen positions. The broad line NMR spectrum shows no line width transition down to 4°K (Richards and Schaefer, 1961), indicating that the barrier height is less than 0.2 kcal mole^{-1}. Spin-lattice relaxation times have also been measured and can be interpreted in terms of a barrier height of 2.0 ± 0.6 kcal if the reorientation is describable in terms of an activation energy (Ibers, 1960). The inelastic neutron scattering spectrum is also indicative of almost free rotation (Janik *et al.*, 1964).

Ammines

Also included in this section should be the ammines, transition metal compounds with NH_3 as a ligand. The hydrogen bonding in these compounds should be of interest in comparison with that found in hydrates. It seems unlikely that an ammonia molecule coordinated to a metal atom could be an acceptor in a hydrogen bond, although pentacoordination might exist. Unfortunately, none of these compounds has been studied extensively by modern structural methods, although the approximate crystal structures are known for several of them. (See, for example, Wyckoff, 1960.)

6-8 HYDROGEN BONDING IN HYDROXIDES

Hydrogen bonding in hydroxides is usually weak and often nonexistent. The negative charge on the OH^- ion obviously makes the ion a poor proton donor. The proton *accepting* power is of course great, and in some circumstances a weak hydrogen bond is formed.

A neutron diffraction study has been carried out on $Ca(OH)_2$ (Busing and Levy, 1957). The location of the hydrogen ions is such that no hydrogen bonding is possible. As shown in Figure 6-33 the structure consists of sheets of hydroxide ions and calcium ions in which the OH ions are well separated. Furthermore, the sheets are stacked in such a way that no close contacts between OH^- ions occur.

The difference between the mean square amplitudes of O and H in the bond direction is 0.0068 A². That calculated from the observed infrared stretching frequency is 0.0087 A², thus providing good evidence that the amplitudes of motion derived from diffraction studies can be related to the vibrational frequencies in a simple way. Similar agreement exists for the amplitude

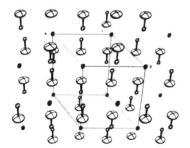 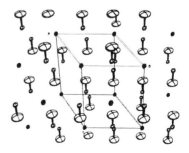

Figure 6-33 *The structure of calcium hydroxide. There is no possibility of hydrogen bonding, as the OH^- ions are well isolated from one another. The calcium atoms are at the cell corners.*

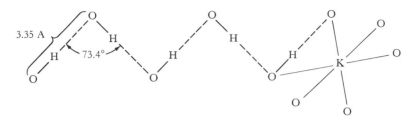

Figure 6-34 *The hydrogen-bonded chains in crystalline potassium hydroxide. The deviation of the O—H vector from the O · · · O line is less than 4°.*

perpendicular to the bond axis, interpreted as being due to a librational motion of the O—H ion, and the librational frequency of 400 cm⁻¹ derived from the infrared spectrum (Hexter and Dows, 1956).

In contrast, the structure of KOH (Ibers, Kumamoto, and Snyder, 1960) involves strings of OH ions (Figure 6-34). Although a neutron diffraction study has not been carried out, the oxygen atom positions have been determined by an x-ray diffraction study. A combination of infrared and x-ray work places the hydrogen atoms nearly along the O—O lines; the oxygen atoms form a zig-zag chain. The O—O distance is 3.35 A and it is inferred that the hydrogen atoms lie no more than 4° off the O—O line. The structure is very similar to the structure of HF insofar as the hydrogen-bonded chains go. The similarity of the structures and the nonlinearity of the chains are perhaps an indication that hydrogen bonds are formed to lone pair orbitals on O and F. The hydrogen bonding here in KOH is much weaker than in HF. The O—H distance is 2.35 A. The O—H stretch frequency of 3600 cm⁻¹ (Snyder, Kumamoto, and Ibers, 1960) compared with 3650 cm⁻¹ in Ca(OH)₂ is a further indication of weak hydrogen bonding.

6-9   A METAL-HYDROGEN-METAL BOND

This chapter would be incomplete without discussion of the possible existence of bonds of the type M—H—M, where M is a transition metal. Perhaps the best example of this is in the compound which has been formulated as $[(C_2H_5)_4N][HCr_2(CO)_{10}]$ by Handy, Treichel, Dahl, and Hayter (1965). The anion presumably has the configuration shown in Figure 6-35. The ion is approximately centrosymmetric, although not required by the crystallographic symmetry (space group $P1$). The position of the hydrogen atom was inferred from the geometry of the rest of the molecule; it was not seen in the x-ray electron density map. A single sharp line in the NMR

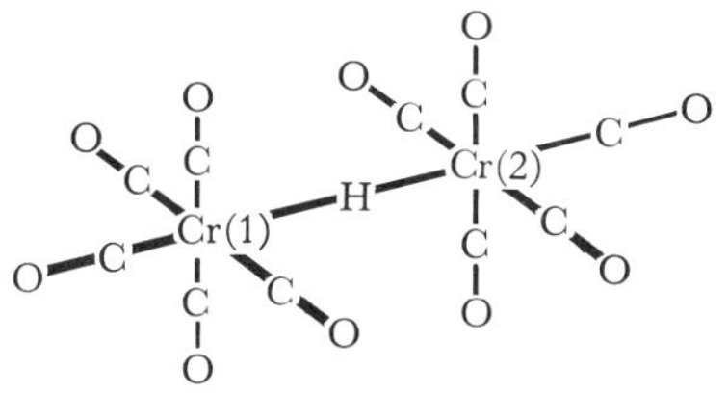

$$HCr_2(CO)_{10}^-$$

Figure 6-35 *A new type of hydrogen bond: a symmetric metal-hydrogen-metal bond.   The hydrogen atom position has not been confirmed by diffraction studies.   This is perhaps an electron-deficient bond of the type found in the boron hydrides.   (From Handy et al., 1965.)*

spectrum occurs at a frequency which is usual for transition metal-hydrogen bonds.   The Cr—Cr distance of 3.40 A would lead to a Cr—H distance of 1.70 A, if the bond is symmetric.   This bond length is about what would be expected from the sum of the covalent radii.   A neutron diffraction study of this or a similar compound would be of great interest, although as usual with possibly symmetric hydrogen bonds, the symmetry may be difficult to establish from diffraction studies (Section 3-7).   The possibly electron-deficient bonding in these compounds is probably more akin to that in the boron hydrides (see Section 1-6) than to the more conventional types of hydrogen bonds.

REFERENCES

Abrahams, S. C. (1962), Crystal and Magnetic Structure of Cupric Fluoride Dihydrate at 4.2° K, *J. Chem. Phys.* **36,** 56.

Abrahams, S. C., and Prince, E. (1962), Crystal Structure of Cupric Fluoride Dihydrate at 298° K, *J. Chem. Phys.* **36,** 50.

Atoji, M., and Rundle, R. E. (1958), Neutron Diffraction Study of Gypsum,
$CaSO_4 \cdot 2H_2O$, *J. Chem. Phys.* **29,** 1306.

Bacon, G. E., and Curry, N. A. (1956), A Neutron Diffraction Study of Sodium
Sesquicarbonate, *Acta Cryst.* **9,** 82.

Bacon, G. E., and Curry, N. A. (1962), The Water Molecules in $CuSO_4 \cdot 5H_2O$, *Proc.
Roy Soc. London* **A266,** 95.

Bacon, G. E., and Gardner, W. E. (1958), The Structure of Chromium Potassium
Alum, *Proc. Roy. Soc. London* **A246,** 78.

Baur, W. (1964), On the Crystal Chemistry of Salt Hydrates, a Neutron Diffraction
Study of Magnesium Sulfate Tetrahydrate, *Acta Cryst.* **17,** 863.

Baur, W. (1965), On Hydrogen Bonds in Crystalline Hydrates, *Acta Cryst.* **19,** 909.

Bernal, J. D., and Fowler, R. H. (1933), A Theory of Water and Ionic Solution, with Particular Reference to Hydrogen and Hydroxyl Ions, *J. Chem. Phys.* **1,** 515.

Bertie, J. E., Calvert, L. D., and Whalley, E. (1963), Transformations of Ice II, III and V at Atmospheric Pressure, *J. Chem. Phys.* **38,** 840.

Bertie, J. E., Calvert, L. D., and Whalley, E. (1964), Transformations of Ice VI and Ice VII at Atmospheric Pressure, *Can. J. Chem.* **42,** 1373.

Bertie, J. E., and Whalley, E. (1964a), Infrared Spectra of Ices Ih and Ic in the Range 4000 to 350 cm^{-1}, *J. Chem. Phys.* **40,** 1637.

Bertie, J. E., and Whalley, E. (1964b), Infrared Spectra of Ices II, III, and V in the Range 4000–350 cm^{-1}, *J. Chem. Phys.* **40,** 1646.

Beurskens, G., and Jeffrey, G. A. (1964), Crystal Structure of Potassium Fluoride Tetrahydrate, *J. Chem. Phys.* **41,** 917.

Brown, A. J., and Whalley, E. (1966), Preliminary Investigation of the Phase Boundaries between Ice VI and VII and Ice VI and VIII, *J. Chem. Phys.* **45,** 4360.

Busing, W., and Levy, H. A. (1957), Neutron Diffraction Study of Calcium Hydroxide, *J. Chem. Phys.* **26,** 563.

Chidambaram, R. (1961), A Bent Hydrogen Bond Model for the Structure of Ice-I, *Acta Cryst.* **14,** 467.

Chidambaram, R. (1962), Structure of the Hydrogen-Bonded Water Molecule in Crystals, *J. Chem. Phys.* **36,** 2361.

Chidambaram, R., Sequeira, A., and Sikka, S. K. (1964), Neutron-Diffraction Study of the Structure of Potassium Oxalate Monohydrate: Lone-Pair Coordination of the Hydrogen-Bonded Water Molecule in Crystals, *J. Chem. Phys.* **41,** 3616.

Clark, J. (1963), Water Molecules in Hydrated Organic Crystals, *Rev. Pure Appl. Chem.* **13,** 50.

Claussen, W. F. (1951a), Suggested Structures of Water in Inert Gas Hydrates, *J. Chem. Phys.* **19,** 259.

Claussen, W. F. (1951b), A Second Water Structure for Inert Gas Hydrates, *J. Chem. Phys.* **19,** 1425.

Craven, B., and Takei, W. J. (1964), The Crystal Structure of Perdeuterated Violuric Acid Monohydrate: The Neutron Diffraction Analysis, *Acta Cryst.* **17,** 415.

Danford, M. D., and Levy, H. A. (1962), The Structure of Water at Room Temperature, *J. Am. Chem. Soc.* **84,** 3965.

El Saffar, Z. M. (1966), Study of the NMR Results in Some Crystalline Hydrates, *J. Chem. Phys.* **45,** 4643.

Eyring, H., Ree, T., and Hirai, N. (1958), Significant Structures in the Liquid State, I, *Proc. Nat. Acad. Sci. US* **44,** 683.

Falk, M., and Ford, T. A. (1966), Infrared Spectrum and Structure of Liquid Water, *Can. J. Chem.* **44,** 1699.

Feil, D., and Jeffrey, G. A. (1961), The Polyhedral Clathrate Hydrates. Part 2: Structure of the Hydrate of Tetra *Iso*-Amyl Ammonium Fluoride, *J. Chem. Phys.* **35,** 1863.

Fuller, W. (1959), Hydrogen Bond Lengths and Angles Observed in Crystals, *J. Phys. Chem.* **63,** 1705.

Garrett, B. S. (1954), Crystal Structures of Oxalic Acid Dihydrate and α-Iodic Acid as Determined by Neutron Diffraction, *U.S. Atomic Energy Commission*, **ORNL 1745.**

Haas, C., and Hornig, D. F. (1960), Inter- and Intramolecular Potentials and the Spectrum of Ice, *J. Chem. Phys.* **32,** 1763.

Hamilton, W. C. (1962a), Bond Distances and Thermal Motion in Ferrous Fluosilicate Hexahydrate: A Neutron Diffraction Study, *Acta Cryst.* **15,** 353.

Hamilton, W. C. (1962b), The Structure of Solids. *Ann. Rev. Phys. Chem.* **13,** 19.

Handy, L. B., Treichel, P. M., Dahl, L. F., and Hayter, R. G. (1966), Structure of and Bonding in $HCr_2(CO)_{10}^-$: The first Known Linear Electron-Deficient X—H—X Molecular System Stabilized by a Three-Center, One Electron Pair Bond, *J. Am. Chem. Soc.* **88,** 366.

Heath, D. F., and Linnett, J. W. (1948), Molecular Force Fields. I. The Structure of the Water Molecule, *Trans. Faraday Soc.* **44,** 556.

Herzberg, G. (1945), Molecular Spectra and Molecular Structure, Vol. II, *Infrared and Roman Spectra*, pp. 207, 282. Van Nostrand, New York.

Hexter, R. M., and Dows, D. A. (1956), Low-Frequency Librations and the Vibrational Spectra of Molecular Crystals, *J. Chem. Phys.* **25,** 504.

Honjo, G., Kitamura, N., Shimaoka, K., and Mihama, K. (1956), Low Temperature Specimen Method for Electron Diffraction and Electron Microscopy, *J. Phys. Soc. Japan* **11,** 527.

Honjo, G., and Shimaoka, K. (1957), Determination of Hydrogen Position in Cubic Ice by Electron Diffraction, *Acta Cryst.* **10,** 710.

Hornig, D. F., White, H. F., and Reding, F. P. (1958), The Infrared Spectrum of Crystalline H_2O, D_2O, and HDO, *Spectrochim. Acta* **12,** 338.

Ibers, J. A. (1960), Nuclear Magnetic Resonance Study of Polycrystalline NH_4ClO_4, *J. Chem. Phys.* **32,** 1448.

Ibers, J. A., Hamilton, W. C., and MacKenzie, D. R. (1964), The Crystal Structure of Sodium Perxenate Octahydrate, *Inorg. Chem.* **3,** 1412.

Ibers, J. A., Kumamoto, J., and Snyder, R. G. (1960), Structure of Potassium Hydroxide: An X-Ray and Infrared Study, *J. Chem. Phys.* **33,** 1164.

Ibers, J. A., and Stevenson, D. P. (1958), Motional Correction to Distances Derived from NMR Data: NH_4Cl, NH_4F, and $N_2H_6F_2$, *J. Chem. Phys.* **28,** 929.

Janik, J. A., Janik, J. M., Mellor, J., and Palevsky, H. (1964), Study of Molecular Rotations in Solids and Liquids by the Inelastic Scattering of Cold Neutrons, *J. Phys. Chem. Solids* **25,** 1091.

Kamb, B. (1964), Ice II: A Proton-Ordered Form of Ice, *Acta Cryst.* **17,** 1437.

Kamb, B. (1965), Structure of Ice VI, *Science* **150,** 205.

Kamb, B., and Datta, S. K. (1960), Crystal Structure of the High-Pressure Forms of Ice: Ice III, *Nature* **187,** 140.

Kamb, B., and Davis, B. L. (1964), Ice VII, the Densest Form of Ice, *Proc. Nat. Acad. Sci. US* **52,** 1433.

Kamb, B., Prakash, A., and Knobler, C. (1967), Structure of Ice V, *Acta Cryst,* **22,** 706.

Larsson, K. E. (1965), Experimental Neutron Scattering Results on Liquids, in Thermal Neutron Scattering (P. A. Egelstaff, ed.), p. 347. Academic Press, New York.

Levy, H. A., and Peterson, S. W. (1953), Neutron Diffraction Study of the Crystal Structures of Ammonium Bromide in Four Phases, *J. Am. Chem. Soc.* **75,** 1536.

Levy, H. A., and Peterson, S. W. (1957), Proton Positions in $CuCl_2 \cdot 2H_2O$ by Neutron Diffraction, *J. Chem. Phys.* **26,** 220.

Manoharan, P. T., and Hamilton, W. C. (1963), The Crystal Structure of Sodium Nitroprusside, *Inorg. Chem.* **2,** 1043.

Marckmann, J. P., and Whalley, E. (1964), Vibrational Spectra of the Ices. Raman Spectra of Ice VI and Ice VII, *J. Chem. Phys.* **41,** 1450.

McMullan, R. K., and Jeffrey, G. A. (1965), Polyhedral Clathrate Hydrates. IX. Structure of Ethylene Oxide Hydrate, *J. Chem. Phys.* **42,** 2725.

Nemethy, G., and Scheraga, H. A. (1962), Structure of Water and Hydrophobic Bonding in Proteins. I. A Model for the Thermodynamic Properties of Liquid Water, *J. Chem. Phys.* **36,** 3382.

Olovsson, I., and Templeton, D. H. (1959), X-Ray Study of Solid Ammonia, *Acta Cryst.* **12,** 832.

Padmanabhan, V. M., Srikantha, S., and Ali, S. M. (1965), Neutron Diffraction Study of Ammonium Oxalate Monohydrate, $(NH_4)_2C_2O_4 \cdot H_2O$, *Acta Cryst.* **18,** 567.

Pauling, L. (1930), The Rotational Motion of Molecules in Crystals, *Phys. Rev.* **36,** 430.

Pauling, L. (1935), The Structure and Entropy of Ice and of Other Crystals with Some Randomness of Atomic Arrangement, *J. Am. Chem. Soc.* **57,** 2680.

Pauling, L. (1960), *The Nature of the Chemical Bond*, 3rd Ed. Cornell Univ. Press, Ithaca, New York.

Pauling, L., and Marsh, R. (1952), The Structure of Chlorine Hydrate, *Proc. Nat. Acad. Sci. US* **38,** 112.

Peterson, S. W., and Levy, H. A. (1957), A Single Crystal Neutron Diffraction Study of Heavy Ice, *Acta Cryst.* **10,** 70.

Plumb, R. C., and Hornig, D. F. (1953), Evidence for One-Dimensional Rotation in Ammonium Iodide, *J. Chem. Phys.* **21,** 366.

Plumb, R. C., and Hornig, D. F. (1955), Infrared Spectrum, X-Ray Diffraction Pattern, and Structure of Ammonium Fluoride, *J. Chem. Phys.* **23,** 947.

Reed, J. W., and Harris, P. M. (1961), Neutron Diffraction Study of Solid Deutero-ammonia, *J. Chem. Phys.* **35,** 1730.

Richards, R. E., and Schaefer, T. (1961), Motional Narrowing and Line Shapes in Some Ammonium Salts, *Trans. Faraday Soc.* **57,** 210.

Rush, J. J., Taylor, T. I., and Havens, W. W., Jr. (1960), Proton Motions in Ammonium Halides by Slow Neutron Cross-Section Measurements, *Phys. Rev. Letters* **5,** 507.

Schlemper, E. O., and Hamilton, W. C. (1966), On the Structure of Trigonal Ammonium Fluorosilicate, *J. Chem. Phys.* **45,** 408.

Schlemper, E. O., Hamilton, W. C., and Rush, J. J. (1966), Structure of Cubic Ammonium Fluorosilicate: Neutron Diffraction and Neutron-Inelastic-Scattering Studies, *J. Chem. Phys.* **44,** 2499.

Shimaoka, K. (1960), Electron Diffraction Study of Ice, *J. Phys. Soc. Japan.* **15,** 106.

Smith, H. G., and Levy, H. A. (1962), Neutron Diffraction Study of Ammonium Perchlorate, *Acta Cryst.* **15,** 1201.

Snyder, R. G., Kumamoto, J., and Ibers, J. A. (1960), Vibrational Spectrum of Crystalline Potassium Hydroxide, *J. Chem. Phys.* **33,** 1171.

von Stackelberg, M., and Mueller, H. R. (1951), On the Structure of Gas Hydrates, *J. Chem. Phys.* **19,** 1319.

Taylor, J. C., and Mueller, M. H. (1965), A Neutron Diffraction Study of Uranyl Nitrate Hexahydrate, *Acta Cryst.* **19,** 536.

Taylor, J. C., Mueller, M. H., and Hitterman, R. L. (1966), Crystal Structure of Thorium Nitrate Pentahydrate by Neutron Diffraction, *Acta Cryst.* **20,** 842.

Taylor, M. J., and Whalley, E. (1964), Raman Spectrum of Ices Ih, Ic, II, III, and V, *J. Chem. Phys.* **40,** 1660.

Wagner, E. L., and Hornig, D. F. (1950), The Vibrational Spectra of Molecules and Complex Ions in Crystals. IV. Ammonium Bromide and Deuteroammonium Bromide, *J. Chem. Phy.* **18,** 305.

Waldstein, P., Rabideau, S. W., and Jackson, J. A. (1964), Nuclear Magnetic Resonance of Single Crystals of D_2O Ice, *J. Chem. Phys.* **41,** 3407.

Wall, T. T., and Hornig, D. F. (1965), Raman Intensities of HDO and Structure in Liquid Water, *J. Chem. Phys.* **43,** 2079.

Whalley, E., Davidson, D. W., and Heath, J. B. R. (1966), Dielectric Properties of Ice VII, Ice VIII: A New Phase of Ice, *J. Chem. Phys.* **45,** 3976.

Wyckoff, R. W. G. (1965), *Crystal Structures*, 2nd Ed., Vol. III. Interscience, New York.

Zalkin, A., Forrester, J. D., and Templeton, D. H. (1964), The Crystal Structure of Sodium Perxenate Hexahydrate, *Inorg. Chem.* **3,** 1417.

Hydrogen-Bonded Ferroelectrics

There are many ferroelectric materials in which the ferroelectric transition seems to be associated with a reorientation of hydrogen bonds. These seem to be of sufficient interest to warrant separate discussion.[1]

A ferroelectric is a material in which there can exist a spontaneous polarization, that is, a spontaneous net displacement between the centroids of the positive and negative charges. A further necessary condition is that it must be possible to reverse the direction of the polarization by the application of an electric field, without causing dielectric breakdown of the material.

There are 32 crystal classes characterized by their point-group symmetries. Of these, eleven are centrosymmetric; they cannot be polar and, *a fortiori*, ferroelectric. Of the remaining 21 classes, only 10 can have a unique polar axis; these 10 have the point-group symmetries C_1, C_2, C_3, C_4, C_6, C_s, C_{2v}, C_{3v}, C_{4v}, C_{6v}. It is necessary that a crystal belong to one of these 10 classes if it is to be a ferroelectric. Again, it should be emphasized that a polar crystal is defined as a ferroelectric crystal only if the polarization can be reversed by an electric field.

As an example, consider the structure shown in Figure 7-1a. This is a polar structure. Application of an electric field might produce the structure of opposite polarity shown in Figure 7-1b. This structure results if every molecule is rotated by 180° about an axis perpendicular to the paper. If this reversal is possible, the material is ferroelectric. At sufficiently high temperatures, thermal agitation might break down the ordering of the dipolar molecules to produce a random structure with no net spontaneous polarization. The material is no longer ferroelectric. The temperature at

---

[1] For more detailed discussions of the theory and properties of ferroelectrics the reader should consult the books by Megaw (1957) and Jona and Shirane (1962).

which this transition from the ferroelectric to the nonferroelectric phase takes place is called the *ferroelectric Curie temperature;* as shown below, it may be determined by an examination of the dielectric constant or specific heat as a function of temperature.

Above the ferroelectric Curie temperature, the crystal is said to be *paraelectric.* The terms ferroelectric and paraelectric have been coined by analogy to ferro- and paramagnetism. Although the terminology is perhaps misleading and unimaginative, it is certainly here to stay. The two phenomena are not entirely analogous.

Many substances which show ferroelectric behavior are disordered in the paraelectric state. The ferroelectric transition is then an order-disorder transition. The structure above the ferroelectric Curie point may be simply a superposition on a microscale of the two polar structures corresponding to the two directions of polarization. This is not always true, however. In ammonium sulfate, discussed below, the transition is probably not of the order-disorder type.

A ferroelectric crystal, by virtue of its spontaneous polarization, always displays a hysteresis loop if the polarization is plotted as a function of applied electric field (Figure 7-2). As the Curie point is approached, the area enclosed by the hysteresis loop will grow smaller, and the loop will become a line passing through the origin at the Curie temperature. A peak in the

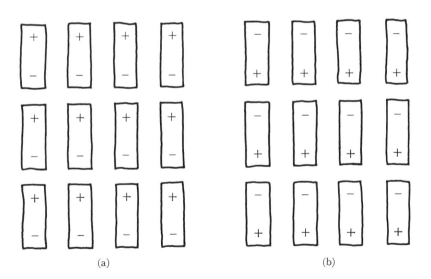

(a)   (b)

Figure 7-1 *Schematic representation of a simple polar structure with two directions of polarization (a) and (b). The individual units may be dipolar molecules. If application of an electric field can produce a change from (a) to (b), the crystal is ferroelectric.*

dielectric constant and in the specific heat, plotted as functions of temperature, are also evident at the transition temperature (Figures 7-3 and 7-4).

The excellent book by Jona and Shirane (1962) presents a table of all ferroelectric crystals known up to 1960. Except for a few complex oxides of transition metals and half a dozen other ionic crystals, most of the compounds tabulated are hydrogen bonded, and the ferroelectric transition is probably associated in part with a change in the details of the hydrogen bonding.

Ferroelectric behavior seems to be relatively common in hydrogen-bonded substances for two reasons. First of all, X—H covalent bonds, and hence most hydrogen bonds, are polar in nature. Any ordering of these dipolar bonds in a crystal class with a polar axis leads to a structure with a polar electric axis. Second, it may often be easy to reverse the polarization direction in such a crystal, because the polarization reversal may be effected simply by breaking or distorting hydrogen bonds which have relatively little energy associated with them. Often, the polarization reversal is obtained merely through the movement of a hydrogen atom from one side of a hydrogen bond to the other:

$$O—H \cdots O \rightarrow O \cdots H—O$$

Sometimes the ferroelectric transition involves the reorientation of ammonium

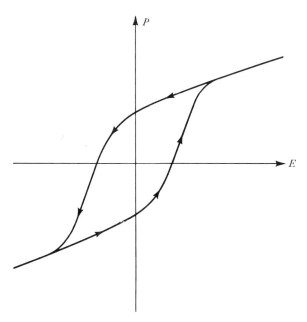

Figure 7-2 *Polarization P versus electric field strength E. The hysteresis loop is characteristic of a ferroelectric crystal.*

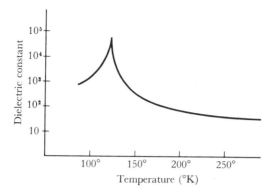

Figure 7-3 *Dielectric constant versus temperature for KH_2PO_4, a typical crystal exhibiting ferro-electric behavior.   The peak occurs at the ferroelectric Curie point; the material is ferroelectric at lower temperatures and paraelectric above.*

ions or water molecules, either of which may easily rotate in a lattice to produce a polarization opposite to the initial one.   We shall discuss below one example of each of these types.

7-1   ROCHELLE SALT

The tetrahydrate of sodium potassium tartrate, $NaK(C_4H_4O_6)\cdot4H_2O$, is the oldest known ferroelectric crystal.   It is also rather special because it

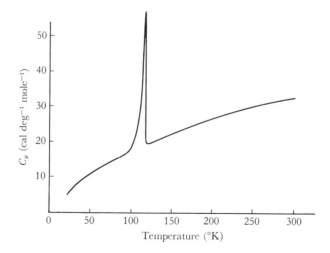

Figure 7-4 *Specific heat versus temperature for KH_2PO_4.   The sharp λ point is typical of many, but by no means all, ferroelectric transitions.*

exhibits two ferroelectric Curie points. It is ferroelectric only between $-18°$ and $24°C$. The crystal structures of the three phases are almost indistinguishable by x-rays, so that the major changes as one goes from one structure to the other must be associated with the hydrogen atoms. An excellent discussion of the structural problem has been given in the book of Jona and Shirane (1962). We shall not repeat this discussion here except to remark that extensive but as yet incomplete neutron diffraction work by Frazer (1966) indicates that the major change taking place at the upper ferroelectric Curie point is the shift of a hydroxyl hydrogen on the tartrate group from a position where it is weakly hydrogen bonded to a carboxyl group oxygen to a second position where it lies in a generally electron-rich area but cannot be associated with a single hydrogen bond. The structure of Rochelle salt is exceedingly complex, and further refinement of the diffraction data is necessary before the structural changes accompanying the transition can be said to be thoroughly understood.

7-2 COLEMANITE

The mineral colemanite, $CaB_3O_4(OH)_3 \cdot H_2O$, is ferroelectric below $2.5°C$ and paraelectric above. The anionic part of the structure is composed of infinite chains in which the four oxygens are involved in B—O—B bridges and the three hydroxyl groups are appendages to the chain attached to the boron atoms. The three hydroxyl groups act as hydrogen bond donors, as does the water molecule. The water molecule and one of the hydroxide oxygen atoms as well as the oxygen atoms in the B_3O_4 framework act as hydrogen bond acceptors.

The structure is monoclinic with four molecules per unit cell. In the ferroelectric structure, the space group is $P2_1$, so that there are two crystallographically independent formula units in the asymmetric unit of the structure. Above the transition temperature in space group $P2_1/a$ there is only one independent formula unit in the asymmetric unit.

The structures of both phases have been studied by neutron diffraction (Hainsworth, 1965). This investigation has shown that the phase transition is an order-disorder transition involving primarily the water molecule and one of the hydroxyls. In the ferroelectric phase, the two independent water molecules have very different environments as shown in Figure 7-5. One of the molecules (B) forms two rather normal hydrogen bonds. (See Table 7-1.) The second water molecule (A) differs from the first by a rotation of about $180°$ approximately around the O_{9A}—H_{96A} bond, which remains a normal hydrogen bond, while the O_{9A}—H_{99A} vector is directed toward a region of generally negative charge but does not form a single strong hydrogen

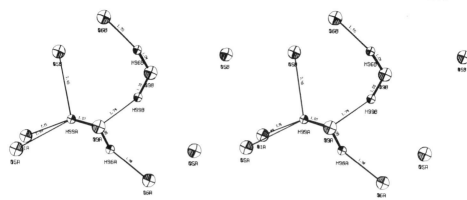

Figure 7-5 *The two independent water molecules in the ferroelectric phase of colemanite. Above the ferroelectric Curie point, there is a center of symmetry half-way between 09A and 09B. This is achieved by disordering the structure so that both types of water molecules occupy each site at random. A rotation around the 09—H96 bond suffices to accomplish approximately this. Notice that each pair of atoms in the drawing except for H99A and H99B is approximately related by a center of symmetry, even in the ferroelectric phase.*

bond. The best description is probably in terms of a trifurcated bond with the parameters of Table 7-1. The structure above the transition has a center of symmetry halfway between O_{9A} and O_{9B} in Figure 7-5. It can best be described in terms of disorder which places both types of molecules in each site.

There are six independent hydroxyl groups in the ferroelectric phase.

Table 7-1 *Hydrogen Bonds in Ferroelectric Phase of Colemanite. Bond Distances Are in Angstroms and Bond Angle in Degrees*

	O—H	H $\cdots$ O	O $\cdots$ O	$\angle$O—H $\cdots$ O
Water B				
O_{9B}—H_{99B} $\cdots$ O_{9A}	1.00	1.74	2.67	154
O_{9B}—H_{96B} $\cdots$ O_{6B}	1.04	1.70	2.72	165
Water A				
O_{9A}—H_{96A} $\cdots$ O_{6A}	0.93	1.98	2.87	157
O_{5A}	1.07	2.33	2.98	117
O_{9A}—H_{99A} $\cdots$ O_{1A}	1.07	2.25	3.20	146
O_{5B}	1.07	2.45	3.12	119
Hydroxyl II	0.98	1.77	2.73	169
Hydroxyl III	1.03	2.28	3.14	141
Hydroxyl IV	0.96	$\begin{cases} 2.31 \\ 2.28 \end{cases}$	2.81 3.11	$\left.\begin{matrix} 111 \\ 145 \end{matrix}\right\}$

Four of these occur in two pairs which are related by the approximate center of symmetry. The hydrogen bond parameters of these two pairs are similar and change but little as the crystal goes through the transition. The acceptor oxygen atom is in each case one of the oxygens in the polyanion chain. The mean hydrogen bond parameters for these bonds (II) are given in Table 7-1. The remaining two hydroxyl groups have very different environments; these are the two groups which lie closest to the water molecules. One of these groups forms a rather weak hydrogen bond to one of the anion oxygens (Table 7-1, III). The other hydroxyl of the pair forms a bifurcated hydrogen bond, one branch to a member of the polyanion chain and one branch to water with the parameters of Table 7-1 (IV). Above the transition these two hydroxyls become equivalent by disordering; both types are found at each of the centrosymmetrically related sites.

The postulated explanation of the mechanism of the transition is adapted from that given by Hainsworth. The water molecule and the hydroxyl group can each exist in two positions of almost equal hydrogen bond energy. Above the transition temperature, the water molecules have sufficient energy to cross the relatively low barrier which must separate the two configurations. It is worth repeating here that low barriers toward librational motions of water molecules in solids often accompany structures where there exists the possibility of bifurcated hydrogen bonds; the result of the low barrier at the high temperature is a dynamically disordered state. The same must be true of the hydroxyl which is disordered at the higher temperature. The reorientation of the O—H group corresponds to a rotation about the B—O bond, so that the angle B—O—H remains constant at about 110°; thus the major change in energy should be that involved in going from one weak hydrogen-bonding situation to another.

As the temperature is lowered, a water molecule may be trapped in one or the other of the two possible orientations. The relative stability of the two positions for the inversion-related atom will then be changed so that it settles into the nonequivalent alternative position. The effect of this ordering on the calcium neighbors of each of the hydrogen atoms is such that they move toward or away from the water oxygens, in a sense following the hydrogen atoms. The influence of this relaxation is spread to the polyanion chains through the hydroxyl group. The strength of the interaction through the water-calcium-hydroxyl-polyanion network is sufficient to ensure that the ordering of one cell exerts a strong influence on neighboring cells to become ordered with the same relative configuration.

The relatively low barriers between the alternative configurations for water molecule and hydroxyl group ensure that the material undergoes a reversal of polarization on reversal of an applied electric field. On reversal, no strong bonds must be broken; it is only necessary to change the orientation of some rather weak hydrogen bonds. The atomic parameters of all the other atoms remain approximately the same as the crystal polarization is reversed or as the crystal is taken through the transition.

Although the absolute configuration of the polarity of the crystal with respect to an applied external field could have been determined by making use of the anomalous scattering of boron (Section 2-7), the high absorption in the crystals due to the presence of ^{11}B made measurement of the effect so subject to error that a definitive answer could not be obtained.

7-3 AMMONIUM SULFATE

Ammonium sulfate, $(NH_4)_2SO_4$, undergoes a ferroelectric transition at 223°K. The structure is orthorhombic, and in the high temperature, nonferroelectric phase, there is a mirror plane perpendicular to the c axis of the crystal. At the ferroelectric transition point this mirror plane is destroyed. The major changes in the structure have been shown by a precise neutron diffraction investigation of both phases (Schlemper and Hamilton, 1966) to be associated with displacements of the two crystallographically independent ammonium ions in the structure. The transition is not of the order-disorder type found in a number of ferroelectric materials, including colemanite discussed above, but involves a change in the hydrogen bonding of the ammonium ions to the sulfate ions which results in stronger hydrogen bonds in the ferroelectric phase. Each of the ammonium ions has only one H · · · O distance less than 2.0 A in the room temperature phase but has three such distances in the ferroelectric phase.

Although the ammonium group which does not lie on the mirror plane shows the greatest changes in orientation at the transition, the loss of symmetry at the transition is best illustrated by consideration of the ammonium ion which lies on the mirror plane above the transition. Figures 7-6 and 7-7 show that below the transition the ammonium ions and sulfate ions shift in such a way that the strongest hydrogen bonds can be formed. This twisting of the groups destroys the mirror plane of symmetry that existed above the transition. The motions are, however, relatively slight (rotations of 15°–25°), and it is easy to see that the reversal in direction of an applied electric field could reverse the direction of the distortion from the more symmetric structure. The hydrogen atom positions shift as much as 0.3 A in passing through the transition. Thus a shift of 0.6 A is necessary in reversing the polarization.

It is interesting that the ammonium group is a less regular tetrahedron in the more symmetric high temperature phase. The H—N—H bond angles for the two groups vary from 100.2 ($\sigma = 0.8°$) to 118.5 ($\sigma = 1.5°$) in the

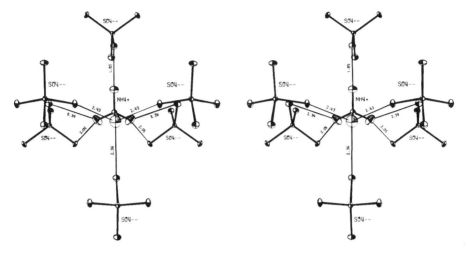

Figure 7-6 *Environment of ammonium (I) in the paraelectric phase of ammonium sulfate.*

paraelectric phase.   Although corrections for thermal motion made in order
to obtain more realistic values for the equilibrium angles might change these
angles slightly, it is clear that the departures from the ideal angle of 109° 28′
are significant for the high temperature phase but may not be for the ferroelectric phase, where the angles range from 106.1° to 114.1°.

The N—H bond lengths do not change significantly between the two

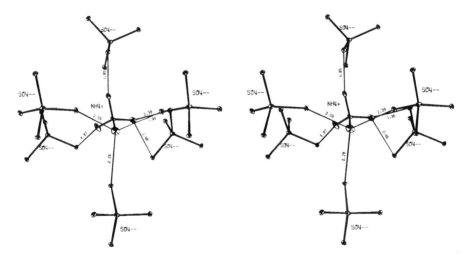

Figure 7-7 *Environment of ammonium (I) in ferroelectric phase of ammonium sulfate.   Note
that the ions have rotated to destroy the mirror plane of symmetry which is so obvious in Figure 7-6.*

phases.   The mean values of the N—H bond length uncorrected for thermal
motion are 0.97 ($\sigma = 0.01$) at room temperature, and 1.01 ($\sigma = 0.02$) at
183°K.   The correction for thermal motion, assuming the "riding" model
(see Section 2-4), results in the more realistic values of 1.06 and 1.05 for the
two phases.

The atomic vibrational amplitudes were also obtained from the crystal
structure refinement.   From these amplitudes, under the assumption that
the ammonium ions move as rigid groups, one can obtain librational frequencies for the ammonium ions.   If the motion can be described as that of a
hindered rotor with a moment of inertia of I about the axis of rotation and
with a cosine shaped potential, the relationship between the frequency of the
transition from the ground to the first excited state ν and the mean square
librational amplitude ω in square radians in given by

$$\omega = \langle \phi^2 \rangle = \frac{kT}{4\pi^2 I \nu^2}$$

(see, for example, Cruickshank, 1956).   On this basis the three calculated
frequencies for ammonium (I) are 124, 149, and 218 cm^{-1} and for ammonium
(II) 129, 186, and 207 cm^{-1} in the room temperature phase.   The root mean
square frequencies for the two ions are 168 cm^{-1} and 177 cm^{-1}.   In the
low temperature phase there is little change in these frequencies, the root
mean square values being 162 cm^{-1} and 158 cm^{-1}.   These results, although
perhaps uncertain by as much as 50% on an absolute scale, are in good agreement with the neutron inelastic scattering results of Rush and Taylor (1965),
who suggested the existence of two librational modes with frequencies of 335
cm^{-1} and 200 cm^{-1}.   The neutron diffraction results show that these two
frequencies may best be associated with anisotropic librations of individual
ammonium groups rather than with two ammonium groups having widely
differing but isotropic frequencies.

The fact that the ammonium groups are in two different environments
is clear from the NMR work.   (See, for example, Blinc and Levstek, 1960.)
The NMR line is narrow at room temperature; this means that the protons
are equivalent on the time scale of the NMR experiment and hence that the
ammonium ions must be reorienting about random axes at frequencies
greater than about 10^5 cycles sec^{-1} (Section 4-1).   There are no changes in
the line width at the ferroelectric transition.   At about -110°C, however,
the line splits into two components, one narrow and one broad.   Down to
$-180°$, this condition persists, suggesting that one ammonium group is still in
"rapid reorientation" while the motion of the other is "frozen-in" (see Figure
7-8).   As the neutron diffraction results have shown, however, the amplitudes
of the hindered rotational motion are not large and are similar for the two
ammonium groups.   This is in agreement with the infrared absorption

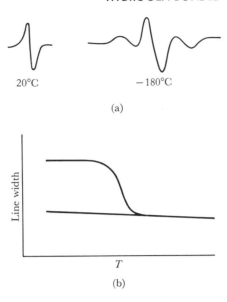

Figure 7-8 *Proton magnetic resonance in ammonium sulfate. (a) The derivative line shapes at two temperatures are shown.   A single sharp absorption is seen at room temperature, while at low temperatures a sharp line is superimposed on a broad line. (b) The two line widths are plotted as functions of temperature.*

frequencies of 360 cm^{-1} and 600 cm^{-1} assigned by Blinc and Levstek to the hindered rotational modes.   The comparison between these experiments emphasizes again that the NMR experiment is measuring something very different from the other experiments, and that "rapid reorientation" is not to be confused with nearly free rotation.

Ammonium sulfate has also been studied recently by deuteron magnetic resonance.   In this technique the resonance line of each deuteron is split by interaction of the deuteron quadrupole moment with the electric field gradient tensor at the deuteron nucleus.   The magnitude of the splitting depends on the angle made between the applied magnetic field and the directions of the principal axes of the field gradient tensor.   Measurement of the splittings as a function of the orientation of a single crystal can thus lead to information on the orientations of the field gradient tensors in the crystal. Now it can be assumed that one of these principal axes for each deuteron lies approximately along the N—D bond.   Thus the orientations of the ammonium groups in the crystal as well as their shapes can be obtained by this technique.   O'Reilly and Tsang (1967) have carried out an extensive series of deuteron resonance measurements for ammonium sulfate as a function of temperature.   For the ferroelectric phase, their results are in good agreement with the neutron diffraction data insofar as they predict the distortions of the ammonium ions to within a degree or two and the orientations to about five degrees. They feel that their results for the paraelectric phase can be explained best in terms of a model which is simply a superposition of the two ferroelectric structures of opposite polarity; such a structure is definitely not compatible with the neutron diffraction results and the interpretation of the deuteron resonance data must therefore be at least partially incorrect. Although the neutron diffraction results could possibly be interpreted in terms of a disordered structure, the two configurations could not differ by as much as do the two ferroelectric structures of opposite polarity; furthermore, the distortion of the bond angles in the paraelectric phase is real and is not compatible with the disordered model proposed in the report of the deuteron resonance data.

7-4 POTASSIUM FERROCYANIDE TRIHYDRATE

The ferroelectric nature of $K_4Fe(CN)_6 \cdot 3H_2O$ (KFCT) was discovered by Waku et al. (1959). The structure has been studied by a variety of techniques, and the basic nature of the ferroelectric transition seems to be well understood, despite the fact that the neutron diffraction work is as yet incomplete.[2] The crystal structure is monoclinic, space group $C2/c$ above the transition, which occurs at $-22°C$, and space group Pc in the ferroelectric phase, where the center of symmetry and the side centering are no longer present.

The structure (Figure 7-9) consists of double layers of the complex ions,

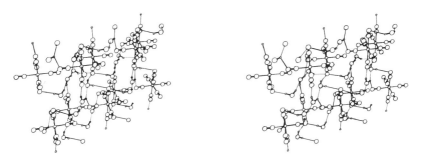

Figure 7-9 *Part of the structure of potassium ferrocyanide trihydrate. The potassium ions are not shown. Layers of $Fe(CN)_6^{4-}$ ions are linked together by hydrogen-bonded water molecules in the intervening layers. The water positions and hydrogen bonds shown are those suggested by Kiriyama et al. (1964) for the ferroelectric phase. Taylor, Mueller, and Hitterman (1967) have shown by a neutron diffraction study that the water molecules are highly disordered in the paraelectric phase.*

[2] This study is being carried out by Taylor, Mueller, and Hitterman (1967) of the Argonne National Laboratory.

perpendicular to the b axis, surrounded by K^+ ions with intervening layers of water molecules. The two-dimensional x-ray work of Kiriyama *et al.* (1964) has shown that there are no significant changes in the heavy atom positions in passing through the transition. Hence the ferroelectric transition is probably associated with reorientation of the water molecules to give different hydrogen bond configurations.

This crystal has been extensively studied by NMR techniques (Kiriyama *et al.*, 1964; Blinc, Brenman, and Waugh, 1961) and by deuteron magnetic resonance (Tsang and O'Reilly, 1965). The combination of these methods with the heavy atom positions from the x-ray work has resulted in probable structures for both phases. It seems certain from these experiments and from the neutron diffraction data that the transition is from an ordered structure below the Curie point to a complicated disordered structure above the Curie point.

The line widths and relaxation times in the deuteron resonance experiment have been used to obtain some information about the molecular motions. First of all, the most important motion in the crystal seems to be the 180° flip of the water molecule about the bisectrix. An estimate of 2.0 kcal mole^{-1} for the activation energy for this reorientation was obtained from the line width data (Section 4-2). Tsang and O'Reilly have pointed out, however, that the absolute value of the correlation time extrapolated to infinite temperature is about 10^4 times as long as that which would be expected on the basis of a torsional oscillator with a cosine-shaped potential. This, together with the fact that the frequency of 200 cm^{-1} estimated for the energy level separation is only in qualitative agreement with the values of 110, 160, and 410 cm^{-1} found by Rush, Leung, and Taylor (1966) in the neutron scattering experiments, suggests that the shape of the barrier is not simple. The latter authors have shown by inelastic scattering experiments that there is no significant change in the rotational freedom of the water molecules at the ferroelectric transition temperature and that the rotational freedom of the H_2O molecules is greater here than in water. The neutron spectrum shows a vibrational peak at 425 cm^{-1} as opposed to 480 cm^{-1} in water (Larsson, Holmryd, and Otnes, 1961). The total cross section slope (Section 4-7) is also higher for KFCT.

At high temperatures the reorientation process which corresponds to the polarization reversal in the ferroelectric phase has an activation energy of about 10 kcal mole^{-1}.

The proton magnetic resonance data of Blinc, Brenman, and Waugh (1961) are in essential agreement with the deuteron resonance data, although somewhat different conclusions were reached regarding hydrogen atom positions. At 20°C a single sharp resonance line is observed, indicating that the molecules are reorienting rapidly about more than one axis, and that the structure is probably completely disordered with respect to the proton positions.   At $-133°C$ a single broad line is seen; the width of this line is approximately that found for other substances with water molecules in rigid lattices. From the point of view of the NMR experiment, the water molecules are "frozen in."   A plot of correlation time versus temperature indicates a barrier toward reorientation of approximately 2.5 kcal mole^{-1}, in agreement with the deuteron resonance data.   At $-58°C$, there are two lines, one narrow and one broad.   This is consistent with the interpretation that there are two types of water molecules, one of which is less firmly hydrogen bonded than the other and is thus able to reorient rapidly at lower temperatures. There is still, however, some long range order in the proton positions which persists up to the Curie point at $-24.5°K$.   There is indeed a sharp change in slope of the correlation time versus temperature curve at the Curie point. An order-disorder transition is consistent with all the evidence.

The resonance work, although extremely useful, is subject to many assumptions and interpretations.   While the determination of hydrogen-hydrogen vectors may be straightforward (see Chapter 3), the assignment of these to a particular structure is not in a structure as complex as potassium ferrocyanide trihydrate.   One must await the neutron diffraction results for a definitive answer, a conclusion which is supported by the discrepancies in the ammonium sulfate results.

7-5   POTASSIUM DIHYDROGEN PHOSPHATE

Perhaps the best understood of the ferroelectrics from a structural point of view is KH_2PO_4.   The ferroelectric transition takes place at $123°K$.   Above this temperature the structure may be described in the tetragonal space group $F\bar{4}d2$; below, in the polar orthorhombic space group $Fdd2$.   The tetragonal c axis becomes the polar axis of the orthorhombic structure.   In both phases the structure may be described in terms of PO_4 tetrahedra, each of which is surrounded tetrahedrally by four more PO_4 groups.   This tetrahedral array of phosphate groups is connected by hydrogen bonds. Since there are two hydrogen atoms per phosphate group, we can assign one hydrogen atom to each of the bonds connecting a phosphate group with its four neighbors.   A neutron diffraction study of the ferroelectric phase (Bacon and Pease, 1955) has shown that two hydrogens are associated with each phosphate group, so that in fact we have $H_2PO_4^-$ ions in the crystal.   The structure is ordered so that the hydrogen atoms are all covalently bound to the phosphate groups at their tops (positive direction of the c axis) (Figure 7-10).   The reversal of the polarization causes the H atoms to move to the

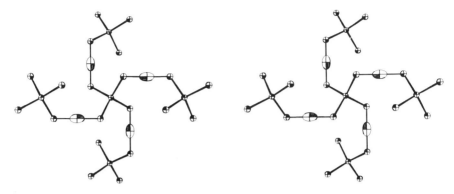

Figure 7-10 *The environment of one $H_2PO_4^-$ ion in potassium dihydrogen phosphate.*

other ends of the O—H · · · O hydrogen bonds, thus becoming covalently bound to the bottoms of the adjacent phosphate groups.

The hydrogen bonds are in fact almost perpendicular to the c axis, and the shift in charge in the hydrogen bonds cannot account for the magnitude of the polarization. However, the diffraction study shows that there are small shifts in the heavy atom positions as well, and a simple point-charge model gives a calculated polarization which is in good agreement with experiment.

Above the transition, the hydrogen atoms become disordered, and the structure can be described in terms of two half hydrogens in each of the four hydrogen bonds that the PO_4 group forms (Figure 7-11). In actual fact, one does not see isolated half hydrogens as in ice, for here the hydrogen bond is very short, about 2.5 A. The scattering density plot shows an elongated

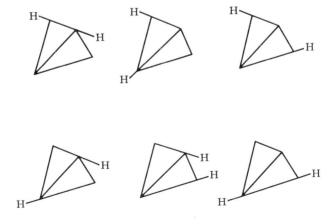

Figure 7-11 *Possible configurations of a single $H_2PO_4^-$ ion in potassium dihydrogen phosphate.*

region of density along the O · · · O direction. This could be due either to the superposition of two half hydrogens or to a centered hydrogen atom undergoing marked anisotropic vibration. The diffraction experiment cannot decide between the two possibilities (see Chapter 3). The infrared evidence seems, however, to lend firm support to the half-hydrogen model. Furthermore, the neutron inelastic scattering experiments, NMR experiments, and Raman spectra indicate that there is no great change in the strength of the hydrogen bond at the transition. Thus, everything points toward the ferroelectric transition in KH_2PO_4 being an order-disorder transition of the simplest type.

It is interesting that the transition temperature in potassium dihydrogen phosphate is raised from 121° to 222°K on deuteration. Furthermore, the shape of the polarization versus T curve changes from that typical of a second-order transition to the more rectangular shape of a typical first-order transition. Blinc (1966) has recently shown that this behavior can be explained on the basis of a very simple model in which an analogy is made to a ferromagnetic transition.[3] In this model, the hydrogen associated with each O · · · O distance is described as existing in two possible states—in one side of the double-minimum potential or the other. An approximate Hamiltonian, analogous to the Heisenberg formalism for ferromagetism, is set up, and the states of the system are determined. The transition is described in terms of parameters which involve the atomic masses as well as the potential energies of interaction. The ratios of these parameters determine whether the transition is first or second order or intermediate.

Further experiments by Bjorkstam (1967) on the deuteron resonance of

[3] See also Blinc and Svetina (1966).

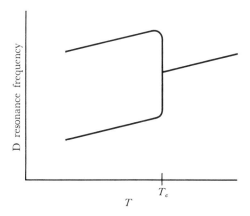

Figure 7-12 *Deuteron resonance quadrupolar splitting in KD_2PO_4 as a function of temperature. T_c is the transition temperature between the ferroelectric and paraelectric phases.*

potassium dihydrogen phosphate have shown that there is an abrupt change in the quadrupole splitting of the deuteron resonance at the transition temperature. Above this temperature, the deuteron is moving from one side of the barrier to the other fast enough to average out the quadrupolar fields at the nucleus, and a single line is observed. Below the transition, the field becomes more asymmetric, and two lines are observed (Figure 7-12).

REFERENCES

Bacon, G. E., and Pease, R. S. (1955), A Neutron Diffraction Study of the Ferroelectric Transition of Potassium Dihydrogen Phosphate, *Proc. Roy. Soc. London* **A230**, 359.

Bjorkstam, J. L. (1967), Deuteron Nuclear Magnetic Resonance Study of the Ferroelectric Phase Transition in Deuterated Triglycine Sulfate and KD_2PO_4, *Phys. Rev.* **153**, 599.

Blinc, R. (1966), Magnetic Resonance in Ferroelectrics, *Proc. Int. Meet. Ferroelec. Prague, 1966*, **2**, 333.

Blinc, R., Brenman, M., and Waugh, J. S. (1961), Proton Magnetic Resonance Study of Ferroelectric Potassium Ferrocyanide Trihydrate, *J. Chem. Phys.* **35**, 1770.

Blinc, R., and Levstek, I. (1960), Nuclear Magnetic Resonance and Infrared Study of Ammonium Sulfate and Ammonium Fluoroberyllate, *J. Phys. Chem. Solids* **12**, 295.

Blinc, R., and Svetina, S. (1966), Cluster Approximations for Order-Disorder Type Hydrogen-Bonded Ferroelectrics. II. Application to KH_2PO_4, *Phys. Rev.* **147**, 430.

Cruickshank, D. W. J. (1956), The Variation of Vibration Amplitudes with Temperature in Some Molecular Crystals, *Acta Cryst.* **9**, 1005.

Frazer, B. C. (1966), private communication.

Hainsworth, F. N. (1965), The Positions of the Hydrogen Atoms and Their Role in the Ferroelectric Behavior of Colemanite. Dissertation, McMaster University, Hamilton, Ontario.

Jona, F., and Shirane, G. (1962), *Ferroelectric Crystals*. Pergamon Press, New York.

Kiriyama, R., Kiriyama, H., Wada, T., Niizeki, N., and Hirabayashi, H. (1964), Nuclear Magnetic Resonance and X-Ray Studies of Potassium Ferrocyanide Trihydrate Crystal, *J. Phys. Soc. Japan* **19**, 540.

Larsson, K. E., Holmryd, S., and Otnes, K. (1961), Cold Neutron Scattering Experiments on Light and Heavy Water, in *Inelastic Scattering of Neutrons in Solids and Liquids*, p. 329. International Atomic Energy Agency, Vienna. (Proc. Symp. 1st, Vienna, 1960.)

Megaw, H. (1957), *Ferroelectricity in Crystals*. Methuen, London.

O'Reilly, D. E., and Tsang, T. (1967), Deuteron Magnetic Resonance and Proton Relaxation Times in Ferroelectric Ammonium Sulfate, *J. Chem. Phys.* **46**, 1291.

Rush, J. J., Leung, P., and Taylor, T. I. (1966), Motions of Water Molecules in Potassium Ferrocyanide Trihydrate, Water, and Ice: A Neutron Scattering Study. *J. Chem. Phys.* **45,** 1312.

Rush, J. J., and Taylor, T. I. (1965), Study of Low-Frequency Motions in Several Ferroelectric Salts by the Inelastic Scattering of Cold Neutrons, *Inelastic Scattering of Neutrons*, Vol. II, p. 333. International Atomic Energy Agency, Vienna. (Proc. Symp. 3rd., Bombay, India, 1964.)

Schlemper, E. O., and Hamilton, W. C. (1966), A Neutron Diffraction Study of the Structures of Ferroelectric and Paraelectric Ammonium Sulfate, *J. Chem. Phys.* **44,** 4498.

Taylor, J. C., Mueller, M. H., and Hitterman, R. L. (1967), A Neutron Diffraction Study of Ferroelectric KFCT ($K_4Fe(CN)_6 \cdot 3D_2O$) above the Curie Temperature, *Abstracts, Am. Cryst. Assoc. Meeting, Atlanta, Georgia, January, 1967*.

Tsang, T., and O'Reilly, D. E. (1965), Deuteron Magnetic Resonance of Ferroelectric Potassium Ferrocyanide Trihydrate, *J. Chem. Phy.* **43,** 4234.

Waku, S., Hirabayashi J., Iwasaki, H., and Kiriyama, R. (1959), Ferroelectricity in Potassium Ferrocyanide Trihydrate, *J. Phys. Soc. Japan* **14,** 973.

<table>
<tr><td>*chapter*
eight</td><td># Outlook for the Future</td></tr>
</table>

The qualitative and many of the quantitative features of the hydrogen bond are well understood. Further quantification of our understanding will undoubtedly increase with time. Old methods will give better results, new methods will be further developed, and the results of theoretical calculations will become increasingly useful.

Infrared Spectroscopy

The availability of far infrared instruments of superior resolution will allow a more detailed exploration of the low frequency modes which are characteristic of hydrogen-bonded groups in solids. Conventional infrared techniques will be improved to afford increased resolution and more meaningful intensity measurements in all regions of the spectrum.

The availability of fast digital computers will become of increasing importance in the interpretation of the complex spectra usually observed in hydrogen-bonded systems. First of all, it is possible to carry out normal coordinate treatments and force-constant refinements for systems with many atoms. More importantly, perhaps, it is possible to compute numerical vibrational wave functions, energy levels, and transition probabilities for extremely anharmonic systems. Extension of such calculations to include coupling of the many anharmonic modes present in hydrogen-bonded systems will lead in the next several years to satisfying and quantitative explanations of the broad and often highly structured A—H stretching modes that are found. The calculation of crystal energies as functions of molecular orientation may lead to a better understanding of the spectra associated with the low frequency rotational and translational modes in solids.

Raman Spectroscopy

In the past, Raman spectroscopy has not been widely applied to hydrogen bonding in solids because of the necessity of having a transparent sample. The availability of very intense laser radiation sources may greatly increase such applications.

Neutron Scattering

Inelastic scattering of neutrons from hydrogen-bonded materials will emerge in the next several years as one of the important experimental techniques. As a form of spectroscopy which has already resulted in much new insight into the low frequency modes, its application to single crystals is just beginning. The ability to study the forces governing intermolecular motions as a function of crystal orientation is an exciting possibility.

Diffraction

Neutron and x-ray diffraction will continue to be the best methods for the study of atomic positions in crystals. The increased awareness of crystallographers of the care that must be taken to eliminate systematic error in their experiments will lead to better data and to geometrical parameters in which one may place more confidence. Detailed studies of the deuterium-hydrogen isotope effect by both x-ray and neutron diffraction measurements will provide a sound experimental basis against which theories of the potential function in these systems can be tested. The precise determination by neutron diffraction of the parameters describing the thermal motion of hydrogen atoms will also contribute greatly to the understanding of hydrogen bond energetics.

Resonance

Nuclear magnetic resonance will continue to give valuable, although usually limited, information on hydrogen bonding. As a quick diagnostic tool, it can give qualitative information concerning thermal motion. When the structure is not too complicated, proton or deuteron resonance in single crystals can be used to obtain approximate positions of hydrogen atoms in the structure. Measurement of the anisotropy of quadrupole coupling constants can lead to information on the electron distribution in hydrogen-bonded systems; such information may be important in understanding the electronic structure of such systems.

Theory

The increasing capability of theoretical chemists to make sound *a priori* calculations of wave functions for complex molecules leads one to hope that a firm quantum mechanical understanding of the hydrogen bond and of the potential function for nuclear motion in hydrogen bonds will soon emerge.

Many exciting steps in this direction were discussed at the EUCHEM Conference on hydrogen bonding at Schloss Elmau, Bavaria, in April 1967. Readers interested in the results–both experimental and theoretical–of that conference should consult volume 1 of the *Journal of Molecular Structure*, where part of the proceedings will be published.

Conclusion

We have attempted in this text to present to the student an introduction to a few of the more important methods used in the study of molecular structure in the solid state. By discussing all these methods in their application to a particular type of system—the hydrogen bond—we have demonstrated that it is the understanding of a phenomenon that should be the result of any chemical investigation. Toward this end it is necessary that all possible methods be brought to bear on the problem. It is of course of the highest importance that each method be applied with care and understanding, but it must always be remembered that this attention to method and instrumentation is only a means to an end.

appendix

Neutron Diffraction Studies on Hydrogen-Bonded Systems

Neutron Diffraction Studies on Hydrogen-Bonded Systems[a]

Compound	Bond Type X···H···Y	X—Y (Å)	X—H (Å)	H—Y (Å)	∠X—H—Y (deg)	Comment	Reference[b]
KHF$_2$	F—H—F	2.26	1.13	1.13	180	Symmetric	1, 2
NaHF$_2$	F—H—F	2.26	1.13	1.13	180	Symmetric	3
Acetamide·$\frac{1}{2}$HCl	O—H—O	2.42	1.21	1.21	180	Probably symmetric	4
KH maleate	O—H—O	2.44	1.22	1.22	180	Probably symmetric	5
KH chloromaleate	O—H—O	2.40	1.21	1.20	175	Symmetric	6
NaHCO$_3$·Na$_2$CO$_3$·2H$_2$O	O—H—O	2.50	1.25	1.25	180	Probably symmetric[c]	7
	O—H···O	2.77	1.01	1.78	167	Mean of two bonds	
KH bisphenyl acetate	O—H—O	2.54	1.27	1.27	180	Probably symmetric	8
HCrO$_2$	O—H—O	2.49	1.24$_5$	1.24$_5$	180	Probably symmetric	9
DCrO$_2$	O—D···O	2.55	0.96	1.59	180	Disordered $\frac{1}{2}$H model	9
KH$_2$PO$_4$ (298°K)	O—H···O	2.49	1.09	1.40	180	Disordered $\frac{1}{2}$H model	10
KH$_2$PO$_4$ (77°K)	O—H···O	2.49	1.05	1.44	180	Ordered ferroelectric phase	11
KH$_2$AsO$_4$	O—H···O	2.52	1.06	1.46	180	Disordered $\frac{1}{2}$H model	12
KD$_2$AsO$_4$	O—D···O	2.52	1.03	1.49	180	Disordered $\frac{1}{2}$H model	12
NH$_4$H$_2$PO$_4$	O—H···O	2.48	1.07	1.41	180	Disordered $\frac{1}{2}$H model	13
	N—H···O	2.91	1.00	1.96	159	—	
Oxalic acid·2H$_2$O	O—H···O	2.52	1.06	1.47	175	—	12
	O—H···O	2.86	0.97	1.94	156	—	
	O—H···O	2.84	0.95	1.91	167	—	
D$_2$O (123°K)[d]	O—D···O	2.76	1.01	1.75	180	Disordered $\frac{1}{2}$H model	14
	O—D···O	2.75	1.01	1.74	180	—	
CrK alum	O—H···O	2.66	1.03	1.63	180	—	15
	O—H···O	2.66	1.02	1.65	170	—	
	O—H···O	2.64	1.03	1.61	180	—	
	O—H···O	2.72	0.95	1.80	159	—	
CsAl(SO$_4$)$_2$·12H$_2$O	O—H···O	2.82	0.94	1.90	165	Water-sulfate	16
	O—H···O	2.77	0.96	1.81	171	Water-sulfate	

	O—H···O					
Cu formate·4H₂O^e	O—H · · · O	2.65	0.97	1.69	166	Water-sulfate	16
	O—H · · · O	2.62	0.98	1.66	163	Water-water	
	O—H · · · O	2.81	0.95	1.88	166	Water-formate	
	O—H · · · O	2.81	1.04	1.79	166	Water-water	
	O—H · · · O	2.78	1.08	1.72	167	Water-water	
	O—H · · · O	2.81	0.97	1.84	176	Water-water	
	O—H · · · O	2.81	1.15	1.90	132	Water-water	
	O—H · · · O	2.76	1.04	1.75	169	Water-water	
	O—H · · · O	2.76	0.91	1.85	176	Water-water	
MgSO₄·4H₂O	O—H · · · O	2.88	0.97	1.92	174	Water-sulfate	17
	O—H · · · O	2.75	0.95	1.82	168	Water-sulfate	
	O—H · · · O	2.84	0.97	1.95	151	Water-sulfate	
	O—H · · · O	3.04	0.93	2.39	127	{ Weak and bifurcated	
	O—H · · · O	3.28	0.93	2.59	132	{ Water-sulfate	
	O—H · · · O	2.86	0.95	2.06	140	Water-sulfate	
	O—H · · · O	2.83	0.99	1.85	174	Water-sulfate	
	O—H · · · O	2.83	0.96	1.90	163	Water-sulfate	
	O—H · · · O	2.73	0.98	1.75	178	Water-sulfate	
CuSO₄·5H₂O	O—H · · · O	2.83	0.94	1.91	168	Water-sulfate	18
	O—H · · · O	2.79	0.96	1.89	154	Water-sulfate	
	O—H · · · O	2.75	0.97	1.79	168	Water-sulfate	
	O—H · · · O	2.70	0.97	1.73	176	Water-sulfate	
	O—H · · · O	2.68	0.96	1.72	173	Water-sulfate	
	O—H · · · O	2.72	0.94	1.79	167	Water-sulfate	
	O—H · · · O	2.79	0.97	1.84	167	Water-sulfate	
	O—H · · · O	2.99	0.96	2.07	161	Water-sulfate	
	O—H · · · O	2.76	0.96	1.81	171	Water-water	
	O—H · · · O	2.76	1.00	1.76	172	Water-water	
Th(NO₃)₄·5H₂O	O—H · · · O	2.95	0.96	2.00	174	Water-nitrate	19
	O—H · · · O	2.90	0.95	1.96	168	Water-nitrate	
	O—H · · · O	2.95	0.98	2.07	148	Water-nitrate	

Neutron Diffraction Studies on Hydrogen-Bonded Systems[a] (Continued)

Compound	Bond Type X···H···Y	X–Y (Å)	X–H (Å)	H–Y (Å)	∠X–H–Y (deg)	Comment	Reference[b]
Th(NO₃)₄·5H₂O	O–H···O	2.70	0.95	1.75	173	Water-nitrate	19
(UO₂)(NO₃)₂·6H₂O	O–H···O	2.70	0.97	1.73	178	Water-nitrate	20
	O–H···O	3.00	0.95	2.18	144	Water-nitrate	
	O–H···O	2.92	0.98	1.94	177	Water-nitrate	
	O–H···O	2.71	0.97	1.74	173	Water-water	
	O–H···O	2.69	0.97	1.74	168	Water-water	
	O–H···O	2.76	0.93	1.85	164	Water-water	
	O–H···O	2.70	0.87	1.85	165	Water-water	
Ca(SO₄)₂·2H₂O	O–H···O	2.82	1.00	1.82	180	Low accuracy	21
		2.82	0.98	1.84	180		
AlOOH	O–H···O	2.65	0.99	1.69	161	—	22
α-HIO₃	O–H···O	2.69	0.99	1.70	173	—	12
α-Resorcinol	O–H···O	2.72	1.02	1.73	164	—	23
Pentaerythritol	O–H···O	2.74	0.94	1.81	171	—	24
CuF₂·2H₂O (298°K)	O–H···F⁻	2.65	0.98	1.69	165	—	25
CuF₂·2H₂O (4.2°K)	O–H···F⁻	2.65	0.96	1.71	168	—	26
FeSiF₆·6H₂O[d]	O–H···F⁻	2.68	0.92	1.86	161	—	27
		2.72	0.92	1.82	169		
CuCl₂·2H₂O	O–H···Cl⁻	3.18	0.95	2.26	164	—	28
Dimethylglyoxime	O–H···N	2.77	1.02	1.91	140	H···H = 2.84	29
Sulfamic acid	N–H···O	2.97	1.03	1.95	169	O···H distance at 2.45 Å not considered to be H bonds by author	30
		2.98	1.03	2.00	169		
		2.97	1.01	1.99	159		
Urea	N–H···O	3.03	0.99	2.06	167	—	31
		2.99	1.00	2.08	151	—	
ND₃	N–H···N	3.35	1.01	2.37	164	—	32

262

Compound	Bond					Notes	Ref.
(NH$_4$)$_2$SO$_4$ (180°K)^d	N—H · · · O	3.04	1.07	2.38	119	—	33
		2.93	1.06	1.91	160	—	
		2.87	1.06	1.82	174	—	
		2.93	1.02	1.92	173	—	
		2.87	1.04	1.85	166		
		3.05	1.06	2.28	129 }	Bifurcated	
		2.92	1.96	2.39	109 }		
		2.90	1.04	1.87	168	—	
(NH$_4$)$_2$SO$_4$ (298°K)^d	N—H · · · O	2.98	1.05	1.96	164	—	
		2.99	1.08	1.97	156		
		3.33	1.04	2.48	139 }	Weak and trifurcated	
		3.19	1.04	2.48	125 }		
		3.19	1.04	2.48	125 }		
		3.15	1.09	2.27	136 }	Bifurcated	
		3.16	1.09	2.14	155 }		
		2.90	1.05	1.85	175	—	
		3.06	1.06	2.36	122 }	Weak and trifurcated	
		3.05	1.06	2.43	116 }		
		3.05	1.06	2.43	116 }		
		3.24	1.07	2.39	135 }	Bifurcated	
		3.08	1.07	2.05	160 }		
(NH$_4$)$_2$SiF$_6$ (cubic)^d	N—H · · · F	3.00	1.06	2.08	155	Dynamic disorder	34
PH$_4$I	P—H · · · I$^-$	4.24	1.39	2.87	172	—	35
Methylglyoxal	N—H · · · Cl$^-$	3.39	1.03	2.51	144	—	36
bisguanylhydrazone		3.21	1.01	2.20	171	—	
		3.27	1.01	2.34	152	—	
		3.16	0.97	2.32	146	—	
		3.15	1.02	2.17	160	—	
		3.48	1.04	2.82	122	—	
		3.45	1.03	2.58	143	—	
		3.51	0.97	2.63	151	—	

Neutron Diffraction Studies on Hydrogen-Bonded Systems[a] (Continued)

Compound	Bond Type X···H···Y	X–Y (Å)	X–H (Å)	H–Y (Å)	∠X–H–Y (deg)	Comment	Reference[b]
Methylglyoxal bisguanylhydrazone	N–H···O	2.90	1.04	1.89	163	—	36
		3.07	1.01	2.08	163	—	
	O–H···Cl⁻	3.09	1.02	2.14	153	—	
		3.15	0.99	2.19	166	—	
Violuric acid·D$_2$O	O–D···O	2.56	1.02	1.54	175	—	37
		2.76	0.97	1.82	162	—	
		2.79	0.94	2.07	131 }	Bifurcated	
		2.96	0.94	2.10	150 }		
(NH$_4$)$_2$C$_2$O$_4$·H$_2$O	O–H···O	2.80	0.97	1.85	168	—	38
K$_2$C$_2$O$_4$·H$_2$O	O–H···O	2.74	0.96	1.80	169	—	39
KH diaspirinate	O–H–O	2.44	1.22	1.22	180	Probably symmetric	40

[a] See Table 6-4, footnote a.

[b] (1) Peterson, S. W., and Levy, H. A. (1952), *J. Chem. Phys.* **20**, 704.
(2) Ibers, J. A. (1964), *J. Chem. Phys.* **40**, 402.
(3) McGaw, B. L., and Ibers, J. A. (1963), *J. Chem. Phys.* **39**, 2677.
(4) Peterson, S. W., and Worsham, J. E., Jr. (1959), U.S. At. Energy Comm. **ORNL 2782.**
(5) Peterson, S. W., and Levy, H. A. (1958) *J. Chem. Phys.* **29**, 948.
(6) Ellison, R. D., and Levy H. A. (1965), *Acta Cryst.* **19**, 260.
(7) Bacon, G. E., and Curry, N. A. (1956), *Acta Cryst.* **9**, 82.
(8) Bacon G. E., and Curry, N. A. (1960), *Acta Cryst.* **13**, 717.
(9) Hamilton, W. C., and Ibers, J. A. (1963), *Acta Cryst.* **16**, 1209.
(10) Bacon, G. E., and Pease R. S. (1953), *Proc. Roy. Soc. London* **A220**, 397.
(11) Bacon, G. E., and Pease, R. S. (1955), *Proc. Roy. Soc. London* **A230**, 359.
(12) Garrett, B. S. (1954), U.S. At. Energy Comm. **ORNL 1745.**
(13) Tenzer, L., Frazer, B. C., and Pepinsky, R. (1958), *Acta Cryst.* **11**, 505.
(14) Peterson, S. W., and Levy, H. A. (1957), *Acta Cryst.* **10**, 70.
(15) Bacon, G. E., and Gardner, W. E. (1958), *Proc. Roy. Soc. London* **A246**, 78.
(16) Kay, M. I., Almodovor, I., Gonzalo J. A., Cromer, D. T., and Okada, K. (1966), U.S. At. Energy Comm. **PRNC-84.**

(17) Baur, W. (1964), *Acta Cryst.* **17**, 863.

(18) Bacon, G. E., and Curry, N. A. (1962), *Proc. Roy. Soc. London* A**266**, 95.

(19) Taylor, J. C., Mueller, M. H., and Hitterman, R. L. (1966), *Acta Cryst.* **20**, 842.

(20) Taylor, J. C., and Mueller, M. H. (1965), *Acta Cryst.* **19**, 536.

(21) Atoji, M., and Rundle, R. E. (1958), *J. Chem. Phys.* **29**, 1306.

(22) Busing, W. R., and Levy, H. A. (1958), *Acta Cryst.* **11**, 798.

(23) Bacon, G. E., and Curry, N. A. (1956), *Proc. Roy. Soc.* A**235**, 552.

(24) Goedkoop, J. A., and Loopstra, B. O. (1959), *Ned. Tijdsch. Natuurkunde* **25**, 29.

(25) Abrahams, S. C., and Prince, E. (1962), *J. Chem. Phys.* **36**, 50.

(26) Abrahams, S. C. (1962), *J. Chem. Phys.* **36**, 56.

(27) Hamilton, W. C. (1962), *Acta Cryst.* **15**, 353.

(28) Peterson, S. W., and Levy, H. A. (1957), *J. Chem. Phys.* **26**, 2200.

(29) Sass, R. L. (1960), *Acta Cryst.* **13**, 320.

(30) Hamilton, W. C. (1961), *Acta Cryst.* **14**, 95.

(31) Worsham, J. E., Jr., Levy, H. A., and Peterson, S. W. (1957), *Acta Cryst.* **10**, 319.

(32) Reed, J. W., and Harris, P. M. (1961), *J. Chem. Phys.* **35**, 1730.

(33) Schlemper, E. O., and Hamilton, W. C. (1966), *J. Chem. Phys.* **44**, 4498.

(34) Schlemper, E. O., Hamilton, W. C., and Rush, J. J. (1966), *J. Chem. Phys.* **44**, 2499.

(35) Sequeira, A., and Hamilton, W. C. (1967), *J. Chem. Phys.* **47**, 1818.

(36) Hamilton, W. C., and La Placa, S. J. (1967), *Acta. Cryst.*, in press.

(37) Craven, B., and Takei, W. J. (1964), *Acta Cryst.* **17**, 415.

(38) Padmanabhan, V. M., Srikantha, S., and Ali, S. M. (1965), *Acta Cryst.* **18**, 567.

(39) Chidambaram, R., Sequeira, A., and Sikka, S. K. (1964), *J. Chem. Phys.* **41**, 3616.

(40) Sequeira, A., Berkebile, A., and Hamilton, W. C., *J. Mol. Struct.*, in press.

[c] This is a two-dimensional study, and the *y* parameters were assumed.

[d] Corrected for thermal motion by "riding" model.

[e] This structure is disordered and was solved in projection only. The accuracy of the results is therefore rather low, as may be judged from the agreement among the O—H bond lengths.

265

Author Index

Subject Index